UNIVERSITY OF PITTSBURGH
School of Engineering Publication Series

No. 2 Industrialization and Development

UNIVERSITY OF PITTSBURGH.
School of Engineering Publication Series

1. Salkovitz, Gerende, & Wingard, *Dimensions of Biomedical Engineering,* 1968
2. Hoelscher & Hawk, *Industrialization and Development,* 1969

Industrialization and Development

H. E. Hoelscher and M. C. Hawk: *editors*
University of Pittsburgh

Proceedings of an International Conference
on the Interdisciplinary Aspects of the
Application of Engineering Technology to the
Industrialization of the Developing Countries
held October 20-25, 1968 at the University
of Pittsburgh

*Sponsored by The School of Engineering
in cooperation with the University Center for
International Studies, University of Pittsburgh*

$\mathcal{S}an \ \mathcal{F}rancisco \ \mathcal{P}ress, \ \mathcal{I}nc.$

255   12th Street, San Francisco, California 94103

Library of Congress Catalog Card Number 73-88723

The march of Providence is so slow, and our desires so impatient; the work of progress is so immense and our means of aiding it so feeble; the life of humanity is so long, that of the individual so brief, that we see only the ebb of the advancing wave, and are thus discouraged. It is history that teaches us to hope.

General Robert E. Lee

Letter to Charles Marshall, 1866; cf H. L. Mencken, "A New Dictionary of Quotations on Historical Principles," 1946, Knopf.

TABLE OF CONTENTS

PREFACE

IT IS A GREAT PLEASURE to welcome you to this truly international conference. Representatives of 21 countries, of many universities and foundations, and of 22 industries are gathered here to discuss the problems of social and economic change in emerging countries via the development of their technological bases—via industrialization.

This Conference had its origins in an earlier meeting held at the Rockefeller University in May, 1966. That meeting, the proceedings of which have just been published, focused on the impact of science on human affairs in India and Pakistan. One of the many results of that meeting was an indication that change in the developing countries should be considered derivative from the development of industries and that this development depended heavily on the interaction of engineers, humanists, political scientists, economists, those in the legal and medical professions, and those in government. The present Conference was designed to provide a vehicle whereby persons of diverse backgrounds and interests could examine together the problems of interfacing the technical and nontechnical professions in the interests of industrialization and, hence, social and economic change.

I am most impressed by the broad and ambitious agenda of this Conference which addresses the worldwide task of industrializing developing countries. It is important that this Conference crosses the interdisciplinary threshold.

We have all read the statistical projections and gloomy predictions for the future. Populations of the world are exploding, shortages in food and industrial productivity are extrapolating sharply, but not sharply enough to cover the rapid increase in population in the developing regions of the world.

I would like to place industrialization and development in an even broader context. The problem of underdevelopment abroad has, I think, a parallel in the growing urban crisis in America and in other developed areas of the world. In the urban, as well as the international, area, there is a crisis of widening economic disparity. At the city level, the affluent become more affluent and the minority ghetto dwellers become more alienated. This is true not only in the United States, but in many areas of Latin America, the Far East, and Europe as well.

At the level of whole nations—the concern of this Conference—the developed countries are enhancing their prosperity while, in the developing countries, gross national products are failing to keep pace with per capita population growth.

The situation is made even more difficult and demanding because we are placed under severe time limitations on two counts. People who are denied rising per capita wealth are, nonetheless, gripped by rising expectations. Therefore nations with such populations are experiencing deepening political and social instability, making for explosive political situations. Second, there now exist on this planet some thousands of megatons of destructive military force which, for the time being, are in the hands of five countries. Thus, the stakes are high and time pressure is upon us; we cannot afford for your task, the agenda of this conference, to go unsolved until the end of this century.

More relevant to engineering technology itself in the crisis of widening economic disparity, I suggest that we are handicapped by specialization— specialization in whatever problem we deal with, whether national or international. As long as our engineers practice only engineering, industrial leaders seek only to make profits, universities only teach and carry on research, or as long as political administrators only govern, we will not be able to solve our problems. We must lift our sights and broaden our objectives; we must have more general political and social criteria than are found in our own disciplines or areas of responsibility.

Finally, the problem of industrializing developing countries is not simply one of productivity. In our cities today, we still have poverty in the midst of riches. For example, in the United States, our air, rail, and roadway transportation systems are declining in effective performance in the face of steeply improving transportation technology. For these reasons, we must be concerned with the functions of design and of distribution and management, as well as with industrial productivity.

This volume contains the Proceedings of the International Conference on the Interdisciplinary Aspects of the Application of Engineering Technology to the Industrialization of Developing Countries. The formal papers from the Principal Participants, those charged with special responsibilities for the Conference subtopics, are presented in their entirety. The discussion papers, workshop reports, and edited reports of discussions at the General Assemblies of the Conference are likewise presented. The chapter headings in this volume are, by and large, the Conference subtopics.

We hope that this volume may be a source of new ideas, many of which may be implemented in our joint international efforts to better the lot of all men and of man's society throughout the world.

Wesley W. Posvar

Chancellor, University of Pittsburgh

FOREWORD

THE UNITED STATES exists today in a shrunken, complex, and interdependent world. New nations with diverse and unfamiliar cultures have emerged. Engineering skills have been responsible for the technical and technological advances made throughout the world, advances which have occurred rapidly but unevenly from country to country. The pressures of population growth and new scientific discoveries have aggravated the present near-revolutionary situation. The impact of our socio-economic system on nations slowly emerging from poverty, and of their systems on our own, has been real but, even now, is only partially apparent and appreciated. Vast regions of the world are underdeveloped, with resources inadequately and often inefficiently utilized. Existing living and economic conditions, as unsatisfactory as they are, are in danger of further retrogression and dramatic improvements are desperately needed.

Every nation in today's world faces many problems. Improved health, exploration and utilization of natural resources, more and better housing, urban planning, better transportation and communications, and expanded educational facilities are but a few of the needs of almost every country, regardless of geographical location and political structure.

The problems of economic development in the newly emerging countries are of major concern to all. International stability cannot be assured so long as a gross disparity exists in the sources of comfort and safety for people of neighbor nations. Thus, it is in our own best interest to assist the nations of South American, Africa, and Southeast Asia to become economically viable.

SCIENCE AND ENGINEERING

There has been talk about the need for increased science in these countries and about the concomitant need for increasing the percentage of their gross national product for pure and basic research. The uninformed often assume that substantially increased attention to science will automatically lead to economic and industrial development. There is ample evidence, however, that this assumption is not valid. The difference between science and engineering is considerable and an understanding of this difference is a key to the planning function for economic development. *Science,* the activity of man concerned with learning, provides some of the inputs to *engineering,* that activity concerned with the use of knowledge for the solution of problems in the real world. Engineering, through its development function, in turn provides the new technologies which allow the continued operation of those existing technologies producing consumer goods. Science is often stimulated into new discoveries by the needs of engineering; thus, although these two activities are coupled through an information feedback, they remain separate and distinct.

We suggest that the industrialization of a developing country is not directly dependent upon its basic research budget, but rather upon the development of its technological base. This is not a simple matter, nor a problem solely for the engineering profession. It is subtle and many disciplines must be involved if the country's problems are to be understood and successfully attacked.

The problems relating to the industrialization and subsequent economic development of such countries revolve about the need for new and/or expanded technologies. Change is needed and such changes must necessarily involve all facets of the social, economic, political, cultural, and technological systems operative within the country. We propose that these interlocking relationships be explored systematically at this Conference so that the processes involved may be better understood and our efforts may become more effective.

THE PROBLEM—TODAY AND TOMORROW

The present world situation is fraught with danger. In 1954, the United Nations estimated that the 1980 population of the world would be approximately four billion. Today, it is clear that estimate was in error by at least half a billion of human beings. The food index, an index of total food available per capita, is paralleling or slightly rising above the population growth-rate curve in the developed regions of the world. However, in the developing regions—the countries of South Asia, Africa, and Latin America—although total food availability is rising dramatically, per capita availability is actually decreasing. The gap between the nourishment available per person in the developed and the developing countries of the world is widening despite the massive efforts devoted to agriculture and food production in the past twenty years. Professor James Bonner of the California Institute of Technology has said[1] that the food projections for the developing regions, either in the relative index or in calories available per capita per day, show a probable downward trend during the next thirty years—a situation which clearly can only lead to world chaos.

Among the best indices of technological development are energy production and consumption. In the United States, electrical energy production during 1965 was about 5000 kilowatt-hours per capita. In this same year, energy production in Chile was about 680 kilowatt-hours per capita, approximately 13 per cent of that in the United States. And Chile is one of the most advanced South American nations. Ecuador, one of the more underdeveloped nations in South America, produced less than 100 kilowatt-hours of energy per capita, approximately 1.9 per cent of that in the United States. India, a much larger nation than Ecuador, and surely much more highly industrialized, produced even less

1. "The Next Ninety Years," *Proceedings of a Conference Held at the California Institute of Technology,* March, 1967; pp. 5–18.

energy—approximately 50 killowatt-hours per capita, less than 1 per cent of that of the United States.

Energy consumption in the developed countries today is equivalent to approximately 12 tons of coal per person and seems likely to grow on a reasonable extrapolation to nearly 100 tons of coal per person by the end of this century. In India, energy consumption per person is approximately 1 per cent of that in the United States and the prospects for growth appear dim. Once again, a marked disparity seems to be widening despite our best efforts to close it.

The per capita gross national product in the United States was $3800 in 1965 and is anticipated to be something like $15 000 by the end of this century. In India, the 1965 figure on a dollar basis was approximately $80—a ratio of 1 to 50 of that in the United States—and, by the end of this century, may possibly extrapolate to something near $130—a ratio of 1 to 120 of that anticipated for the United States. While the absolute magnitude of these numbers and the relevance of an Indian gross national product converted to U.S. dollars may be questioned, a diminishing ratio must be considered significant.[3]

Finally, the world's waste products—currently about 5 lb per person per day—generate heat under reasonably active conditions at a rate of about 1000 watts. Our civilization also generates noise in large, but thus far nonmeasureable, quantities. No basis for quantifying this pollutant is yet available. Waste, heat, and noise must be considered important contaminants and the source of important future problems. Those extra half billion people who will probably populate the world in the year 2000 will produce 2.5×10^9 lb of waste per day or, at a density of 1—that of water—a square mile covered to a depth of 2 ft every day. The heat they will generate will be sufficient to boil an amount of water equal to a lake 10 miles long by 10 miles wide and 10 ft deep every hour of the day.

These are physical problems, problems of science, of engineering, of technology. We have great faith that solutions can and will be found. However, these physical problems carry with them economic, sociological, political, and cultural problems even more staggering, more difficult to identify, more nearly impossible to quantify, and perhaps more drastic in their effect on our civilization. We do not have equal faith that the solution to these problems can or will be found. Science and engineering have long had the advantages accruing from modeling and analytical techniques which provide important points of attack, methods of tests, and techniques for problem solving. But the almost-sciences and the professions other than engineering, and perhaps, medicine, have not had the advantages of the analytic tools available to science and engineering.

2. *Ibid.*

3. These are figures of Professor Harrison Brown of the California Institute of Technology, *Ibid.*, pp. 12–15.

THE ROLE OF THE UNIVERSITIES

University faculties throughout the United States are concerned with the problems of the developing countries. These faculties often have devoted themselves with dedication and enthusiasm to problems which are more than slightly apart from the real need. The development of educational programs in India geared to highly theoretical, sophisticated, or narrow Western specialties cannot be expected to assist the industrialization of that country. Many professionally trained university personnel who have been concerned with the problems of the developing world have not had the advantage of the practical experience of those who have faced specific industrial problems in the developing countries. The scope and magnitude of the problem have not always been apparent to those in the universities. We must call attention to the fact that a successful program of industrialization will necessarily involve all disciplines commonly represented in any major university.

It also seems obvious that the universities of the world must accept the challenge of preparing young men and women for participation in the effort to solve the problems of the developing countries. Such preparation must be different from anything available today. It must be broad in its coverage of the traditional academics, penetrating to the problem structure for which it is designed. It must produce graduates able to integrate knowledge from many fields, thus synthesizing something new, something not now available. Such programs must provide more than rearrangements of old cliches for new times. They must be different in ways not now obvious. University curricula for such efforts need to be developed and, to provide a start, we need the results from this Conference.

LACK OF RELIABLE DATA

The task before the Conference is made more difficult by the absence of reliable statistical data on the past growth of the developing countries and to their present political, economical, and technological status. A significant portion of Chapter 11 of vol. I of the new monumental work by Gunnar Myrdal entitled *The Asian Drama* (New York: Pantheon, 1968), is devoted to the unrealiability of statistical information about the national output and the structure of these economies. The problems of information gathering within these countries, the questions of a proper basis for comparison with conditions elsewhere, the uncertainty of exchange rates and of the real value of money in these countries, and the difference from country to country in the meaning and significance of figures reported, supposedly on the same basis, make our task more difficult. It is important, therefore, that we utilize the knowledge, understanding, experience, and expertise of the principal participants and their associates at this Conference. How then to evaluate, to assess, to anticipate the problems arising from the nonscience and the almost-sciences, from the professions which are not blessed with analytic tools and methods based soundly in fact and theory? How can the interface between the two, mismatched, married today under the force of necessity, be smoothed for effective cooperation on the problems of both?

CHARGE TO THE CONFERENCE

These are the problems to which this Conference must address itself. We ask that in approaching them you focus on three very general questions:

1. How is the process of economic development via industrialization in the developing countries dependent upon or related to the specific subtopic for which you have accepted responsibility? The articulation, the delineation of that problem structure is clearly a necessary precursor to further consideration of the problem area.

2. What is the present state of our knowledge in each of these subject areas insofar as the problem structure of each subtopic has been identified? What experience have we both nationally and internationally? What do we know that can be brought to bear upon the problem structure?

3. What are the "next steps?" What should be the directions for the immediate and the near future, for government-sponsored development and university study, to further the understanding of the problem structure previously identified and to relieve the pressures which that existing problem structure and our state of ignorance about it have generated? What can we do now, in the immediate and near future, to solve the problems which impede economic and social development via industrialization?

This is the charge to our Conference: identify the problem structure, assess what we know, and articulate directions for the immediate future in the marriage of the physical and the nonphysical problems of our present world. Surely these are worthwhile goals.

ACKNOWLEDGMENTS

This Conference is sponsored by the School of Engineering of the University of Pittsburgh in cooperation with the University's newly formed Center for International Studies. The University of Pittsburgh has a long history of interest and involvement in development and education throughout the world. Its faculties have long been working in many countries. The formation of the new Center for International Studies is but further evidence of our deep institutional commitment to worldwide education and development. We firmly expect that many things will eventuate at our University as a consequence of this Conference.

The School of Engineering and the University Center for International Studies gratefully acknowledge the splendid cooperation of the many segments of the University community. Each of the several schools, colleges, centers, and administrative offices assisted in the detailed planning and effective operation of the Conference. University personnel were fortunate in having, as members of the Conference Planning Committee, several experienced representatives from government, industry, international organizations, and foundations. University personnel also contributed their time and talent to serve as members of the various committees, workshop rapporteurs, faculty hosts, and chauffeurs. Special hostesses for the Conference participants were selected from members of student societies and from the secretarial staffs of various schools within the University. The Conference owes much of its success to the financial assistance rendered by the National Science Foundation, the Ford Foundation International Dimensions Program of the University of Pittsburgh, the Union Carbide Corporation, the Wellington C. Carl Fund of the Pittsburgh Foundation, and the Gulf Oil Corporation. We appreciate the encouragement and endorsement given by the Agency for International Development and the American Society for Engineering Education. The recorders used in the workshop sessions were furnished by the Dictaphone Corporation. We are grateful to all these organizations for their help in bringing this Conference to fruition.

Most important, the University of Pittsburgh is indebted to the more than 100 participants who came from 21 countries to consider the many and diverse problems relating to the industrialization of the developing nations. Their experience, energy, and enthusiasm were evident throughout the Conference, assuring its ultimate success.

H. E. Hoelscher
M. C. Hawk

Subtopics of the International Conference on
The Interdisciplinary Aspects of the Application of Engineering
Technology to the Industrialization of the Developing Countries

Goals of Industrialization—A National View

—An International Overview

The Role of the Engineer in the Industrialization of the Developing Countries

An Interdisciplinary Study of the Application of Engineering Technology to the Industrialization of the Developing Countries:

—The influence of the availability or nonavailability of natural resources

—The influence of the economic structure and financial resources

—The influence of the availability of desired human resources, such as entrepreneurs, managers, engineers, technicians, skilled, semiskilled, and nonskilled labor

—The influence of social and cultural environment

—The influence of the legal structure

—The influence of political environments

—The influence of the availability of technical assistance, bilateral or multilateral aid, both in terms of economic assistance, the transfer of technology, and the building of an appropriate technological base

—The influence of indigenous research and development efforts

—The influence of public health

The Role of International Organizations and the Governments of Developed Countries Toward an Increased Effectiveness in the Application of Engineering Technology to the Industrialization of the Developing Countries

The Role of National Governments Toward an Increased Effectiveness in the Application of Engineering Technology to the Industrialization of the Developing Countries

The Role of Private Industries in the Developed Countries Toward an Increased Effectiveness in the Application of Engineering Technology to the Industrialization of the Developing Countries

The Role of National Private Industries Toward an Increased Effectiveness in the Application of Engineering Technology to the Industrialization of the Developing Countries

The Role of Universities in the United States Toward an Increased Effectiveness in the Application of Engineering Technology to the Industrialization of the Developing Countries

The Role of National Universities, Government or Private, Toward an Increased Effectiveness in the Application of Engineering Technology to the Industrialization of the Developing Countries

An Interdisciplinary Team Approach from the Nonengineering Point of View

An Interdisciplinary Team Approach from the Engineering Point of View

OPENING SESSION STATEMENTS

Dr. Charles H. Peake
Provost, University of Pittsburgh

Dr. Nicky Beredjick
UNIDO

Dr. Charles H. Peake, Provost of the University of Pittsburgh, presented his thoughts about possible roles for a university in the field of international studies and about the necessary commitment of higher education in the United States to this activity. Dr. Nicky Beredjick of UNIDO formally opened the Conference and introduced the first speaker.
Their introductory comments follow.

The Editors

OPENING SESSION STATEMENTS
Charles H. Peake

THERE ARE FOUR principles which I believe essential to the University of Pittsburgh's or any university's playing an effective role in international affairs, including technological development.

First, in its formal educational programs, the university must commit itself to the international dimension, free itself insofar as possible from ethnocentricity, be sure that every appropriate basic and professional discipline incorporates the dimension concerned with other cultures of the world so that, for example, a valid international social science system can emerge and so that graduates are intellectually equipped to participate in the solution of world problems.

Second, in order to achieve these educational ends, the university must appoint, in every possible department and school, faculty members who have the commitment to and expertise in the international dimension of their respective disciplines.

Third, there must be a university-wide administrative vehicle to facilitate the interaction of the faculty members from all parts of the university who have this expertise and who need to work cooperatively on complex, interdisciplinary research projects. Such is the function of our University Center for International Studies. Our Center also provides a vehicle for institutional aspects of technological development—problems which a complex university is almost uniquely equipped to investigate. The wealth of ideas, analyses, and problems produced here by the distinguished participants will give an enormous impetus to the future cooperative study, research, and related activities conducted by our Center for International Studies, in which the School of Engineering, of course, will be a major participant. Through the Center, we shall continue the significant relationships established by this Conference.

Fourth, a university, having such a formal educational context, such a faculty, and such an organization is able, I think, to function institutionally as an instrument in international development undertakings.

In my opinion, and in the opinion of most of my colleagues, this can best be done when we keep in mind that we are part of a world-wide system of universities whose first duty is to transmit knowledge, to develop the power of using knowledge, and to create new knowledge to advance the state of the art in every basic and applied discipline. This common concern for personal professional development is the fundamental bond between one university and another in whatever parts of the world they may be and constitutes the primary basis for fruitful interaction between and among them—institution-to-institution interaction based on reciprocity and mutual concern. The initiative, the planning, and the administration must lie within the respective universities. There must be cooperative research undertakings, exchange of faculty and students, and personalized professional relationships extending over time. We must eschew the broker's role. When an American institution has a comprehensive international educational context in its formal program, the essential principle of reciprocity can be readily implemented, and one university will not be working for another university; they will be working together in their common interest and to their mutual advantage.

Nicky Beredjick

I CONSIDER IT a privilege and an honor to preside over the opening session of the University of Pittsburgh's International Conference on Interdisciplinary Aspects of the Application of Engineering Technology to the Industrialization of Developing Countries. It gives me great pleasure to convey to you the best wishes of the United Nations Industrial Development Organization for the success of this endeavor. The University of Pittsburgh's initiative to hold a conference on some interdisciplinary aspects of development and specifically industrialization at this time is commendable. These days, we often hear about the need to build "bridges" across the great divide between East and West. I believe that there are few who will deny that there exists between South and North a veritable precipice of separation that we should earnestly endeavor to scale. This is not the time and place to cite the well-known statistics on population, per capita income, food and agricultural production, and manufacture and trade. All of you, I am sure, know that new and intensified efforts are required by the "have" countries on behalf of the "have not." Let us for a moment see how this general state of affairs may affect this Conference and in what small way it can make a contribution.

It goes without saying that for the developing countries to catch up, an accelerated process of development will have to be undertaken first and foremost through the totality of efforts by the developing countries from within, supplemented, but not superseded, by all the aid that can be mustered from outside, whether from international organizations or from developed countries on a bilateral basis. Industry is one of the most dynamic sectors of any economy and, as such, its accelerated development contributes significantly to the overall development of a country. Of the many aspects which govern the successful development of industries in developing countries, one is the successful transfer and adaptation of technology. This brings us directly to the crux of the Conference.

Many of us who have labored in one field or another on behalf of the less developed countries have come to realize that the successful establishment and operation of industries often is governed by a host of interdisciplinary factors and not exclusively by the application of engineering technology. As a member from the Center for the Study of Democratic Institutions recently put it very aptly, development is a total problem where many disciplines meet: technology, economics, political science, demography, sociology, geography, and ecology among others. Much of our current thinking is characterized by a gross underestimation or perhaps misunderstanding of the complex issues at stake.

Dean Hoelscher is one of the vigorous proponents of the idea that, in order for engineers and other "industrializers" to have a systematic approach in coping with interdisciplinary problems when confronted with them in developing countries, they must be well prepared first by formal education. It became clear to Dean Hoelscher that the majority of engineering schools in the United States have no established formal courses designed to teach students such a subject and, thus, the idea for this Conference was born.

It is sincerely hoped that, when all the speeches have been made, discussions concluded, and reports completed, we will be able to look back to not "just one more conference on a timely subject of interest," but to a milestone evolving into an increased recognition in educational institutions in the United States and elsewhere of the need to redesign curricula of higher education to prepare graduates better for the many interdisciplinary problems they will encounter and upon which the success of their work may very well depend.

KEYNOTE ADDRESS

Detlev W. Bronk
President, Rockefeller University

TWO YEARS AGO the Rockefeller University and the University of the State of New York sponsored a Conference on Science and the Human Condition in India and Pakistan. Many scientific societies and federal and private foundations aided in making that Conference a truly memorable discussion of the role of science and engineering in the development of South Asia.

The theme of the present Conference is rooted in the origins of human cultures and their spread by the migrations of peoples and the adventurous journeys of explorers. From inquisitive and creative tribes, knowledge and newly invented tools were carried to less creative societies so that, from the more advanced, the more primitive learned how to control natural forces. As the routes of commerce lengthened, traders for rare goods became important agents in the development of distant lands; in return for goods they bartered tools and left glimpses of new knowledge brought from their homelands.

As knowledge became organized and modern science evolved, seekers and traders of knowledge became the most significant of merchants.

When, in 1609, the Accademia dei Lincei made plans to establish nonclerical monasteries for international cooperation, it proposed that discoveries of the laws of nature "be communicated without delay from each house to all the sister houses throughout the then known world."

Subsequently, Francis Bacon proposed that, in his imagined House of Solomon, there be twelve scientists who should go from country to country for exchange of knowledge derived from experimental investigations. Significantly, those twelve were to be called "Merchants of Light." In fulfillment of the Baconian ideal, The Royal Society he envisioned has, throughout its three centuries, fostered international cooperation for the furtherance of science. For centuries the functions of the Merchants of Light have been the duties of the Foreign Secretary.

During the growth of colonial empires in the seventeenth and eighteenth centuries, the role of science and technology in the relations between nations broadened in scope. There was little "exchange of knowledge derived from experimental investigations" between scientists of undeveloped countries and of the mother nations, but the exploration of unexplored lands revealed new knowledge of the earth and of previously unknown flora and fauna. The science and technology that had been developed in Europe were used to exploit the resources of the conquered colonies for the material benefit of the conquerers.

Only slowly did colonists use scientific knowledge discovered in Europe for the development of their new homelands.

Such was the history of our country. The records of The Royal Society of London, of the Académie des Sciences of Paris, and the archives of other learned societies of Europe are replete with accounts of observations made by their naturalists and explorers on the American continent. But the American colonists themselves were too busy applying science in the building of a new nation to have time for the development of an indigenous science and technology. True, Benjamin Franklin and David Rittenhouse were exceptional experimentalists and were deemed worthy of election to fellowship in The Royal Society of London for Improving Natural Knowledge. But it is significant that, when Franklin and his associates founded the American Philosophical Society in Philadelphia in 1769, they stated that its purpose was to be "promoting useful knowledge." Useful and practical were primary ends of the colonists' curiosity; nevertheless, the quest for understanding was deeply rooted in the spirit of their ancestors who had been nurtured in the European tradition. One is reminded of this by the 1769 "Advertisement" of the first volume of the *Transactions of the American Philosophical Society:*

> The American Philosophical Society think it their honor to follow that illustrious body The Royal Society of London in their endeavors for enlarging the Sphere of Knowledge and Useful Arts. And though, in Countries where the Arts and all useful Improvements have arrived almost at their maturity, the following Work may scarce be considered as a mite thrown into the common treasury; yet here, where they are but in their infancy, it may be received as some accession to our smaller Stock.

As we consider the role and status of science and engineering in developing countries, it is well to recall that 150 years passed before American science reached the state of maturity referred to in the "Advertisement." Engineering competence is essential to the development of a strong national economy, but a strong national economy is a prior essential for the furtherance of basic research. Therein lies the importance of "Applying Engineering Technology to the Industrialization of Developing Countries" as a prelude to a nation's partnership in the worldwide scientific endeavor.

Another phase in the development of international relations between scientists and engineers has had its origin in the development of modern warfare. The nature of armed conflicts between nations has been influenced by the course of technology from the days of primitive man. Of that we are reminded by the work of Leonardo da Vinci, by the introduction of the fore and aft rig in Drake's Navy, and latterly by the spectacular achievements of Vannevar Bush and his Office of Scientific Research and Development. In obvious and subtle ways, wars between nations and preparations of war have influenced the progress of science as well as the relations between nations.

The National Academy of Sciences was founded during our Civil War in order to mobilize scientific talent in support of the Federal forces. Half a century later, the Academy increased its capacity for scientific service to our Army and Navy by creating the National Research Council of scientists and engineers who represented many technical and scientific societies. Thus war stimulated a new era of science in the United States.

At the close of World War I, members of the Academy and founders of the National Research Council recognized that the security of our country in an era of scientific warfare would depend upon competent scientific manpower. So also would the vitality of our industries. Accordingly, in order to increase the number and improve the training of able scientists, the Academy and Research Council established National Research Council Fellowships for postdoctoral study. From 1920 to 1940 more than a thousand young men and women were enabled to study and develop their research skills under leading scientists, mostly in Europe during the first decade and then later in our own expanding laboratories. The influence of this program of advanced training was so great that Graduate Dean Sir Hugh Taylor of Princeton was moved to say that, if there was any one factor more responsible than others for our success in World War II, it was the National Research Council Fellowships.

During this Conference on the Application of Engineering to the Industrialization of Developing Countries, I would not stress unduly the role of warfare in the furtherance of science. But the history of science and of warfare amply record how the development of each is influenced by the other.

I was vividly reminded of this by a dramatic scene in an airport at Teheran early on a June morning in 1945. The Germans had recently surrendered in the European phase of World War II and, as Coordinator of Research for the United States Army Air Forces, I was one of a group of Americans on my way to the 220th anniversary of the Academy of Sciences of the USSR. As our staff car approached the airfield that had been build by the Allies, we stopped to permit a train of 100 camels to pass slowly. As this ancient mode of transportation passed before us, an Air Force C-47 transport plane, followed by its B-17 bomber escort, roared down over the camel train. I recall Irving Langmuir then saying: "Engineering technology that has made possible the battles of the skies will make ancient Persia restless for material change and will doom the camel train."

As we flew on to Moscow, we asked ourselves, "Why is the Akademia Nauk celebrating its 220th anniversary with guests from many countries of the world?" To celebrate survival and victory and release from the horrors of war? Yes. Also, the day-long parade of modern weapons demonstrated to the people of Russia and their allies that they had achieved the power to wage a technological war. The presence of hundreds of distinguished scientists who came as guests from the major nations, excepting the vanquished enemies, was evidence that Russia had reached scientific maturity. Representatives of less developed countries were shown the capacity of Russian engineers to give them technical assistance in return for new alliances. Of special interest for the Russian academicians was the opportunity to gratify the traditional desire of scientists to confer with their colleagues from other countries.

A year later the National Academy of Sciences, of which I was then Foreign

Secretary, and the American Philosophical Society were hosts at a second conference of scientists and engineers from the academies of many countries. There was no display of weapons, no talk of the technology of warfare. The subjects most discussed during that week were those that had relevance for this gathering:

How could scientists pool their resources for rebuilding the scientific endeavor and technological industries of war-impoverished countries?

International cooperation in scientific programs of worldwide scope. Plans for the fulfillment of hopes that science and technology would enable all nations, and especially the less developed, to acquire the material needs and benefits they required without recourse to war.

It was a time of hope and faith in the beneficent powers of science and technology. The United Nations and UNESCO were being born, the Marshall Plan was to be activated, as was the Agency for International Development; the North Atlantic Treaty Organization was established; worldwide air lines and communications systems were shrinking the world. In all of these great aspirations and endeavors of world-conscious men, science and technology have played a major role.

As I think back through the fast moving decades since those postwar conferences in Moscow and Washington, I have tried to recall the dominant motives, the reasons for the widespread increase in public support of science and the causes of the forward surge of scientific endeavor. I will speak of four.

After years of restrictive dictators, the poverty of exploited people, and a destructive war, men craved an outlet for their creative spirits. After destruction came the wish for creation.

Despite the fervent desire for peace that followed 1945, there was but fragile hope that further wars would be long delayed. Accordingly, science continued to be supported in many countries in order to build instruments of war. "Modern arms for free men" expressed the hope that technology could build the defenses of peace.

But thoughtful scientists gave to science a higher and more enduring mission: to eliminate some of the most virulent causes of war. Francis Bacon said it thus: " . . . to enlarge the bounds of human empire, to the effecting of all things possible for all people, through a knowledge of the causes and secret motion of things." We could see no prospect of a peaceful world if one half had knowledge and physical resources for a satisfying life while the other half were slaves to poverty and ignorance of natural forces. We had faith that science could peacefully provide the material benefits that needy nations had sought fruitlessly to acquire through war.

In the preamble to the Charter of UNESCO, there is this noble passage: "Since wars begin in the minds of men, it is in the minds of men that the defenses of peace must be constructed." One might also say: "Since wars are caused by the inhumanity of men, it is by the humane wish and acts of men that the defenses of peace must be constructed." Food for life can be increased by the use of science, disease can be cured and prevented, unlimited growth of unwanted populations can be limited, the life of man can be made more meaningful and rewarding.

The will to know and apply the laws of nature, to defend our freedom to be what we can be, to live peacefully, to aid the needy in their quest for a healthy and satisfying life—those I think were the four motives that fired the ambitions of scientists and engineers during this past quarter century and inspired the faith of those who gave us generous support for our research and engineering.

The need for modern technology in developing countries is so vast and the opportunities so challenging that we need competence and courage to meet the challenge and humility to admit that there are limits to what we can do: limits imposed by natural laws, the limits of a finite world for an ever increasing population, limits set by man's apathy, will, and desires.

How to use engineering technology to satisfy the aspirations of people in developing countries are the topics of this International Conference. I have confidence in the wisdom of the discussions and proposals; I hope that those from "developed" countries will have adequate modesty to question whether all of the characteristics of their cultures are so desirable that they justify the imposition of their ways of life on "developing" countries. I hope that generous instincts to be helpful will not lead to blurring of the precious diversity of culture. Different ways of life preserve the indentity of nations and enrich all nations.

As you discuss the Interdisciplinary Aspects of the Applications of Engineering Technology to the Industrialization of Developing Countries, I hope you will often ask: "Develop what to what and why?"

1

GOALS OF INDUSTRIALIZATION
Principal Paper—Alberto Tangari
Discussion of Paper by Alberto Tangari
Principal Paper—A. J. Aizenstat

The first working session of the Conference was devoted to a discussion of the
goals of industrialization, both national and international.

The Editors

GOALS OF INDUSTRIALIZATION—
A NATIONAL VIEW

Principal Paper by Alberto Tangari

IN EVERY COUNTRY the problem of economic growth has to be solved by increasing capitalization and human capabilities in order to raise productivity of capital and labor and improve living conditions. Historical experience has shown that various means have been used to attain this goal, and Brazil is not an exception from the general rule. In fact, despite certain structural maladjustments which are responsible for its difficulties, Brazil has been registering a reasonable rate of development. Its potentialities in human and natural resources are the bases for acceleration of the process.

ECONOMIC GROWTH AND INDUSTRIALIZATION

It is already common knowledge that only a fundamental change of the economy through industrialization will enable a country to grow rapidly. Nevertheless, it is imperative that serious efforts be made to overcome certain limiting factors which still persist. Although Brazil has entered the industrial phase, its rate of growth is lower than that of industrialized countries, thus increasing the gap that separates us from these countries. This is the major problem of the modern world, and the one responsible for social tensions generated by the eagerness for rapid improvement of living conditions. A certain rate of absolute growth is not sufficient for underdeveloped countries; it is necessary that the relative growth compared to that of industrialized nations bring forth gradual disappearance of the gap between the two.

The Brazilian gross national product at 1966 prices increased from 16.2 billion "new cruzeiros" in 1947 to 44.3 billion in 1966—a cumulative growth of 172 per cent, representing a 5.6-percent annual average variation. Deducting the demographic growth, Brazil has an average "per capita" growth of 2.5 per cent annually.

The country's economic growth, which implies improved agricultural technology, better commercial organization, and gradual elimination of handcraft activities, will supply a considerable increase of manual labor, to which should be added the regular growth of population. The most important role of industry will be that of absorbing this human potential to reach a satisfactory level of production.

One of the most important items of economic development lies in the change of occupational distribution, resulting in a decrease of the population engaged in agricultural activities in relation to the entire economically active population. Thus the difference between the per capita income of a developed country and that of an underdeveloped one corresponds to a greater percentage of the population in the primary sector. As long as this difference persists between the "per capita" incomes, the differences of demographic distribution will also remain.

In the United States, for instance, it was possible to obtain, in about 50 years, a reduction from 50 per cent to about 10 per cent of the share of population engaged in primary activities. The Soviet Union, with a more concentrated effort, saw the share of population engaged in primary activities fall, in ten years, from 80 to 58 per cent. In Brazil, this populational transfer started to accelerate only after World War II. Until 1920, 69 per cent of the population was engaged in rural activities. By 1940, this proportion had decreased to only 65 per cent. At present it is estimated that 49.6 per cent of the Brazilian working population is engaged in the primary sector and 14.6 per cent in the secondary sector. In the industrialized regions, the picture is considerably better but, even so, compared to more developed countries, there is a large percentage of labor that must be released from the primary sector. It is obvious, therefore, that this displacement or rural population should be consistent with a well-balanced economic development. In other words, it is necessary that there should be, not a reduction, but an increase, of agricultural production through mechanization.

ORIGIN OF THE BRAZILIAN INDUSTRY AND GRADUAL REPLACEMENT OF IMPORTS

At the end of World War II, Brazil began to increase diversification of its internal production. Industrialization became the factor that led to changes in the social and economic structure. Until recently the dynamic sector of our economy was formed by export of primary products. The growth of per capita products depended, almost exclusively, on our capacity to import, depriving the economy of its own internal dynamism.

Since primary products are of low elasticity of demand, external economic fluctuations cause similar fluctuations in our economic system through higher or lower export prices. During the 1920–1929 period, the growth of per capita national gross product was 2.5 per cent, due mainly to the improvement of import capacity. From 1929 to 1937 the percentage was only 0.3 per cent, which meant that per capita national gross product had become stagnant owing to a decrease of import capacity. Between 1937 and 1947, the growth of per capita product maintained an unsatisfactory level, remaining at 0.7 per cent because imports were kept in abeyance during the World War.

However, the prevailing export economy in Brazil, typically colonial, has gradually transformed itself into an internal market economy, in which the main growth factor became related to investments through incentives, being no longer dependent on the external demand for primary products. This does not imply that we overlook the primary sector of the economy. Indeed, we still depend fundamentally on the income provided by this sector and promote investments which rely on the importation of equipment and raw materials.

The first phase of important industrial expansion resulted from the first World War, when the difficulties of foreign supply stirred up the initiative spirit, and the coffee export revenues supplied, at the same time, markets and funds for the first industrial investments of some importance. Still, due to the coffee economy, the Center-South regions of the nation were able to install basic services for power and transportation which favored market expansion for the first consumer goods ever produced.

Industrial development at that time limited itself almost exclusively to textiles and food products. When the Second World War began, the lack of entrepreneurship became evident as restriction of a market of 40 million inhabitants (and with a reasonable consuming power in some regions) to a severe dependency on external supplies of every kind. The effects of protecting Brazilian industry, as a result of the conflict itself, enabled investors who had gathered sufficient capital and knowhow to produce certain goods and to dominate their respective areas in the market. This period of industrial effort had an essential advantage: It revealed the potentials of the domestic market already in existence in Brazil. The lack of governmental economic policy, however, created distortions which caused immediate problems for the development of the industrialization process.

The exchange and import control system established at that time favored the so called "essential" imports, leaving the attractions of the domestic market for the production of consumer goods, thus stimulating the installation of highly profitable light industries to the detriment of basic sectors which had relatively low returns and demanded long-term investments. The resultant postponement of the installation of heavy industry and infrastructure sectors caused a "bottleneck" in our development.

At the end of this period, Brazil had an industrial complex of some importance whose survival was dependent on the importation of equipment and raw materials. But the deterioration of international commercial relations—decreasing export prices and increasing import prices—and the relative stagnation of exports reduced the country's capacity to purchase, at a time when demands for import had increased.

PLANNING FOR INDUSTRIAL DEVELOPMENT

The modernization of the country's total economic structure sectors—administrative, financial, tax, and technological—called for coordinated action through predetermined programs. Therefore, since World War II, various plans and programs have been launched aiming at a development level in accordance with the aspirations of the Brazilian people.

The initial step was the installation of the Volta Redonda Steel Mill by Companhia Siderúrgica Nacional with the collaboration of the United States government in 1944. This mill supplied the rolled steel market with the necessary material to establish a mechanical industry.

In 1947, another step toward planning appeared, the SALTE Plan (Salide Alimentação Transporte Energia), conceived during the government of President Dutra and encompassing health, food, transportation, and power. This plan, however, had no chance of being implemented and was abandoned by the next government.

Not until 1953 was the federal government able to rely upon a serious study of the country's economic structure, its failings, and its needs. This study was carried out by the Joint Brazil-United States Development Commission, created through an agreement between the Brazilian and United States governments in 1950. This Commission developed from two former missions: the Cooke Mission (American Technical Mission), which strove to stimulate local production of essential goods during World War II, and the Abbink Mission (Joint Brazil-United States Technical Commission), which undertook a general survey of the Brazilian economic and financial problems. The Joint Development Commission completed 41 projects, including re-equipping the railway system and main ports, expansion of generating capacity of electric power, and some major plans in the fields of agriculture, industry, roads, and storage. Training programs for Brazilian experts in American universities were included.

The implementation of these projects required about US $388 million in foreign loans and large investments of local currency. The results of this joint study were very useful, giving great impetus to the surge of industrial progress which started in 1956.

In order to help the Commission's development projects, an official financial agency was created to supply the necessary funds for fixed investments: the Banco Nacional do Desenvolvimento Econômico (National Bank for Economic Development).

During 1956—at the beginning of Juscelino Kubitschek's presidency—the foundations for industrial progress and economic growth were laid by the government's setting 30 goals through which to attain predetermined levels of development in the several sectors of the economy such as power, transportation, food, basic industries, and education. For the execution of this program, the government placed great stress on the participation of private enterprise and promoted favorable psychological conditions to attract businessmen to share in the governmental efforts. The Plan of Goals was successful.

Goal 27, the establishment of the automotive industry, is a perfect example of coordination between government and private enterprise. The government established a plan of incentives which temporarily exempted from taxation the importation of equipment and accessories not yet produced in the country. At the same time, private enterprise committed itself to a graduate annual increase in the volume of automotive components that had to be produced in the country.

A horizontal structure was adopted for the Brazilian automotive industry: the final assembly of the vehicle was entrusted to large international automobile enterprises, while the manufacture of component parts was committed to Brazilian enterprises. The obligation to promote progressive integration was left to the big automobile companies. In this way the assembling companies were compelled to give their suppliers the necessary technical, financial, and economic assistance. Because the automotive industry is very strict with regard to specifications and tolerances, a new mentality for industrial production was created based on quality control, insuring a direct improvement in general production techniques.

Thus, a country which had depended solely on imports for the supply of automotive vehicles, with the resultant and onerous disbursement of currency, saw its automotive production rise from 30 500 units in 1957 to 225 400 in 1967. The installation of the Brazilian automotive industry not only supplied the market with vehicles required for land transportation, but promoted the establishment of more than 50 000 new jobs in assembly lines alone, not to mention the job opportunities created by the production of components and accessories, auxiliary industries, workshops, and service stations. The government also derived large benefits from the production of automotive vehicles, as considerable taxes were collected for application to other sectors, such as hospitals, schools, roads, communications, and oil and power production. Through the automotive industry, a real transfusion of technology from developed countries was injected into the Brazilian economy.

The implementation and development of this industry in Brazil is a convincing example of the value of a well-planned and well-executed industrial project for developing countries.

As a result of the growth of the automotive industry, the manufacture of tractors also progressed, the starting point of a modernization process in agriculture through mechanization. Furthermore, the manufacture of machine tools for metal working was developed and, in a short time, the country was in a position to export lathes in reasonable quantities.

In 1961 and in 1964, "Three-Year Plans" were outlined. However, they produced few practical results and served principally to correct distortions by curbing an inflationary trend without impairing industrial progress.

STRATEGICAL PROGRAM FOR DEVELOPMENT

The present government, under the leadership of President Arthur da Costa e Silva, after analysis of the country's economic situation in depth, launched the "Programa Estrategico de Desenvolvimento" (Strategic Program for Development), which is to be carried out during the three-year period of 1968–1970, but whose repercussions should be felt in the future.

The basic goals of this "Program" are:

1. to accelerate economic development and, at the same time, to curb inflation;

2. to use the benefits of development to promote social progress; and

3. to expand opportunities for manpower employment.

In order to reach these goals, the economic policy will follow these prerequisites:

1. balance-of-payments control;

2. elimination of regional and sectorial economic disparities, which bar market expansion and hinder the fair distribution of social benefits;

3. execution of social and economic reforms in order to modernize the country's institutional structures, especially university reform, the administrative

reform including reform of the statistical system, land reform, and expansion of scientific and technological research; and

4. maintenance of the current climate or order and institutional stability.

Through the combination of these measures, the government intends to reach a 6-percent annual growth rate, at least, for the gross national product during 1968–1970. If this goal is attained, the gross national product should reach the level of NCr$84 400 million in 1970 (at 1968 prices) or an equivalent of US $22 810 million.

Priority is given to the consolidation of basic industries in the capital goods area, bearing in mind (a) the tendency of the "traditional" mechanical and electrical industry to grow profitably in developing countries in view of the high absorption of semiqualified labor and to create, at the same time, opportunities for exportation; (b) the promotion of important forward and backward linkages; (c) the sector's inherent capacity to encourage and stimulate scientific and technological development; and (d) its role in assuring greater autonomy to domestic development, strengthening the already high possibility of transforming financial savings into real investment.

We are also paying attention to the strengthening of the intermediate goods sector (steel, chemicals, nonferrous metals, nonmetallic minerals, ore, paper, cellulose), which is important owing to (a) greater use in this area of Brazil's comparative advantages, especially those related to steel and aluminum metallurgy; and (b) the stimulating effects for the installation and expansion of the industries that absorb those basic products. Modernization of our traditional industries that produce consumer goods (textiles, clothing, shoes, food products and beverages), with the merger of some industries, eventually will exert a beneficial effect on the above priority through the purchase of capital and intermediate goods necessary to accomplish the program.

Regarding the control of inflation, the goal is to reduce, each year, the upward trend of prices and to create a process of gradual stabilization. At the same time, the government and official agencies are pledged to reduce their permanent budget deficits.

CONCLUSION

The picture thus outlined shows the importance of industrialization as a factor of progress for Brazil. Brazil is a continental country, with a huge territory (8 500 000 km²) and an estimated population of 85 000 000 growing at a rate of 3.1 per cent annually under very adverse conditions. Nevertheless, all this plus the exhausting tropical climate in many coastal areas, the failure to discover and develop large-scale petroleum sources or first-grade coal, the formidable geographic barrier of the Serra do Mar (a chain of mountains close to the ocean), the way in which the major rivers in the Brazilian hinterland flow into the interior rather than to the coast, the extremely hilly nature of hundreds of square miles of the hinterland closest to the coast, and the fact that so much of the country consists of tropical forests where soils are subject to rapid leaching and erosion when the land is cleared constitute an exciting challenge to man's creative and technical capacity.

Only through industrialization, supported by proper technology, can Brazil break through the barriers that prevent its admission among the fully developed countries.

DISCUSSION OF THE PAPER BY ALBERTO TANGARI

IN THE LIGHT of a conference on development and industrialization held earlier this year in Lebanon, Mr. Hassan Saab of Lebanon emphasized several points concerning the goals of industrialization in developing countries.

1. The far-reaching effects of industrialization in a developing country not only create or improve industries, but also restructure the various sectors of the economy, if not all sectors of life as well.

2. The Lebanese engineer, whether educated at one of the two schools of engineering in that country or at a university outside Lebanon, has not yet come into his role as a pioneering participant in the industrialization of his country. He is still much more a technician, limited to one field or another and not a real participant in the process of industrialization. One of the tasks at this Conference should be to seek ways and means of transforming the engineer from a mere technician into a developer.

3. The Lebanese have come to realize that whether or not the nation possesses natural resources, human resources, or financial resources, what really matters in the process of industrialization and development is political structure. If the political structure is strongly committed to development and industrialization, the nation can make the best possible use of all other resources. If there is no committed political leadership, there unfortunately is a waste of resources and efforts. This is a very delicate problem. Men know how to produce engineers but, since the days of Plato, they have been asking themselves how to form proper political leaders. This challenge should be one of the challenges to this Conference.

On the second point made by Mr. Saab, Dean Harold Hoelscher commented that one of the major problems today is how to improve the communications between engineers and political scientists. The situation in Brazil geographically is very interesting from the point of view of a systems engineer. There is a well-developed thin coastal strip and a very large underdeveloped center, conditions that systems engineers have looked at a number of times under other related circumstances for different purposes. Recently, a team of political scientists, engineers, and computer personnel reported on a computer model for the socio-economic structure for Caracas in Venezuela. This computer model is primitive but a step forward in the efforts of engineers, scientists, and mathematicians to work with political scientists on problems that relate to the total social technology and structure, political structure, of the country.

Commenting on the remarks made by Mr. Saab and Dean Hoelscher, Mr. Maximo Halty-Carrere presented some information on a recent study made by the Organization of American States based on the experience of entrepreneurs opening new ventures in the industrial sectors of Latin American nations. Surprisingly enough, OAS found that, in Latin America, about 30 per cent of new businesses were installed, organized, and carried out by technical professionals: engineers, chemical engineers, and others. Mr. Halty-Carrere felt that it is interesting and encouraging that the engineering profession is concerned with economic programs and with the need to speed up the development process.

Mr. Lawrence Bass further commented that, in India, 15 per cent of all the grain in the field is lost before it reaches the consumer and that in some sections, the loss is much, much higher. There are also astronomical losses of perishable fruits and of vegetables, milk, and meat. This is a systems problem: how to conserve the agricultural products through some present processing and some better method of transportation to speed up the delivery to the consuming areas, and through a better direction system so that the products can be distributed economically.

Several questions were put to Mr. Tangari about his paper and the development of Brazil.

1. Mr. Jesse Perkinson asked if, in the development plans and organizations that exist in Brazil, there is a way in which the scientific and engineering community has a voice in this planning; if there is a routine for the input of this aspect of development planning and how it is organized.

Mr. Tangari replied that, in Brazil's Ministry of Industry and Commerce, there is an industrial commission consisting of nine executive groups. In each executive group, there are one or two engineers supplied by the Armed Forces. The Army in Brazil initially had the task of establishing engineering schools so that military engineers are traditional and very helpful. For instance, when Brazil began its automotive industry, four or five engineers helped in the planning from the technical point of view and were concerned with the initiation of production in Brazil and with the means of controlling this production. At present, about 15 engineers are working with the government on development.

2. Mr. Howard Hamilton asked whether any provision has been made in Brazil's tax structure to encourage entrepreneurship on the part of individual engineers and investors as a team, not as existing companies.

Mr. Tangari replied that there were no such provision as yet; however, in Brazil's law, there is a provision for funds to help companies in planning, but not to help individuals. Brazil wants to help these companies improve their systems, methods, and hiring of technical people and to rationalize the production.

3. Mr. Tangari replied to a question from Mr. Nicky Beredjick about arrangements and regulations which govern the development of the Northeast of Brazil by saying that the Northeast and North regions are not as well developed as the Central or Southwest regions. The government has decided to establish some provisions in the income-tax law to attract money to the Northeast region and has created an organization, SUDENE (Superintendencia do Desenvolvimento do Nordeste), for the region's development. SUDENE receives plans from private organizations and plans for industrial projects made by engineering people, technicians, or economists. If the proposed program proves good for the region, the government allows the people who developed this plan to receive money from the income-tax department in order to operate the projects.

4. Mr. Mordecai Lador asked about the Brazilian government's efforts in the Northeast towards industrialization of agricultural processing. Mr. Tangari replied that in the Northeast region, the most important problem is to give the region's 70 000 000 people an opportunity to work. At the sugarcane plantations, the people have not sufficient income to live on and buy things. Therefore, the government started an industrial program to provide jobs and income so that the people could buy some foods from agricultural organizations. However, at present, the government cannot afford two programs, and is therefore taking care of the industrial sector and forfeiting the agricultural. Next year, perhaps the government can give more attention to the agricultural sector.

5. In reply to a request from Mr. Julien Engel to elaborate on the government's stated objective of strengthening the scientific and technological capabilities of Brazil, Mr. Tangari replied that the government is just beginning this important work. This year it will enlarge its financial resources for hiring technical people. In addition to the original Institute of Technology, there are many good institutions in São Paulo. Brazil is studying and learning about a national research organization; for instance, it soon will establish an Institute of Technology with the help of the United States.

6. In reply to a question from Mr. Merton Barry about whether the Brazilian government was prepared to prevent such negative side effects of industrialization as water and air pollution. Mr. Tangari replied that the government has started studies of pollution in Rio de Janiero but that there are not any serious pollution problems in Brazil as yet.

There were two questions from the floor. The first concerned bottlenecks in the industrialization process in Brazil. Mr. Tangari replied that the main bottleneck is in the internal market. Brazil's population has little buying power. The government is trying to provide better living conditions for the people in order to expand the internal market. He felt that there is also a lack of technology appropriate to Brazilian conditions and the government now is trying to establish some Institutes of Technology to study conditions and made changes in foreign technology for Brazilian production. The third bottleneck is the financial system. There is a good financing system to help the industry sell heavy goods. Therefore, in the internal business, industries are not in a good position because of the lack of financial support.

The second question from the floor concerned Brazil's degree of emphasis on agricultural development. Mr. Tangari stated that Brazil now is beginning to pay attention to agricultural development. In the past, implements, tractors, and fertilizers were not available to give to the agricultural people. Because importation of equipment is very expensive, the government decided to develop industries to help the agricultural sector. After the mechanical industry started in Brazil, the government was in a position to offer tractors and other implements to the farmers. Since petroleum products have improved, some fertilizer plants have been started, based upon private initiative. Nitrogen in the phosphoric fertilizers also is being produced although Brazil still must import potassium.

GOALS OF INDUSTRIALIZATION—
AN INTERNATIONAL OVERVIEW

Principal Paper by A. J. Aizenstat*

INDUSTRIALIZATION is indeed a very complex phenomenon which permeates all of man's endeavors. As the major single determinant of the human environment, it marks the wave on which mankind is moving from a past dependent on the haphazard play of natural forces to a self-made future. In this sense, its broad goals tend to merge with what our particular vision of the future happens to be. But I do not propose to discuss a particular futuristic "scenario." Rather, I will concentrate on some of the more immediate prospects which seem to me particularly relevant to the theme of this Conference.

ROLE OF INDUSTRY

Over the last decade a fairly wide consensus has crystallized on the role of industrialization in the process of development. As Secretary-General U Thant put it: "There is no longer any substantial controversy about the importance of industrialization as the main path of economic growth for developing countries." A reflection of this consensus was the establishment, less than two years ago, of a special United Nations Industrial Development Organization (UNIDO) with the aim of assisting the accelerated industrialization of developing countries. UNIDO's functions, which range from advice on the formulation of policies and industrialization programs to advice related to the selection of individual projects and technological processes, involve essentially the mobilization of national and international resources in concerted efforts to create a modern industrial sector in areas which, so far, have remained outside the mainstream of the Industrial Revolution. The establishment of international machinery for this purpose is also a measure of the growing internationalization of the underlying problems which I propose to discuss in the hope of stimulating their further discussion at the workshops of this Conference.

THE STATUS QUO

Because of their accumulated capitalization and technological capability, the industrial countries have enjoyed almost automatic growth at a fairly high rate over the last two decades. In contrast, the developing countries, whose economies are still highly dependent on exports of raw materials and staple farm products, have remained largely stagnant, as has their relative industrial output, which over the past half century has stayed at about 6 or 7 per cent of total world manufacturing.

It is true that a number of developing countries have managed to make important strides forward. In some instances industrial production of individual developing countries has risen at the high rates of between 7 and 9 per cent per

---

*The views expressed in this paper are the sole responsibility of the author and do not necessarily reflect the position of the organization with which he is connected.

annum. But this applies mostly to a few oil-rich countries or to those others where special circumstances have contributed the resources necessary for a high rate of capital investment. For the vast majority of the almost 2.5 billion people who live in developing areas, grim reality is reflected in very low per capita income rate growth, ranging from about 2 per cent in Latin America and East Asia to about only 0.5 per cent in South Asia.

Thus, the general position of the less-developed countries seems to have been little affected by the intensive development efforts over the last two decades. At least the efforts seem to have been inadequate to overcome the sizable obstacles to development which operate in most of the poor countries. In light of this experience and of the obvious link between modern industrial production and selfsustained economic progress, it is hardly surprising that the drive for accelerated industrialization should have become the most urgent goal of the developing countries.

A VIEW OF THE FUTURE

If the "development gap" has failed to yield to past efforts, prospects for the future appear even less promising. At present the low-income areas contain about 65 per cent of the world population but produce less than 15 per cent of the total world output. According to the well-known projections of the Hudson Institute, by the year 2000 the population of the less-developed countries will increase to 75 per cent of total world population, but their share in world production will still account for the same 15 per cent. To put it differently, the total output of the industrialized nations is currently more than 12 times that of the developing countries. In the next 30 years the difference is expected to widen to 18 times, which means that the "development gap" will increase during the balance of this century by about 50 per cent if current trends continue.

In the face of lagging development achievements and still poorer prospects for the future, there has been an increasing realization that the process of industrial development is becoming not only more complex but that its very nature is changing as a result of the accelerated rate of technological innovation. Not so long ago, let us say in the early 1960s when the first Development Decade of the United Nations was proclaimed, the goals of industrialization might have been conceived in terms of the traditional pattern of industrial development: the historical path followed during the last 150 years by the now industrialized powers. But, in the rapidly changing world of the 1960s, it is becoming increasingly doubtful that the gap between richer and poorer countries can ever be closed or even narrowed by pursuing objectives geared to an economic structure inherited from the 19th century. The vigorous leaps made by the highly industrialized countries, who are now in the midst of what has already been called the Second Industrial Revolution, seem to have lifted the issues of industrialization out of their traditional context and planted them in a new and as yet uncharted territory.

THE NEW CONTEXT

It may seem far fetched to talk about the latter-day sophisticated technology as a prospect for the still backward economies of the developing countries, but the disappointing achievements of the last 20 years, in spite of considerable development efforts, call for a reappraisal from broader perspectives. Furthermore, the new challenge, which indeed will multiply the obstacles in the path of industrialization, also holds out new hopes for the developing countries. For it is not only those who are still in a pre-industrial era who are confronted with the new problems of the Second Industrial Revolution; its effects are also felt by those' countries which have successfully reached the industrial stage. The industrialized countries of Western Europe, for example, are deeply concerned about their own ability for retaining their industrial status in the face of the rapidly rising rate of technological innovation. In all likelihood they will be increasingly forced to seek not only closer international cooperation but a full restructuring of economic relations to meet these problems in their proper context *as a world-wide phenomenon*. In making the necessary global arrangements, it will not be possible to exclude the developing world nor to maintain it in its traditional peripheral position as a supplier of raw materials and agricultural products.

Some of these arrangements have begun emerging in the form of regional groupings of countries and common market associations. But these attempts have so far been undertaken mostly within the narrow framework of traditional economic thinking and with considerable deference to more immediate goals.

THE TECHNOLOGICAL GAP

It is, of course, impossible to anticipate precisely the type of arrangements that will be required; on balance they will come about as adaptations to the rapidly changing industrial environment. In recent years, and again as a result of rapidly changing technology, considerable concern has been expressed from many quarters about the so called "technological gap." For the developing countries this is not an entirely new problem. For a long time they have been aware of the inadequate attention given to the problems of technology of the poor countries because most technological research was taking place in the industrialized areas. But now the same problem is being confronted by high-income countries whose markets and production structure are unable to meet the increasing cost and pace of technological development. The transfer of existing technology, important as it may be at certain stages and in particular applications, cannot solve the problem in the long term. It would only tend to give permanence to the "gap" in terms of the time required by the recipient country to assimilate imported technology while the supplying countries forge ahead at newer levels, even more difficult to attain. Therefore the question is not so much one of transferring technology as of spreading the capability for technological innovation.

ROLE OF THE INTERNATIONAL CORPORATION

A close look at the historical experience indicates that successful industrialization was always associated with the attainment of domestic technological capability by the country concerned. Nowadays modern industrial technology is in many ways the creation of the business enterprise. While it is true that research sponsored by academic and other noncommercial sources has played an important role in the advancement of science and technology, it is within the framework of the business corporation that management, research, and engineering provide the kind of interaction and practical teamwork which has led to the accelerated flow of new technological applications. Thus, the large industrial corporation has become both a source and a vehicle of technical progress. In practice, the large corporation is acting as the central catalyst in the expansion and direction of technological research in universities, foundations, and similar institutions. Its relations with the government also have become both more intimate and more complex. But, above all, the large business enterprise is emerging as a truly worldwide international business corporation characterized by a shift of interests and outlook from operations in a single country to operations on a broad international scale.

In adapting itself to the requirements of the Second Industrial Revolution, the international corporation is creating a phenomenon of *de facto* internationalism unparalleled in any other branch of human endeavor.

This phenomenon is still, however, in its infancy and in many ways falls short of the kind of international cooperation that will be required to release fully the energies of all the peoples of the world and make them participants in a truly worldwide framework of international production. Ultimately, it should involve not only an international approach to markets or income but, most importantly, an internationalization of the productive functions and their division among different areas so as to ensure their best contribution in both the traditional fields of labor, raw materials, and transport as well as in the new and specialized areas of technology and research.

There are many possibilities for extending cooperation between large international corporations and different forms of production encountered in developing countries. The emerging international corporation has shown considerable ability in adapting to the requirements of different political and economic environments. There also is proof of its ability to associate elements from different markets in an integrated and more efficient production process. Opportunities for this type of cooperation will multiply greatly when an appropriate form of international chartering is devised to meet the requirements of internationally integrated production and the expanding variety of arrangements under which companies in different countries could supply, exchange, or pool their technological, managerial, and financial resources for industrial production.

Thus, the Second Industrial Revolution, while lengthening and adding complexity to the goal of economic progress through industrialization, also is offering new hopes by opening broader perspectives for international cooperation and industrial integration on a worldwide scale. This is especially encouraging at a time when prospects for successful industrialization at the national level appear somewhat dimmed for a large number of developing countries. The hope that the productive machine created by the technological advances of the past few generations will abolish poverty from the face of the earth may be, after all, vindicated if a truly international community of production emerges as a result of the compelling requirements created by modern technology.

2

THE ROLE OF THE ENGINEER
Principal Paper—Wesley L. Orr
Discussion of the Paper by Wesley L. Orr

The engineer brings a particular set of interests and a special training to the development process. Traditionally, he has been deeply involved in "modeling." The paper by Wesley L. Orr illustrates an engineering approach to the modeling of economic growth.

The Editors

A MODEL OF ECONOMIC GROWTH

Principal Paper by Wesley L. Orr

THE OBJECTIVES of engineering and economic development are essentially the same. Both strive to increase utility per person over time and space. As we examine the meaning of utility we realize that, in an engineering and economic sense, the people of the world are concerned primarily with increases in consumption and in wealth. More analytical thought and statistical research have gone into the subject of consumption, or rather into its close relative, income, than into the subject of wealth. Nevertheless it is assumed in this paper that both wealth and consumption are important criteria of economic development. By means of a rather simple macromodel of a closed economy and of real goods and services, we attempt to show the relationship of growth of per capita consumption and growth of per capita wealth to other pertinent economic variables.

The model is introduced with a basic array that displays the definitional connections between the variables. The basic array is then illustrated by a hypothetical example which demonstrates a dynamic economy in equilibrium. This is followed by examples indicating the consequences of increasing and decreasing the proportion of output which is saved. Several equations are derived which relate the variables in a more general way. Finally, the implications, limitations, possible modifications, and uses of the model are discussed. It should be noted that these are period analyses where, as is customary, all changes are assumed to occur instantaneously at the end of the period.

THE BASIC ARRAY

The basic array (Fig. 1) is a simple statement of relationships. The array is entered at the upper left-hand corner with a statistic of total population. Just under population is the statistic of total workers and its relation to population. Under this is the statistic of output and its relation to the number of workers. In the center of the column is the statistic of total consumption and its relationship to output.

At the bottom left-hand corner the array is again entered with a statistic of total wealth. The column progresses upward through the total production capital and output statistics to the total consumption statistic in the center with each showing its relation to the previous entry.

All statistics in the first column pertain to conditions during period n. Statistics in the second column are concerned with conditions during period $n + 1$. The second column follows the outline of the first with the exception that the period subscripts $n + 1$ are used instead of n.

The two columns are connected by two entries. The first entry shows the relation between populations in periods $n + 1$ and n where Δ_n is the rate of population growth. The second entry indicates the relation between

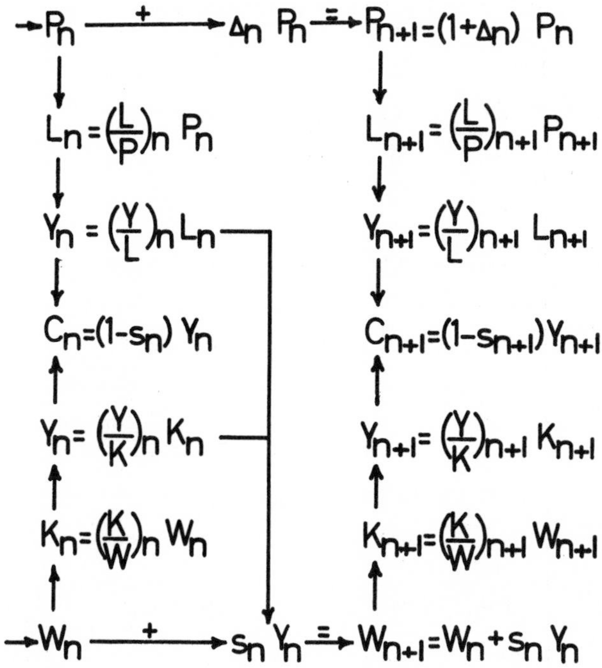

$$\rightarrow P_n \xrightarrow{\ +\ } \Delta_n P_n \equiv P_{n+1} = (1+\Delta_n) P_n$$

$$L_n = \left(\tfrac{L}{P}\right)_n P_n \qquad L_{n+1} = \left(\tfrac{L}{P}\right)_{n+1} P_{n+1}$$

$$Y_n = \left(\tfrac{Y}{L}\right)_n L_n \qquad Y_{n+1} = \left(\tfrac{Y}{L}\right)_{n+1} L_{n+1}$$

$$C_n = (1-s_n) Y_n \qquad C_{n+1} = (1-s_{n+1}) Y_{n+1}$$

$$Y_n = \left(\tfrac{Y}{K}\right)_n K_n \qquad Y_{n+1} = \left(\tfrac{Y}{K}\right)_{n+1} K_{n+1}$$

$$K_n = \left(\tfrac{K}{W}\right)_n W_n \qquad K_{n+1} = \left(\tfrac{K}{W}\right)_{n+1} W_{n+1}$$

$$\rightarrow W_n \xrightarrow{\ +\ } s_n Y_n \equiv W_{n+1} = W_n + s_n Y_n$$

n and $n+1$ are subscripts denoting the period (usually one year)
P is the total population
Δ is the rate of population growth per period
L is the labor force
Y is the output of real goods and services net of actual depreciation of wealth
C is consumption during the period
s is the proportion of Y which is not consumed
K is production capital
W is wealth

FIG. 1.—The basic array.

wealth during period $n+1$ and wealth during period n. Wealth is accumulated by the portion s of output which is saved (that is, which is not consumed). In the interest of simplicity, it is assumed that saving s is net not only of depreciation on production capital but also of depreciation on all wealth—in other words all depreciation is consumed. This might be a serious oversimplification although possibly not much more so than assumptions generally made in national accounting. Later in this paper, a method will be shown for correcting the oversimplification, at the cost, however, of complicating the model.

ILLUSTRATIVE ARRAY NO. 1

The basic array is illustrated by three hypothetical examples or Illustrative

	units	n	ratios	$n+1$	ratios	$n+2$	ratios	$n+12$
P	millions of persons	200	1.015	203	1.015	206		
L/P	ratios	0.4	1.000	0.4	1.000	0.4		
L	millions of persons	80	1.015	81.2	1.015	82.4		
Y/L	ratios $/person	7500	1.034	7759	1.034	8026		
Y	billions of $	600	1.050	630	1.050	662		
Y/K	ratios	1/1.6	1.000	1/1.6	1.000	1/1.6		
K	billions of $	960	1.050	1008	1.050	1058		
K/W	ratios	1/2.5	1.000	1/2.5	1.000	1/2.5		
W	billions of $	2400	1.050	2520	1.050	2646		
C/Y = $1-s$	ratios	0.8	1.000	0.8	1.000	0.8		
C	billions of $	480	1.050	504	1.050	529		
C/P	$ per person	2400	1.034	2483	1.034	2568	1.403	3603
W/P	$ per person	12 000	1.034	12 414	1.034	12 812	1.403	18 017

FIG. 2.—Illustrative array No. 1.

Arrays. All three begin at period n with a closed economy in equilibrium where the following data are given: population P, 200 million; labor force L, 80 million; output Y, $600 billion; total wealth W, $2400 billion; total production capital K, $960 billion; saving s, 0.2 of output; and population growth ratio, 0.015. If it is assumed that the ratios remain fixed then the array constructed in Fig. 2 illustrates continuing equilibrium.

In this and the following illustrative arrays, the ratios occupy alternate columns and alternate rows; the statistical entries occupy alternate, separated spaces. The system in Illustrative Array No. 1 (Fig. 2) is in dynamic equilibrium. The periodic growth rates of per capita consumption and per capita wealth are equal and constant at 0.034.

ILLUSTRATIVE ARRAY NO. 2

Illustrative Array No. 2 begins with identical entries for period n. The first column is the same as in Illustrative Array No. 1 but, now, after being in equilibrium with a saving ratio of 0.2, the saving ratio is raised to 0.3 for the second and all following periods. The ratios Δ, L/P, and K/W are held constant, which seems intuitively reasonable for a short term.

The ratio Y/K also is held constant, which is not quite so reasonable. The relationship between Y/K and Y/L is complicated and a detailed analysis is beyond the scope of this paper. It is generally recognized that an increasingly larger proportion of the total work load is being transferred from people to machines. This substitution tends to increase Y/L at the expense of Y/K. There is, however, little factual information available on Y/K or K/W ratios. A submodel is needed to relate Y/K and Y/L; it should be of special interest to engineers.

In Illustrative Array No. 2 an increase in saving, from 0.2 to 0.3, results in a decrease in the growth rate of per capita consumption during period $n + 1$ from $+0.035$ to -0.073. For the very short run, therefore, consumption welfare benefits from increased consumption. But for the following period, $n + 1$, this rate jumps to 0.059 and will remain at that high level so long as the saving ratio remains at 0.3. For the long run, it is obviously advantageous to increase the saving ratio. Ten years later, period $n + 12$, the per capita consumption will be \$4184 with the 0.3 saving ratio and only \$3603 with a 0.2 saving ratio. It is interesting to speculate about the atti-

	units	n	ratios	$n + 1$	ratios	$n + 2$	ratios	$n + 12$
P	millions of persons	200	1.015	203	1.015	206		
L/P	ratios	0.4	1.000	0.4	1.000	0.4		
L	millions of persons	80	1.015	81.2	1.015	82.4		
Y/L	ratios \$/person	7500	1.059	7943	1.059	8413		
Y	billions of \$	600	1.075	645	1.075	693		
Y/K	ratios	1/1.6	1.000	1/1.6	1.000	1/1.6		
K	billions of \$	960	1.075	1032	1.075	1109		
K/W	ratios	1/2.5	1.000	1/2.5	1.000	1/2.5		
W	billions of \$	2400	1.075	2580	1.075	2774		
C/Y $=$ $1-s$	ratios	0.8	0.825	0.7	1.000	0.7		
C	billions of \$	480	0.941	452	1.075	485		
C/P	\$ per person	2400	0.927	2224	1.059	2356	1.776	4184
W/P	\$ per person	12 000	1.059	12 709	1.059	13 461	1.776	23 905

FIG. 3.—Illustrative array No. 2.

tude of savers when they observe that an increase in saving results in a decrease in consumption. Such speculation may be incorporated as a sub-model of this model and tested dynamically against historical reality.

Illustrative Array No. 2 also shows that the rate of growth of wealth does not follow the pattern of the rate of growth of consumption but jumps immediately from 0.034 to 0.059 and remains at that higher level as long as the saving ratio remains at 0.3. The longer term effect of the higher savings ratio is indicated by comparing the $n + 12$ per capita wealth of \$23 905 at the 0.3 saving ratio with the \$18 017 amount at the 0.2 saving ratio.

These effects are shown in reverse in Illustrative Array No. 3 in which s is reduced to 0.1 and Y/L again is allowed to adjust to this change, with the other ratios remaining constant.

ILLUSTRATIVE ARRAY NO. 3

From Illustrative Array No. 3 it can be seen that a decrease in saving will produce a short-term (one period) increase in consumption followed by a much lower, steady-state, per capita consumption growth rate.

These hypothetical examples illustrate only a sample of the results that ensue from changing the value of a parameter. Instead of an array, it would be useful and elucidative to develop equations which, in single statements, would relate the parameters of interest. Several such equations are derived below.

MODEL EQUATIONS

Let α be the ratio of per capita wealth during period $n + 1$ to the per capita wealth during period n. Then

$$\alpha = \frac{(W/P)_{n+1}}{(W/P)_n} \quad \text{and from the Basic Array}$$

$$= \frac{\dfrac{W_n + s_n Y_n}{(1 + \Delta_n)P_n}}{\dfrac{W_n}{P_n}} = \frac{W_n + s_n (Y/K)_n (K/W)_n W_n}{W_n(1 + \Delta_n)}$$

$$= \frac{1 + s_n (Y/K)_n (K/W)_n}{(1 + \Delta_n)}$$

The per capita rate of growth of wealth is, therefore, a positive function of saving, the output-capital ratio, and the capital-wealth ratio; and an inverse function of the population rate of growth. In the hypothetical, steady-state Basic Array (Fig. 1),

$$\alpha = \frac{1 + 0.2 (1/1.6) (1/2.5)}{1.015} = 1.034$$

Let β be the ratio of per capita consumption during period $n + 1$ to the per capita consumption during period n. Let β_1 be this ratio in terms of the K and W equivalents of Y.

	units	n	ratios	$n+1$	ratios	$n+2$	ratios	$n+12$
P	millions of persons	200	1.015	203	1.015	206		
L/P	ratios	0.4	1.000	0.4	1.000	0.4		
L	millions of persons	80	1.015	81.2	1.015	82.4		
Y/L	ratios $/person	7500	1.010	7574	1.010	7649		
Y	billions of $	600	1.025	615	1.025	630		
Y/K	ratios	1/1.6	1.000	1/1.6	1.000	1/1.6		
K	billions of $	960	1.025	984	1.025	1009		
K/W	ratios	1/2.5	1.000	1/2.5	1.000	1/2.5		
W	billions of $	2400	1.025	2460	1.025	2522		
C/Y $=$ $1-s$	ratios	0.8	1.125	0.9	1.000	0.9		
C	billions of $	480	1.153	554	1.025	567		
C/P	$ per person	2400	1.136	2727	1.010	2753	1.102	3035
W/P	$ per person	12 000	1.010	12 118	1.010	12 238	1.102	13 491

FIG. 4.—Illustrative array No. 3.

$$\beta_1 = \frac{(C/P)_{n+1}}{(C/P)_n} = \frac{\dfrac{(1-s_{n+1})\,Y_{n+1}}{P_{n+1}}}{\dfrac{(1-s_n)\,Y_n}{P_n}}$$

$$= \frac{1-s_{n+1}}{1-s_n}\frac{(Y/K)_{n+1}}{(Y/K)_n}\frac{(K/W)_{n+1}}{(K/W)_n}\frac{W_{n+1}}{W_n}\frac{P_n}{P_{n+1}}$$

$$= \frac{1-s_{n+1}}{1-s_n}\frac{(Y/K)_{n+1}}{(Y/K)_n}\frac{(K/W)_{n+1}}{(K/W)_n}\alpha$$

$$= \frac{1-s_{n+1}}{1-s_n}\frac{(Y/K)_{n+1}}{(Y/K)_n}\frac{(K/W)_{n+1}}{(K/W)_n}\frac{1+s_n(Y/K)_n(K/W)_n}{1+\Delta_n}$$

Note the close relationship between this consumption formula and the wealth formula. The conditions which lead to an increase in the rate of growth of per capita consumption also lead to an increase in per capita wealth. Under steady-state conditions the rates are identical.

Checking this formula against the steady-state Basic Array by substituting the values used in Fig. 2, we obtain

$$\beta_1 = (1)(1)(1)\frac{1 + 0.2\,(1/1.6)(1/2.5)}{1.015} = 1.034$$

Let β_{2a} be the ratio of per capita consumption during period $n + 1$ to the per capita consumption during period n in terms of s, Υ, and Δ:

$$\beta_{2a} = \frac{(C/P)_{n+1}}{(C/P)_n} = \frac{\dfrac{(1 - s_{n+1})\Upsilon_{n+1}}{P_{n+1}}}{\dfrac{(1 - s_n)\Upsilon_n}{P_n}} = \frac{1 - s_{n+1}}{1 - s_n}\,\frac{\Upsilon_{n+1}}{\Upsilon_n}\,\frac{1}{1 + \Delta_n}$$

Substituting the hypothetical, steady-state values used in Fig. 1, we have

$$\beta_{2a} = (1)(1.050)\,\frac{1}{1.015} = 1.034$$

Continuing this derivation by letting β_{2b} be the same ratio but after substitution of L and P equivalents for Υ, we obtain

$$\beta_{2b} = \frac{\dfrac{(1 - s_{n+1})\,\Upsilon_{n+1}}{P_{n+1}}}{\dfrac{(1 - s_n)\,\Upsilon_n}{P_n}} = \frac{\dfrac{(1 - s_{n+1})(\Upsilon/L)_{n+1}(L/P)_{n+1}P_{n+1}}{P_{n+1}}}{\dfrac{(1 - s_n)(\Upsilon/L)_n(L/P)_n P_n}{P_n}}$$

$$= \frac{1 - s_{n+1}}{1 - s_n}\,\frac{(\Upsilon/L)_{n+1}}{(\Upsilon/L)_n}\,\frac{(L/P)_{n+1}}{(L/P)_n}$$

and for the steady-state values used in Fig. 1,

$\beta_{2b} = (1)(1.034)(1) = 1.034$

Two rather drastic simplifications should be noted. First, depreciation was allowed to flow through consumption, reducing the number of variables by one. Depreciation dW on all wealth, including production capital, now will be introduced at the entry which connects wealth through time. W_{n+1} then will equal $W_n + s_n\Upsilon_n - d_nW_n$.

The second major simplification was the closed economy limitation. This limitation will now be relaxed by introducing exports, in the form eW, to the entry which connects wealth through time; W_{n+1} finally equals $W_n + s_n\Upsilon_n - d_nW_n - e_nW_n$.

Introducing this expanded concept into our original equation we obtain,

$$\beta_1 = \frac{1 - s_{n+1}}{1 - s_n}\,\frac{(\Upsilon/K)_{n+1}}{(\Upsilon/K)_n}\,\frac{(K/W)_{n+1}}{(K/W)_n}\,\frac{1 - e_n - d_n + s_n\,(\Upsilon/K)_n(K/W)_n}{1 + \Delta_n}$$

Applying this to our original steady-state Basic Array, but letting s increase to 0.3 (it is now gross of depreciation), and letting e equal 0.01 and d equal 0.03, we have

$$\beta_1 = (1)(1)(1)\frac{1 - 0.01 - 0.03 + 0.3(1/1.6)(1/2.5)}{1.015} = 1.020$$

For a solution, the conditions of equations β_1 and β_{2b} must be satisfied simultaneously.

In this skeletal form the model can be easily disaggregated or submodels attached appropriately. Parallel or tandem stems may be incorporated; some thought has been given to the addition of parallel stems involving monetary and fiscal concepts.

When the parameters are analyzed thoughtfully the inherently inter-disciplinary nature of economic development is demonstrated. What, for instance, are the factors which will increase s, Y/K, K/W, Y/L, L/P, and decrease Δ and real d? Exports are a special case and a supplementary model is needed to relate e over time.

The model, or modifications of it, may prove useful as a tool for forecasting and planning. It will focus attention on what is relevant and on the amount of relevance. The model also should be useful as an aid in understanding the actual mechanism of economic growth. In particular it may call attention to the part that wealth accumulation plays in improving human welfare. For the very poor it is, undoubtedly, the amount of goods that are available for consumption that is of utmost importance. But for those who have risen above the level of the very poor—perhaps already a majority of the earth's people—it may be the desire for wealth that drives men to greater accomplishment.

DISCUSSION OF THE PAPER BY WESLEY L. ORR

THE DISCUSSION of Professor Orr's paper centered primarily about (1) the roles of engineers in building models and developing nations; (2) the roles of political and social institutions in model-building and development; and (3) how model building should be done and how it should be used. The following synopsis reflects the questions and opinions of the discussants, as well as the answers and views of Professor Orr.

ROLES OF THE ENGINEER

Engineering is need-oriented. Initially, society's needs were primarily physical. Engineering became crystalized in the application of physical sciences, in the solution of physical problems, and in the creation of tools with which to solve these problems. This is feasible in a developed country where there are many kinds of professionals, where there are more engineers and mathematicians. But, since there are fewer categories of available skills, in a developing country the need is for flexibility, for innovation. However, it requires a great deal of strength to prevent a developing country from innovating for innovation's sake.

The Engineer as an Innovator. How should engineers help developing countries bring about innovation? The most immediate way of solving the problem of hunger in developing countries would be to produce more agricultural products. This, however, may not really be the best way of solving the problem. A preferable alternative could be birth control or a technology which satisfies and provides security to the population in other than physical-science-oriented, technological ways.

Who is the best engineer for a developing country? Not necessarily the physical-science-oriented engineer from the United States. Dr. Bugliarello did not think that, when a developing country looks to the United States for the best engineers, it gets the type of engineers it truly needs. He felt that a developing country requires an engineer who has the ability to make decisions in the light of few data; who has the ability to decide whether he is going to invest in a model in achieving new concepts, or in getting more data; who has the ability to decide whether he wants a mathematical model or physical model. The developing countries thus need innovative engineers who can help them go their own way.

The Engineer as a Carrier of Methodology. The second role of the engineer in developing countries is as a carrier of methodology to a different social economic situation. Such an engineer may have a limited knowledge of social science. Even so, he must be willing to try to understand this new situation because, as a carrier of methodology, he is a carrier of an aptitude for methodology and (according to Dr. Bugliarello) that is perhaps far more important to the developing country than the content of methodology.

The Engineer as a Social and Political Activist. According to Dr. Bugliarello, the engineer, as an agent of change, has two additional roles: a social and political force and an entrepreneur.

As a social and political force, the engineer should learn to be a decision maker. This implies that, when he makes decisions in social and political contexts, he must become politicized. He must understand the special groups, the economic forces that drive the people. He cannot remain science-pure. He cannot sit and make models; he must understand how they can be brought into being. And he must be, furthermore, willing to take action, not only by learning where the pressure groups are, but also becoming a member of a pressure group. He must influence opinion, he must acquire controls of the mechanism that build up knowledge, and create in the country that body of knowledge he thinks requires control. Thus he must acquire understanding of the compote of the universities.

As Professor Orr commented, an engineer should have an interest in any one of the parameters of the model ratios, thus indicating an interdisciplinary effort in industrialization. Dr. Sabato agreed that engineers are, as any other people, members of society but he added that the developing country, the engineer's society, is in a continuous crisis and the engineer must assume his role in that crisis. Most engineers from developing nations are trained in foreign countries. In these countries they receive all the information about ten subjects, but very little about historic processes. Thus, the indigenous engineer must learn to understand the historical processes and the crisis of his own nation.

The Engineer as an Entrepreneur. In Dr. Bugliarello's opinion, the primary role of an engineer in a developing country is as a doer, an entrepreneur. How can an engineer contribute as an entrepreneur? There are several facets to every country's economy: agricultural, mineral, manufacturing. Engineers already have made an enormous contribution to agriculture in the United States. It is difficult in a developing country to do anything about manufacturing for competition on the world market. Such a nation can manufacture for its own consumption, but cannot compete in a world market. Thus the engineer can make a considerable contribution by developing processes to utilize the natural wealth of a country.

In this context, Professor Orr commented that the engineer has two roles or functions that affect growth. First, he creates new forms of utility, thus increasing the total demand for goods and labor. Second, he produces old goods with greater efficiency, thus releasing labor. Taken together and in balance this becomes a spiral of growth. The concept of the two functions operating in unison constitutes a model of growth. Mr. Halty-Carrere felt that the engineer's roles as innovator and entrepreneur are complementary. To be a doer in an undeveloped country, it is necessary for an engineer to appraise and know the political context in which he must work.

THE ROLES OF POLITICAL AND SOCIAL INSTITUTIONS IN MODEL-BUILDING AND DEVELOPMENT

The discussants felt that it is very important to understand how various kinds of political institutions function and the roles that they play. Furthermore, engineers need an understanding of the sociological aspects of all the various kinds of institutions that are involved as vehicles through which engineers can function. One of the greatest shortages in the world today are vehicles in the form of institutions, vehicles through which development can take place. It was also felt that, unless there was a greater stress at the Conference on the institutional structures that are involved in industrialization, the participants would be missing a very, very important opportunity to understand what causes development to take place.

Every facet of Professor Orr's models involves institutions. This institutional structure has developed in the United States and in other nations of the world over a period of many years. It was suggested that a study be made of this institutional structure, including political institutions and the role that they play. Professor Orr agreed that engineers must work with institutions, which also can be fed into very good models. He also agreed that awareness of the political situation is important. This area, too, has its model aspects, and a model of political manipulation can be built just as well as one of physical manipulation.

A DISCUSSION OF MODEL BUILDING

Regarding economic models, it has been suggested that one may not assume that every member in a society will behave like a rational man. This applies to developed countries such as the United States as well as the developing countries. Thus, the feasibility of including other factors such as political mechanisms, social organizations, and psychological attitudes in more comprehensive development models was questioned. Professor Orr thought that model building can be done with social systems.

A model is a tool used by engineers. It is not infallible and it emphasizes the fact that there must be better communication between engineers and people in the political and social sciences, that the solution does not lie in technology alone, but in a combination of all inputs.

The Lack of Data. In this beginning stage of model building and model-use, one of the biggest problems is data. There are not enough data, even from countries such as the United States, to do a decent job with even a simple model.

Suggested Uses for the Model. One discussant cautioned against the practice of judging the efficiency of a model by its ability to predict. Professor Orr's model was considered to have as its greatest value the ability to lay out the context in which development can be done. It shows structure and dynamic relationships.

It was suggested that, in addition to trying to depict the influences of capital, labor, and production, Professor Orr's model should incorporate the variability of the output per capita which is actually the productivity of capital inputs. This element, in terms of time and the perspective of time, is where the engineering elements really bring the most important contributions. Professor Orr agreed and suggested that sub models could be built and put in the parameters.

Model Building for Savings in a Democracy. Savings are important for the takeoff of an economy and are a phenomenon that can be traced back at least as far as the Industrial Revolution in Great Britain. At that time, development was further aided by the fact that wages did not quite keep up with the new industrialization and that the entrepreneurs thus had an advantage. But today, with labor unions and other social organizations, that is not likely. Therefore, how does an engineer or an economist persuade a developing country to save 3 per cent rather than 2 per cent on a democratic basis? The Soviet Union's policy of keeping savings at the desired level by decree would seem to give that system an advantage. How, in a democratic environment, is an electorate—the consumers—persuaded to save more, even though that will, as the model shows, give it a temporary disadvantage? The only answer to such questions is that the value of the model ultimately is to demonstrate what needs to be discovered, what types of technology can be fed into the model, and what needs to be known.

BIBLIOGRAPHY

Barna, Tibor, ed. *Structural Interdependence and Economic Development.* New York: Macmillan, 1963.

Beach, E. F. *Economic Models.* New York: John Wiley, 1957.

Boulding, K. E. *Economic Analysis,* vol. 2, 4th ed. New York: Harper and Row, 1966.

Chenery, H. B., and P. G. Clark. *Interindustry Economics.* New York: John Wiley, 1967.

Duesenberry, J. S. *Business Cycles and Economic Growth.* New York: McGraw-Hill, 1958.

Hamberg, D. *Economic Growth and Instability.* New York: W. W. Norton, 1956.

Keirstead, B. S. *The Theory of Economic Change.* Toronto: Macmillan, 1948.

Lewis, J. P. *Business Conditions Analysis.* New York: McGraw-Hill, 1959

Lutz, F. A. and D. C. Hague, ed. *The Theory of Capital.* New York: Macmillan, 1963.

Neisser, Hans, and Franco Modigliani. *National Incomes and International Trade.* Urbana: University of Illinois Press, 1953.

Shell, Karl, ed. *Essays on the Theory of Optimal Economic Growth.* Cambridge: MIT Press, 1967.

Tinbergen, Jan, and Hendricus C. Bos. *Mathematical Models of Economic Growth.* New York: McGraw-Hill, 1962.

Organization for Economic Cooperation and Development. *Quantitative Models as an Aid to Development Assistance.* Paris: Organization for Economic Cooperation and Development, 1967.

United States Bureau of the Census. *Historical Statistics of the United States.* Washington, D.C.: U.S. Government Printing Office.

——————. *Long Term Economic Growth, 1860–1965.* Washington, D.C.: U.S. Government Printing Office.

——————. *Statistical Abstract of the United States.* Washington, D.C.: U.S. Government Printing Office.

3

NATURAL RESOURCES

Principal Paper—Ralph L. Miller
Discussion of the Paper by Ralph L. Miller
Commentary—E. T. Culver
Commentary—Kenneth F. Vernon
Report of Workshop 1—Norman K. Flint,
Rapporteur

The second topic of the Conference was the "Influence of the Availability or Nonavailability of Natural Resources." It seems evident that industrialization can take place only if the mineral resources of the country are known and if certain minimal levels are available to support the activity.

The Editors

INFLUENCE OF THE AVAILABILITY OF MINERAL RESOURCES ON INDUSTRIALIZATION

Principal Paper by Ralph L. Miller

ONE OF THE MOST pressing problems the world faces today is how to upgrade the way of life of the millions upon millions of our earth's inhabitants who exist at a bare subsistence level. Industrialization, to the extent that it is feasible and practicable, is one approach to the problem; all developing countries would benefit from increased industrialization since it would raise the economic base and bring more material benefits to the people.

The particular facet of industrialization considered in this paper is the influence of the availability or nonavailability of natural resources. Natural resources include such diverse things as fish and fowl, timber, crops, and scenery. The resource to which I shall confine my remarks, and which particularly concerns industrialization, is minerals.

THE IMPORTANCE OF POSSESSING MINERAL RESOURCES

To a geologist, the term "minerals" is inclusive, embracing metals, nonmetals, fuels, and water. There has long been a tendency to categorize nations into three poorly defined groups on the basis of their possession of minerals—the haves, the have nots, and those in between. In this context, the haves are considered to be blessed with bountiful supplies of basic minerals and thus to have the potential to achieve a high degree of industrialization; most of these so-called have nations started along the road to industrialization in the last century. The have nots, either because of their small geographic size or because of unfavorable geology for mineral deposits, are considered to have little potential for industrialization and are, for the most part, consigned to the role of agrarian nations. The in-betweens are presumed to have a few mineral commodities that can be exploited but to lack supplies of the basic minerals; hence, they never can be expected to achieve the degree of industrialization of the haves.

There is some truth in this rough grouping of countries in terms of their mineral potential for industrialization but, at best, the concept is a halftruth, and even this halftruth is subject to change with time. The possession of mineral deposits of large diversity and quantity is a valuable, but not necessarily indispensable, requirement for increasing industry in developing countries. No nation is completely a have-not nation in the realm of minerals.

In an effort to introduce an analytical element into the consideration of what controls the average standard of living of a society, a colleague in the U. S. Geological Survey, Dr. Vincent McKelvey (1959), has considered the major elements that control a country's human welfare and has expressed the interrelationship of these elements in an equation:

$$L = REI/P$$

in which
L = level of living or level of well-being
R = useful consumption of all kinds of raw materials
E = useful consumption of all forms of energy
I = useful consumption of all forms of ingenuity
P = the number of people who share in the total product of the numerator of the equation

McKelvey's equation is conceptual rather than truly mathematical because numerical values cannot be assigned to all the elements. Reflection will show, however, that it is valid as a concept. None of its elements is reducible to zero because, in such case the society would cease to exist. The product of raw materials times energy times ingenuity is roughly a measure of the degree of industrialization of a country. In a country where large quantities of raw materials (regardless of their source) and large quantities of energy per capita are consumed, and abundant human ingenuity—political, socio-economic, and technological—is applied in transforming the expenditure of raw materials and energy into meaningful products for the benefit of citizens, a high level of living must exist. The equation thus permits examination of the availability of minerals to a nation in the light of its effect on the standard of living. It is evident that while R (raw materials) includes more than minerals, minerals are an important segment of raw materials. Very few nations have achieved a high level of per capita income without a solid base of mineral resource development. The main exceptions are Switzerland, the Netherlands, Denmark, and New Zealand; each of these nations is, in its own way, a rather special case. It is also evident that while E (energy) includes expenditure of human and animal energy, the overwhelming source of energy utilized in advanced economies today is derived from the mineral fuels—coal, oil, gas, uranium and allied radioactive minerals, and from water for hydroelectric power. Finally, I (ingenuity), as it applies to the mineral factor in the economy, embraces primarily science and technology or, in this instance, geology, hydrology, mining, metallurgy, and hydrologic engineering. However, I also includes the political and socio-economic ingenuity essential to permit minerals to be developed and utilized constructively.

Let us look now at each of these mineral components of industrialization in the light of the position of developing countries with respect to them, and examine what may be done to upgrade that position.

EXPLOITATION OF MINERALS FOR EXPORT

In the McKelvey equation, the consumption of raw materials involves minerals, regardless of whether they are produced domestically or are imported. It is apparent, however, that, whenever a country possesses minerals within its own borders that can be produced competitively to supply domestic industries, much money devoted to foreign imports is saved and is available for other internal uses or external purchases. Industrialization is far easier economically with abundant supplies of readily producible minerals. In fact, the cost of importing minerals, particularly minerals of large bulk, has been a major factor in discouraging the development of manufacturing industries in many countries, thus requiring the import of many finished products to supply the needs of citizens who can afford to buy. Therefore, exploitation of minerals for export benefits the national economy and indirectly assists in the promotion of internal industry.

No country on earth to my knowledge is completely devoid of mineral resources. I do not know what mineral products may be mined or quarried in the litte principalities of Liechtenstein and Andorra, but both are blessed with fresh water supplies, the most valuable mineral commodity of all.

In general, the larger the country, the greater its chances for having a variety of mineral deposits, some of which may be economically exploitable. But of even more importance than size is the variety of geologic types of rock, ages of rock, and geologic structures within the national boundaries.

In the past 20 years it has been one of the cornerstones of technical assistance to developing countries to make a quick inventory of natural resources of the country in order to determine which resources have potential for development or for increased production. An inventory can indeed be taken for many types of natural resources—for example a census can be taken of livestock, and land under cultivation or timber resources can be quite accurately assessed with extensive use of airphoto interpretation. In the minerals field, however, the word "inventory," in the sense of assessing the mineral resources of an underdeveloped and little-known country, has no real meaning. Many mineral deposits are concealed beneath obscuring mantles of vegetation, soil, or barren rock. Some deposits have been found almost by accident, perhaps by a curious local inhabitant bringing in unusual looking specimens for identification; others have been found by more knowledgeable prospectors deliberately searching for economic deposits. But most mineral deposits are found, particularly in this day and age, in developed and developing countries alike, by geologists and geophysicists trained in the intricacies of their science, who familiarize themselves with what is known of a large region, develop all possible new information about the region, and then search in the most favorable parts of the region for clues that indicate the presence of one or a set of valuable minerals. Thereafter in the exploitation of an ore deposit, the geologist, the mining engineer, and the mineral economist all join forces.

In most countries of the world, and particularly in those of considerable size, the known ore deposits are but a part, and probably only a small part, of the mineral wealth that ultimately will be found. Concealed deposits will be discovered by utilizing sophisticated exploration techniques. New technological, economic, or political changes and developments will move some deposits from the submarginal into the exploitable category. New uses will be found for minerals now considered worthless. So I reiterate, making a quick inventory of the mineral resources of a developing country is an exercise in semantics, not in practicalities. Granting that one cannot make a realistic inventory of a nation's mineral resources, nonetheless one can search for mineral commodities that, if present, would help uplift a nation's economy.

Minerals for Export. I invite your attention now to the more important mineral commodities for developing countries. These commodities may be broken down into two categories: (1) minerals that can be produced largely for export, and (2) minerals produced principally for internal consumption. Minerals present in large quantities that can be produced and sold on the world market serve, among other things, to bring in foreign exchange, which may be used for many other desirable objectives. In this connection, we must not lose sight of the fact that the ownership of minerals rights in most developing countries is vested in the government and may not be transferred to private entities. Concessions for exploration or exploitation are granted, however, to individuals or companies. Governments of a considerable number of countries derive a major part of their revenue from minerals produced for export—witness metals mining in Chile and Peru, or petroleum production in Venezuela, the Middle Eastern countries, and Libya.

The major minerals that can be exported in large quantities are principally the metals—gold, silver, copper, lead, zinc, and iron—and the fuels—oil, gas, coal, and recently, uranium ore. Although many other metals are produced for sale in the world market by developing as well as developed countries, the above are the most important because they are used so widely in industry and have every prospect of continuing to be in demand for many years to come. In the developing countries, only small quantities of the above minerals are consumed internally, although the utilization of fuels for domestic power for human use and for industry should be a part of any fuel production industry in an underdeveloped country.

Minerals for Internal Consumption. Another group of minerals that are sometimes called the nonmetallics, but which increasingly are referred to as "the industrial minerals," are particularly important for internal consumption. Possession of mineral supplies, and particularly of the industrial minerals, that can be produced for internal consumption, provides the basis for starting new industries that will directly benefit consumers in a developing nation.

In the latest edition of a volume entitled *Industrial Minerals and Rocks,* published by the American Institute of Mining, Metallurgical, and Petroleum Engineers, the list of industrial minerals begins with abrasives and asbestos and ends with wollastonite and zirconium. In between are 53 other mineral and rock types or groups, among them many of the most important commodities for internal use in building and feeding its industries. Consider for a moment what some of these minerals and rocks are, and it is immediately apparent how difficult it is to do without them in a developing and industrializing economy—limestone and dolomite, crushed stone, construction stone, sand and gravel, cement materials, clay, salt, sulfur, glass sand, and fertilizer minerals, to mention only a few of the most important. It is hard to overestimate the usefulness of these rather prosaic industrial minerals in developing industries. For example, in a publication of the Department of Commerce issued 14 years ago, the uses of one of these commodities, limestone, were divided into five broad categories—agricultural, construction, chemical and industrial, metallurgical, and refractory. In the chemical and industrial category, 22 uses were listed and, in the metallurgical category, 32 uses. There are now probably many more industrial uses for limestone. I cite these examples to emphasize how important the possession of key industrial minerals is to the industrial development of a country, and how handicapped a country is when it is trying to develop and has to import the more vital of these industrial minerals. Imagine having to import sand and gravel for making concrete. Fortunately most countries of the world, developed and developing alike, have supplies of at least some of the more common and more useful industrial minerals. The job is to find them.

FUELS

Coal—Possession of an abundant supply of one or more of the mineral fuels has been a principal component influencing successful industrialization. Historically coal has played a vital role in fomenting the development of industry, as petroleum and natural gas do today, and atomic energy looms on the horizon as an important contributor for the future. While quite a few countries, including most of the larger ones, have usable supplies of coal, many others have little or none. In fact, 16 nations of the world produce 95 per cent of the world's coal, leaving only 5 per cent for all the other nations. I personally believe that deposits of lignite which might be exploitable on the site to produce electricity are more widespread than commonly realized, and might enhance the energy supplies of some developing countries.

Oil and Gas—Oil and gas deposits are more widespread in the world than are economic deposits of coal, and the end of the story of their discovery is by no means in sight. Indeed, with the rapid development of techniques for finding and producing oil on the continental shelves, it can be anticipated that some seaboard nations which are not now in the petroleum picture will join the ranks of the haves in the next few decades, to the very considerable benefit of both their financial situation and their supply of domestic energy for human and industrial utilization. The prospects for energy-poor developing countries also are becoming brighter because atomic reactors in the near future probably can provide power at lower cost than the conventional fuels in areas remote from the seaboard and thus can supply power for new small domestic industries.

Water—The subject of water supply for human use, for industrial use, and for hydroelectric power in developing countries is so vast and has so many ramifications that I could not do it justice in this paper. However, I do want to make several points. One can do a reasonably good job of inventorying the surface water supply of a country, including hydroelectric potential, by stream gaging and other techniques. Determining the supplies of ground water is much more difficult. It is both a hydrologic and a geologic problem. It is, however, most important in arid and semi-arid countries and in countries with long dry seasons, because the ground water supply of the world exceeds the supply in the world's rivers by a factor of about 50.

In the last few years the U. S. Department of the Interior has been conducting extensive research in desalinizing salt and brackish water and I think the time is not far off when it will be economically feasible to process sea water as well as surface and subsurface supplies of saline waters on land to fit them for industrial use. This should be of tremendous benefit to new small industries in developing arid countries for, as stated earlier, water-poor countries or parts of countries lack one of the principal ingredients for successful industrialization—abundant supplies of fresh water. The development of unknown or unused supplies of ground water and the conversion of unusable saline waters to usable form can do much in the future for these water-poor countries. The ground water geologist, the chemist, and the hydrologic engineer all join forces in this task.

FINDING AND UTILIZING MINERAL RESOURCES

How then does one go about helping a developing country begin to find out what its mineral resources are and begin to utilize them? This problem breaks down into three different parts. First, one should learn what the rocks, the structures, the tectonic history, and other geological aspects are. In the United States, this job started systematically about 150 years ago and it will probably still be continuing 150 years into the future. Federal and state governments and the universities have been the principal contributors in this learning process. Many hundreds of feet of bookshelves and many map cases in large geologic libraries are filled with published material presenting the geology of the United States in all its manifold aspects.

Second, this storehouse of knowledge should be put to constant use by other geologists who specialize in resource studies—the iron specialists, the petroleum specialists, the ground water specialists, the fertilizer specialists, and many others. Some of these resource specialists work for the federal government, some for state governments, some for universities, but many work for industry. The background knowledge they use as guides in their search for economic deposits of minerals is the wealth of regional geologic knowledge accumulated over the years.

And third, after a geologist (or prospector) has found a mineral deposit of possible economic value, the engineer should take over, working at times in collaboration with the geologist, at times independently. The size and grade of the deposit must be determined, the mining and metallurgical problems assessed; and finally the mineral economist must determine whether the whole package, once tied together, can constitute a viable economic enterprise.

NEED FOR SCIENTISTS AND ENGINEERS

The situation in the average developing country is that the geology and the mineral resources are very little known. How do we find out what the geology of the country is like—what different geologic environments and geologic structures are there, and what geologic events have occurred that would favor the existence of certain types of minerals and be inimical to others?

Assessing the economic mineral potential and finding means of exploiting it is a long-range job requiring educated and experienced scientists and engineers. But where are the scientists and engineers to do this work?

Several years ago, I analyzed this important question of technical manpower for the Central American countries. The figures I arrived at are shown in Table 1.

TABLE 1.—Geological scientists in Central American countries, 1966.*

Country	Native	Foreign	Total Population	Area (square miles)
Guatemala	8		4 285 000	42 042
El Salvador	6		2 824 000	8259
Honduras	0		2 200 000	44 482
Nicaragua	7	10	1 597 000	57 145
Costa Rica	11	1	1 391 000	23 421
Panama	3		1 210 000	28 576
Totals	35	11	13 507 000	203 925

Region			People	Area (square kilometers)
Central America	1 native geologist per		400 000	15 000
United States	1 native geologist per		6500	390

*Includes geophysicists and geochemists.

If far too few trained geologists are present in Central America, as Table 1 shows, there must be even fewer mineral engineers and economists to follow after the geologist and the prospector.

EDUCATION, TRAINING, AND INSTITUTION BUILDING

The jobs that need to be tackled are twofold: (1) education and training of nationals in the geologic and minerals engineering disciplines, and (2) institution building within the framework of the government and the universities to provide jobs and a livelihood for the technicians after completion of the training period, so that they can work at the regional and economic geology of their countries on a continuing basis.

If geologists and mineral engineers are not present in adequate numbers, are they being educated and trained? In many developing countries, they are not. Outside technical assistance is needed, almost required, to start things moving. This impetus may take the form of minerals' investigations by teams of foreign geologists and geophysicists. In many instances, the procedure has been to conduct airborne surveys, geophysical and geologic, with follow-up studies on the ground, searching for specific mineral commodities. The United Nations has conducted a number of such surveys and, in some countries, these studies have been successful in locating and proving up with the drill one or more potentially economic ore bodies. But once the team of experts leaves the local scene, all too often the country remains exactly where it was in terms of any continuing activity directed toward carrying on the work of learning the geology of the country and carrying on the search for additional deposits.

Departments of geology and mining engineering are either nonexistent or woefully inadequate in the universitites of most of the developing countries. Until young men and women have an opportunity to get a minerals education, only an occasional new face will be added to the roster of geologic and minerals experts available for work in their own countries. In almost all the developing countries, national universities need to initiate or strengthen departments of earth science and engineering in order to provide technicians for mineral discovery and development. In addition, government institutions need to be initiated or strengthened in almost all the developing countries to carry on long-range programs in earth science and engineering to foster the exploration for, the development of, and the use of mineral wealth, and thus directly or indirectly to promote greater industrialization and hence greater material benefits for the citizenry.

Men and women from the developing countries are the students, the scientists, and the engineers who should tackle the job of doing the geology of their countries in long-range programs. Whatever the minerals potential turns out to be, and there will be some minerals potential in every country, the educational and investigative effort will be useful and the results will be used.

SUMMARY AND CONCLUSIONS

I have touched on a number of different matters involving or related to the importance of minerals in fomenting and assisting industrialization in developing areas of the world. To summarize:

1. The possession of mineral deposits of large diversity and quantity is a valuable but not necessarily an indispensable requirement for increasing industry in developing countries. No nation is completely a have-not nation in the realm of minerals.

2. Exploitation of minerals for export benefits the national economy and thus indirectly assists in the promotion of internal industrial enterprises.

3. Possession of supplies of minerals, and particularly industrial minerals,

that can be produced for internal consumption provides the basis for starting new industries that will directly benefit consumers.

4. Assessing the economic mineral potential and finding means of exploiting it is a long-range job requiring educated and experienced scientists and engineers.

5. National universities need to start or to strengthen departments of earth science and engineering in almost all the developing countries to provide the technicians for the work of mineral discovery and development.

6. Government institutions need to be started or strengthened in almost all the developing countries to carry on long-range programs in earth science and engineering to foster the exploration for, the development of, and the use of mineral wealth.

DISCUSSION OF THE PAPER BY RALPH L. MILLER

POINTS BROUGHT up in the discussion of Mr. Miller's paper are summarized below:

1. The problem behind developing technicians who can find and exploit mineral resources is how to instill a desire in young people to become geologists and minerals engineers. There is no desire if there is no work and there will be no work unless investments are made in the country. There is no question of the resources that exist in Latin America. The greatest development of these mineral resources has been made by foreigners, by foreign companies, and by countries who need the resources that are there. However, although Argentina has tremendous resources which have been mapped, they have not been developed. Investors in Argentina want a quick return and do not want to get involved in the long-run effort which most mineral investments require. Thus there are no jobs for geologists and no one cares about becoming one. If anyone wants to become a geologist, he comes to the United States where he can get a job. Thus the biggest problem seems to be to encourage or try to encourage the investment atmosphere so that there will be work carried out on a national basis, and the desire will be established in young nationals to enter the mineral resources field.

2. One of the newer developments in foreign operations in developing countries is the provision for scholarships and technical training by the companies utilizing the minerals. This is beginning to encourage and provide an opportunity to those who are sufficiently interested to go on in these technical fields. There are organizations in some of the developing countries where geologists and scientists can get jobs. Almost invariably the development of an institution in the mineral field within a university or within government is the work of one man. And when one man comes along who has the vision, he can start something that will continue. Thus, the need is for a stimulus, internal or external.

3. The above is both right and wrong. It is right in the sense that if there is no investment, there will be no use for geologists and engineers. But how many geologists and mining engineers are produced in the Middle East where the biggest investment of oil has been, how many in Africa, how many in the Congo where investment in the copper industry began with World War I?

The biggest investment in Argentina in minerals has been from Argentines in the oil company. Thus, oil production in Argentina for the past twelve years has been Argentine, mainly because the School of Geology in Argentina has been a strong one. The School was founded at the end of the last century. All the resources were small but were used by the Argentine oil industry to explore and develop the oil in Argentina. If it were not for the geologists existing in Argentina, there could not be an oil industry in Argentina.

PRAGMATIC ASPECTS
OF RAW MATERIALS AVAILABILITY

Commentary by E. T. Culver

AS A PARTICIPANT representing industry, I am going to present some views based on practical experience. First I will present a number of apparent anomalies, observed or observable, in several raw materials situations in developing countries throughout the world. Then, using these facts as a background for further consideration, I will try to derive a basic conclusion concerning raw material supply for industrialization.

The various "economic" tests applied to raw materials sources for steel are broadly applicable to mineral supplies for most other basic industries. The word "economic" is intended to cover, under one blanket, an extremely broad range of technological and commercial disciplines and studies; in fact, it is *the* key word in this brief dissertation.

The country of Brazil recently announced to the world what appears to be a fine example of a nonfact. Geologists searching in the State of Pará have discovered some thousands of millions of tons of high-grade iron ore. Why is this a nonfact? Brazilians will tell you that, with their current proven and probable reserves of iron ore, they could supply the entire world's needs for the next 100 to 150 years. Thus, finding an additional several billion tons is not a matter of crucial economic interest.

Brazil's Santa Caterina coal is high in ash, high in sulfur, and makes poor coke. Yet many thousands of miners and their families depend on this industry for a livelihood. The government, determined to maintain production, fixes by law the amount (40 per cent) of Brazilian coal to be used in the manufacture of coke for the steel industry. The president of one of the large Brazilian steel companies has publicly stated that it would be more economical for him to buy Santa Caterina coal as required by law and dump it. He would much prefer to use 100-percent imported, high-grade coking coal in his ovens, and thereby reduce the cost of finished steel products by a very substantial margin. Therefore, again, having raw materials available can be relatively unimportant and may even prove to be something of a curse.

Consider another case in point: a Near Eastern country desiring a steel plant to help ease its balance-of-payments problems. In a preliminary review, the country stated that it had modest reserves of iron ore analyzing about 23 per cent iron (today's shipping ores run 57 to 63 per cent and higher iron). The ore cost was about $1 per ton at an inland mine head. Considerable research on beneficiation had turned up no common acceptable method of upgrading, but considerable confidence was expressed that a way would eventually be found. In a direct attempt at conservatism, my corporation accepted the assumption that beneficiation to perhaps 45-percent iron content would be possible. By a series of rough approximations, it estimated that ore concentrate delivered at a coastal steel plant site would cost of the order of $20 per ton. It also was forced to observe that high-grade, imported ore could be landed at the same plant for $8–9 per ton. Were this country's natural resources available or nonavailable?

Japan is the supreme example of a have not nation in terms of raw materials for steelmaking, and yet it is second only to the United States and the Soviet Union in world production. True, it has a large home market and, to the consternation of certain other steel producers, has developed a sizable export market. But the major raw materials are almost 100 per cent imported.

Chile, with only a 9 000 000 population, many of whom are not members of the money economy, has a major and flourishing steel industry. Its situation is the opposite of Japan's. Chile has the raw material, the iron ore, but only a very small market. Its dependence obviously is on exports. Nigeria has a bright internal market outlook but, so far as is known at present it possesses only relatively low-grade ores and no coking coal. To date it has not been able to initiate its long-cherished dream of an integrated steel-plant operation. One Far Eastern country—Singapore—with no iron ore, no coal, no assured fresh-water supply, relatively high-cost power, and a miniscule home market, nevertheless sees a bright future for a large, modern steel plant. Recall again, please, that the basic criteria being developed here are just as applicable to fertilizers or petrochemicals, to cement or brick making, and to any of several industries under investigation by developing countries, as they are to iron and steel.

Searching the above cases for a common denominator seems to be a fruitless task; yet, obviously, there must be some mutual and pertinent feature of these raw-material situations which makes them worthy of consideration as a group. In both have and have not countries there can be found examples of an entire range of production efficiencies expressed as the cost, actual or theoretical, of a ton of crude steel. Some have nots can export in the face of world competition; some haves require protective tariffs to assist large but uneconomical industries.

As a method of leading up directly to the conclusion, let us investigate in some detail just how much is implied by the positive statement one often hears in a developing country, "We have the necessary raw materials for this new _____ industry."

I submit the statement says that:

1. At one or more specific geographical locations there are certain minerals, fossil fuels, chemicals, or byproducts of another operation which constitute a basic supply for our planned industry.

2. We own or have rights to this material, or we have a longterm, firm commitment from the owners to sell at a specific price.

3. We have drilled and tested and analyzed geological information sufficiently to prove that we have reserves to carry the industry at least through obsolescence of the process and/or the equipment.

4. We have the mechanical means of recovering these raw materials from subsurface sources.

5. We have the manpower and infrastructure available at the site (or

accounted for in our financial calculations) to recover these materials from the ground.

6. Through research and testing, we have established that the crude materials can be converted to a size or form or degree of purity such that they can be effectively used in our industry.

7. We have the transportation system adequate to move bulk quantities from remote places to the point of manufacture; or, conversely, we are prepared to move our operation to the source of supply and ship the product to market.

8. After having considered this matter from the standpoint of the over-all national economy and the viability of the new industry itself, we have decided that this single source of raw material provides the most economical answer to our supply problem.

Note that the list concluded with the all-important concept of economical operation. Here then is the real test of the effect of the availability or nonavailability of raw materials. The illustrations given earlier serve to demonstrate this theory in actual operation.

The mere presence of raw materials is no guarantee of a viable project, just as their absence is certainly no bar to industrial development. Raw materials of high quality, present in sufficient quantities and economically available for use through new or existing recovery and transportation systems, can be a major driving force behind the urge toward expanded industrialization. But raw materials are not the basic consideration; they are, strictly speaking, only a contributory factor. Given a proven market, the financing to support construction, and the technology with which to build and operate, raw materials are seen more correctly as playing a somewhat subsidiary role. If a project is otherwise viable, due diligence will, in all probability, disclose several reasonable sources of materials, and the principal exercise will merely be one of establishing the economics of various imported and domestic supplies. True, there can be serious problems in technical diplomacy when local sources are downgraded or disregarded, but the only ultimate and true basis for industrial enterprise, whether in the public or private sector, is economic viability. The exploitation of domestic raw materials, except in the case of direct export, is a secondary consideration.

INFLUENCE OF THE AVAILABILITY OR NONAVAILABILITY OF NATURAL RESOURCES

Commentary by Kenneth F. Vernon

THE INFLUENCE of the availability or nonavailability of natural resources on industrial and technological development is an interesting subject because, although the presence of natural resources is very important to industrial development, the resulting levels may vary widely. As used herein, "development" means a series of actions which create and sustain a certain level of living, as distinguished from activities which require a continuous input from the outside to maintain that level of living.

In considering this subject I should like to follow the example used by Dr. Miller and try to set up an equation. The first term of the equation would be *natural resources* (things to work on); the second term would be *technology* (things to work with); and the third term would represent the *stimulus* and the lubrication which causes and assists technology to work.

In a perfectly straightforward situation these three terms would add up to a more or less static level of industrial growth. But I think that, in the ideal situation, there is a continuing interaction among the three. Improved technology identifies and unlocks more resources; the challenge of currently unusable resources stimulates more research to develop new methods. This interplay works best when there is a stimulus—continuous net positive yield of income or benefit from these activities which is immediately available to expand the industrial processes and, in addition, to increase the level of fundamental and applied research. In other words, the ideal situation occurs when the total is greater than the sum of its parts.

The direction that the technological development of any country may take is affected strongly by the presence or absence of various types of natural resources. The presence of a particular combination of resources exercises a strong causative relationship upon the development of particular technical skills. For example, India and Pakistan place great importance on the training of irrigation engineers because of the urgent necessity in these countries for constructing and operating highly developed irrigation systems with which to grow agricultural products. Initially, as a result of the interaction of land and water without artificial drainage facilities, salinized and waterlogged land was created. This required what might be called a second level of technology—the ability to diagnose and correct the problems that had been created—and, at a third level, an ability to prevent their occurrence. As this latter process developed, it became possible to introduce and support new methods of agriculture, together with improved seed strains. The cumulative effect of these technological inputs has been to increase crop production three to four times. A fifth level of effort now emerging is the improvement of harvesting methods, such as by introduction of the mechanical harvester. Thus, a new round of problems, created by the increased quantities of crops coming from the fields, is evidenced by the strain and need for improvement in the transportation, storing, and marketing of crops. The solution of these problems will require the attention of personnel trained in the art of moving food crops to market or, in terms of my equation, the initial availability of the land and water resources, the conditions favorable for agriculture, and the chain of events that have evolved through their use will require the creation of an agro-industrial complex. If sufficient stimulus is present, this industry will grow naturally rather than be poured in and sustained from the outside. Also, because of other current activities in the two countries, many of the tools by which the problems will be solved can be produced within the countries themselves, thus creating and supporting an additional level of industrial activities.

The above example is quite a clear-cut demonstration of the selfsustaining interaction of resources and technology. However, there are other situations where the selfgenerating and expanding development does not occur. In such situations, where there is energy without minerals or vice versa, there can be created at best only a limited extractive industry which will result in a low-level industrial development over the long term. That is not to deny that it may yield relatively high returns in the short run.

The extraction of petroleum in the Middle East is a case example of such a situation. While the extraction and transportation of petroleum has seen many technological improvements (one of the latest steps being the development of the supertanker), this industry has not created a selfgenerative industrial development in the countries supplying the crude oil. In making that statement, I am not overlooking the fact that Kuwait has a high level of consumer enterprise through the wise application, by the government, of the revenues received from oil sales. However, in some of the Middle Eastern countries, the oil revenue is known to have travelled to numbered bank accounts in Switzerland or into dubious investment properties in Beirut. Be that as it may, in Kuwait, roads, schools, hospitals, air conditioning, and the like have received much attention. Labor is attracted from all over the world and there is considerable activity in the petroleum-producing fields and in urban consumer services. However, this prosperity is dependent upon the continued need for petroleum by Europe and the United States and upon the continued ability of Kuwait to supply the petroleum. The industry and the resultant economic development, therefore, are resting on an uncertain base.

In this situation the inputs are all from the outside and the products are all exported. At best, the populations live in a sort of uneasy euphoric state so long as market conditions are favorable. When conditions change or when other localities can offer their products at a lower price, the present state of well-being will come to an uneasy pause. The economy is not selfgenerating.

It is possible to ameliorate the limited outlook by expanding the application of the second and third terms of the equation and create diversification of the industry. At the present time, great quantities of natural gas are being flared to the atmosphere in a complete waste of an irreplaceable natural resource. These natural-gas supplies could be transformed through industrial processes into various forms of fertilizers or fertilizer intermediates which are essential in the race between the world's population and its food supply.

At the present moment there are some imbalances in the worldwide equation of supply and demand. There is a supply capacity in the United States and Europe which exceeds the immediate demand in those areas. On the other hand, there is an under-capacity in the less developed parts of the world. Therefore, Europe and the United States are currently shipping to the lesser developed areas and there is a slightly less than enthusiastic desire by companies to invest in new facilities anywhere.

This situation is expected to continue until about 1972. However, for the period beyond 1972, new plant capacity must be installed. It is possible and, we may hope, likely that some of the new plant capacity will be installed in some of the less developed areas such as the countries around the Persian Gulf. If so, that will broaden the industrial bases of those countries and make them less concerned about technological or economic obsolesence.

REPORT OF WORKSHOP 1

Norman K. Flint, Rapporteur

THE PANEL—Messrs. Miller, Vernon, Culver, and Flint—addressed itself first to the scope of natural resources. Natural resources may be divided into two broad categories which are by their nature completely different: renewable natural resources and nonrenewable natural resources. The importance in the economy of a developing country of the renewable resources—crops, timber, livestock, fisheries—was recognized but, inasmuch as no member of the panel had experience in depth with these renewable resources, it agreed to confine discussion to nonrenewable resources, which are divided into four major groups:

Metallic minerals
Industrial minerals
Mineral fuels
Water (which in a sense is a renewable resource, but nonetheless a mineral)

The principal paper and two commentaries pointed out, from differing viewpoints, that the possession of mineral resources is a desirable but not indispensable requirement for the development of industries based on mineral raw materials.

THE PROBLEMS

The panel recognized, discussed, and was in agreement on the following five problems involving mineral resources in developing countries:

1. The nature and extent of the mineral potential, including all four categories of minerals as previously listed, need to be determined. In most developing countries the basic geology is poorly known and hence the favorable environments for minerals also are inadequately known. The short-range and long-range prospects for finding economically exploitable minerals require much additional basic and applied research.

2. Countries that have revenue-producing minerals such as oil or metals need to invest a part of that income back in basic research and development directed toward diversification of their industry so that, in time, they will not be dependent on just one commodity.

3. The education and training of technical, managerial, and fiscal personnel for the development of viable industries based on mineral raw materials is seriously deficient in almost all developing countries.

4. There is need for a regionalizing effort in many potential mineral-based industries whereby smaller countries can pool their resources and marketing outlets for mutual benefit. A small country that alone could not possibly support a mineral-based industry such as cement because of its own limited needs, may be able to support one if the needs of several nations will be served.

5. Investment in mineral exploration and development, whether by internal or external capital, is an enterprise fraught with risk. A favorable investment climate is needed whereby reasonable returns can be anticipated from successful mineral ventures. Without such a favorable climate mineral exploration and exploitation will not ensue.

THE PRESENT STATE OF KNOWLEDGE OF MINERAL RESOURCES IN THE DEVELOPING COUNTRIES

The panel concluded that the state of knowledge regarding the problems outlined above varies from country to country. In general, the technology and capabilities needed for an accurate analysis of the value and utilization of mineral resources are deficient in most of the developing countries. Hence, these need to be transferred from the developed countries to the developing countries.

RECOMMENDATIONS

The workshop agreed that the problems previously identified for the most part suggest their own solutions, but three specific recommendations were made:

1. Nationals should be trained in earth sciences and mineral technology in their own countries to the maximum extent possible so that early in their indoctrination they become involved in the mineral science and technology of their own country. This will necessitate bilateral and multilateral aid, including aid from private industry. It should be emphasized that aid programs of this type must be undertaken on a long-range basis.

2. The establishment or development of national mineral-oriented institutions needs to be encouraged and supported. These institutions should be charged with the task of finding methods for the effective use of capital to provide for basic research studies and to plan for the development of mineral resource industries where these are practical and promise to be useful. These national institutions need to be cognizant of all aspects of the mineral-based industries, from the earlier phases such as determination of the size and grade of a mineral deposit through the mining, milling, packaging, and transportation stages to the final stage of marketing or utilization of the product. The possession of a mineral resource has no value if the whole package is not an economically viable enterprise. The workshop did recognize, however, that at times tangible social benefits may accrue to an otherwise uneconomic mineral-based industry. These may make a marginal or submarginal mineral-based industry defensible, because it provides employment and hence saves substantial expenditures for social welfare or relief.

3. One of the major problems in many developing countries is getting started on the needed basic and applied geology because of lack of understanding, enthusiasm, or examples of what such a program should include. In some of these countries, the one or very few technicians or political leaders who understand the need and try to do something about it may be like voices crying in the wilderness.

One approach that has been successfully used in Guatemala and may well be applicable in other countries is to enlist the support of a university professor in a United States graduate school, presumably a professor already interested in Latin America, who will assign to advanced students doctoral dissertations that include the basic geological survey and the mapping of areas such as quadrangles in the developing country. Arrangements for such a program require the strong support of technical (political) leaders in the host country who will provide counterparts and logistic assistance as well as organizational connection and support. Over a period of years, not only new and important geology will get done and published, but the interest of national counterparts and of government officials can also be stimulated. This, in time, can result in new or increased efforts to undertake geologic investigations as an internal national program. The expense for the work of doctoral condidates is almost negligible, consisting of per diem and travel expenses for them and their

46

field assistants, and an occasional trip to the country by the sponsoring professor. What has worked well in Guatemala might work equally well in other developing countries. The same procedure for stimulating activity in needed areas also might prove successful for mineral-economics and marketing studies.

CONCLUSIONS

Mineral resources are important both for export and for internal consumption in promoting industrialization in developing countries, but they are not indispensable, as has been demonstrated in Japan. Long-range programs need to be developed to investigate, on a continuing basis, the basic geological configuration of developing countries and to explore more intensively those areas most favorable for mineral commodities of potential value. True conservation means the exploration for, efficient production of, and wise use of natural resources to provide the greatest possible good for the largest number of people.

REFERENCE CITED

McKelvey, V. E., "Resources, Population Growth, and Level of Living," *Science* 129: 875–881, 1959.

4

THE INFLUENCE OF ECONOMIC STRUCTURE AND FINANCIAL RESOURCES ON ENGINEERING TECHNOLOGY FOR DEVELOPING COUNTRIES

Principal Paper—Jack Baranson

Commentary—Walter Chudson

Commentary—W. Paul Strassman

Report of Workshop 2—Arnold Kroner, Rapporteur

This chapter is devoted to an analysis of the availability of financial resources in a viable economic structure, on both of which the development process obviously will depend.

The Editors

THE INFLUENCE OF ECONOMIC STRUCTURE AND FINANCIAL RESOURCES ON ENGINEERING TECHNOLOGY FOR DEVELOPING ECONOMIES

Principal Paper by Jack Baranson[1]

ECONOMIC STRUCTURE and the availability of financial resources have a strong bearing upon a country's technological structure. Economic structure covers a wide range of conditions including market size, income levels, the functioning of price mechanisms, and the availability of capital resources and foreign exchange. Market size determines the scale of production, income levels influence product design, and factor prices have a direct bearing upon the choice of production techniques. Supply and demand structure, in turn, are strongly influenced by economic policies. For example, industrialization programs based upon protection and import substitution nurture small-scale, poor quality, and generally inefficient industry. An official of a leading automotive manufacturing firm once remarked that his company would grow tomatoes in Antarctica if the protective tariff were high enough. This extreme has almost been reached in Chile where domestic content on automotive products runs nearly eight times international costs.

Technological adjustment does afford a developing economy an opportunity to utilize its resource endowment more effectively by economizing on "scarce" resources and making more intensive use of its "abundant" factors. But the limits of technological adjustment and managerial efficiency are set, in a very real sense, by the prevailing economic policies, given the stage of industrial development. Engineers are typically called upon to design plants and equipment under existing supply and demand conditions. A much more challenging role for engineers would be to design industrial systems which economize on scarce or underpriced factors, such as foreign exchange and managerial skills, and make more extensive use of relatively abundant factors, such as low-level skills and raw materials. There is also a specialized need for intermediate technology to serve markets of limited size at transitional stages of industrial development.

APPROPRIATE TECHNOLOGY FOR DEVELOPING ECONOMIES

Industrial products and production techniques designed for affluent economies and high-volume production are often ill suited to the low incomes and limited markets of developing economies. Technologies need to be adjusted to the purchasing power, market size, and factor availabilities of a particular economy. The fact is, the premature introduction of advanced techniques can retard long-

---

[1] The opinions expressed are the author's and do not necessarily reflect the policy or views of the World Bank. This paper is based in part on Dr. Baranson's book *Industrial Technologies for Developing Economies* which is to be published by Frederick A. Praeger.

term growth. The advanced continuous-flow techniques introduced on a massive scale in Soviet metal-fabricating industries during the 1930s resulted in widespread underutilization of scarce capital and mangerial resources. These advanced techniques required a high degree of inter-plant dependence, tight production schedules, and rigid standards specifications for materials and parts—all of which were lacking or deficient in the Soviet economy. Intermediate technology geared to the emerging levels of technical skills and managerial organization would have been more appropriate.

Resource "abundance" and "scarcity" are themselves functions of the technology that can be brought to bear. In general, capital, foreign exchange, and trained labor and management are considered "scarce" as compared to unskilled labor and certain natural resources which are relatively "abundant." In the industrial development of Great Britain and the United States during the nineteenth century, a substantial portion of technical innovation was in response to factor scarcities of industrial labor in the United States and of land and fuel resources in Great Britain. In the early phases of Japanese development, capital scarcity was in part overcome by using factor equipment more intensively on multiple shifts and with more labor assigned to tend and repair machines.

There are several reasons for the underutilization of abundant factors in developing countries. To begin with, the effective use of abundant resources also depends upon the availability and utilization of concomitant scarce factors. Developing economies often lack essential industrial capabilities or human resources to organize, manage, and control production. This is why Professor Hirschman favors capital-intensive techniques that are "large-scale, process-oriented, and machine-paced" to conserve scarce managerial capabilities to plan, coordinate, schedule, and control production. In mainland China the failure of small-scale blast furnaces using labor-intensive techniques is attributed to low quality of coking coal and high transportation costs to service widely dispersed units.

A second element inhibiting the full use of abundant factors relates to the limited capability of developing economies to adapt or convert techniques to available factors. Countries such as India have been criticized for failing to make adequate use of labor-intensive techniques as Japan did in its early stage of industrial development. Even today, Japan has a dual sector of subcontractors—with limited capital resources, paying lower wages, and utilizing labor-intensive techniques—to serve the larger capital-intensive industrial complexes. Japan's success in export markets has been attributed to its ability to transform factors and adapt facilities to changes in world demand.

A third limitation is that quality and precision requirements place absolute limits on the technical feasibility of substituting human skills for machine capabilities. A dilemma often is posed by the payoff between machine sophistication and the human skill requirement: sophisticated equipment that requires a minimum of the operator's skills usually requires high levels of planning, coordination, and maintenance skills. Simpler equipment places a heavier burden upon supervisory and operative skills to adjust tolerances, pace the feeding materials, and control quality and specifications of finished parts.

Fourth, there is the aspect of factor price distortion. This means that, although a factor may be abundant in an aggregate, relative sense for the economy at large, for a particular firm unskilled labor may be overpriced or capital goods underpriced relative to productivity. This, in fact, is the case in most underdeveloped countries. In other words, if the price mechanism were functioning, scarcity would be reflected in higher prices. Entrepreneurs responding to market prices of capital and labor tend to spend more on machine equipment than on labor-saving substitutes. Where market prices fail to reflect relative resource scarcities, costly and cumbersome controls often are necessary to ration scarce resources and minimize windfall profits.

Other factors indirectly affecting economic structure include labor practices, managerial attitudes, and government investment policies. For example, certain labor force characteristics include make-work practices and an insistence upon artisan craftsmanship which interfere with quality control and the adaptation of machine-intensive techniques. Lack of competition in an economy militates against adopting optimal techniques. This may explain in part the findings of a recent study on the international diffusion of direct reduction techniques in steel making, which indicated a very low rate of acceptance even though the processes were labor saving and more economical at low production volumes. Government policies toward foreign collaboration also have a direct bearing upon efficacy in implanting industrial technologies. While recognizing that foreign collaboration fills vital development needs during critical transitional periods of industrialization, most governments seek to limit foreign participation in terms of ownership, management, and the employment of foreign technicians. This propensity to discriminate against, and be hostile toward, foreign enterprise has been an important deterrent to development.

IMPACT OF ECONOMIC STRUCTURE UPON TECHNOLOGICAL DEVELOPMENT

Repeated reference has been made to the growing technological gaps between industrially advanced and developing areas of the world. It is important to distinguish among the potential gains to productivity and the industrial growth rate derived from improvements in management, in economic policy, and in technological structure. The latter refers to induced characteristics of plant size and production scale, the accommodation of techniques to factor scarcities, specialization, and interdependence among plants contributing to related end-products, and the types of managers and innovators associated with production modes. Market development also has been repeatedly cited as the prime mover in technological development. Technological adjustments can be made only within the allowable frame of economic policy and managerial capability.

Because of certain protectionist policies, the potential gains from technology and management are severely constrained.

The general tendency among developing economies in Asia and Latin America has been to industrialize in an extensive range of processing and manufacturing industries—everything from steel and cement to heavy equipment. Inevitably, this approach has resulted in spreading thin the critical but scarce technical and managerial skills needed to run industrial plants and handle modern technologies. Technological absorptive capacities have been even further strained as developing economies have advanced from simple consumer goods, such as home appliances and bicycles, to the much more complex producers' and consumers' requirements such as diesel engines, electrical transformers, railroad locomotives, and hydro-electric turbines—all of which most industrializing countries are now attempting to manufacture themselves rather than import from abroad.

In addition, policies aimed at progressive autarky have fostered a seller's market which tends to undermine technical standards throughout the economy. These policies have also contributed to a widening of the technological gap between the developing and more advanced economies. Product designs and techniques for the small-scale, protected markets lag behind latest developments because of the high conversion costs for low-volume production. These technologies have a built-in obsolescence and are rarely able to survive in competitive world markets. Protectionist and import-substitution policies also contribute to the high costs and inferior quality that characterize procurement and production in developing countries. Industrial firms are compelled by domestic content regulations to duplicate too broad a spectrum of manufacturing industries, a task that becomes progressively difficult in proportion to the sophistication of the transplant and its dependence upon special capabilities and skills.

In Argentina, for example, over a dozen firms manufactured more than 65 major types of passenger cars and light trucks for a market of 200 000. The result was an industrial plant ten times what is required to produce this number of vehicles under competitive conditions. Intensified competition among too many producers for the limited-size, protected market contributed to the proliferation of models and makes, which compounded the diseconomies of scale. As a result, production costs in Argentina average two to three times above international standards. The high cost and poor quality nurtured by protective systems undermine the entry into world markets which could eventually help overcome scale disadvantages.

In the heavy mechanical industries of Argentina, the tendency toward broad product diversification to maintain production in underutilized installed plant capacity stretched technical resources and compounded diseconomies of scale in a market of limited size. Boom-and-bust economic cycles endemic to Argentina contributed to the tendency to overdiversify as a means for utilizing installed capacities. Firms that began in shipbuilding eventually moved into production of locomotives, industrial boilers, oil refinery equipment, structural shapes for bridges and oil wells, cranes, grain silos, and escalators.

REQUIRED TECHNICAL ADJUSTMENTS
TO ECONOMIC STRUCTURE

In industrially advanced countries, product design and production engineering generally occur as separate functions. In an industrially advanced country, it is feasible to separate the functions because the production engineer is able to draw on a vast range of industrial resources and capabilities. But this is rarely the case in underdeveloped countries where the range of industrial capabilities is limited. For this reason, it is especially important in developing countries to design products that incorporate both market demand and productive capability characteristics. This calls for a unified concept of design combining both product design and production engineering. The time and resources it takes to make the necessary adjustments depend on the size of the gap, the absorptive capabilities of the recipient groups, and the prevailing level of protection. The technological absorptive capability of a country such as Japan stands in marked contrast to that of countries such as India or Mexico.

Japan has the engineering and technical skills to convert foreign techniques to domestic conditions. During economic boom periods, production orders come in much more rapidly than most demands for new machine tools can be filled. Japanese industrial firms are able to subcontract to the large number of small shops and factories found in Japan today. Hundreds of technical drawings must be made to convert machine-intensive into labor-intensive techniques. These drawings require the large number of engineers and technicians available in Japan today. A second factor unique to Japan is her highly skilled and abundant industrial labor force. When modern machine techniques are converted to more labor-intensive techniques, heavier demands are made upon machine operators to read blueprints, set up tools, and substitute human skill for machine accuracy. A third element of technological flexibility that exists in Japan, but is generally lacking in underdeveloped countries, is the system of subcontractors that work as segments of industrial complexes. To function effectively, these small machine shops and factories must be able to coordinate their activities within the larger industrial complexes. This includes meeting engineering standards and production schedules and presumes a high degree of effectiveness in industrial organization.

Principles of value engineering (or functional analysis) could be applied to these and analogous industrial design problems. Design engineers must decide whether to relax materials standards, change manufacturing specifications, or, as a last resort, redesign components or parts to accommodate local materials, customer usage, or inability to handle a particular production technique. As an example of specialized product needs, in developing countries where crop yields per acre are low, harvesting combines require "big mouths and small stomachs;" in agricultural sectors with higher crop yields, the need is for "small mouths and big stomachs." Climate, terrain, and crop differences also necessitate product design variations in the harvestor's "pick-up" mechanism. For passenger vehicles designed for use in a country such as India, the following design adjustments would be desirable: higher ground clearance to avoid ruts in the road, added protection for the gas tank, heavy-duty air cleaner for dustier climates, gasoline filter on intake spout, oil pan shaped to maintain lubrication level at steeper incline (as on farm tractor), larger radiator with greater heat-dissipating capacity for hot climates, additional insulation for electrical system against dampness and water, and a higher-frequency horn for congested traffic areas.

As for adjustment in production techniques, cars and light trucks have been redesigned to minimize tooling costs and economize on low-volume production runs. This has been done by using straight-line bodies, thereby avoiding expensive investments in contoured dies and developing a family of models using interchangeable body elements. Much less expensive press-bends are used to shape angular edged fenders, hoods, and side panels. For example, an American steel company designed and built a series of vehicles based on standard mill forms which required minimum investments in forming and fabricating equipment even though they retained functional and style requirements. Interchangeability among body elements and multipurpose use of the end product also were maximized in order to reduce capital outlays for machine tooling. Three different vehicle types were designed based upon more than twenty interchangeable parts, including door and body panels, bumpers, grill elements, and molding frames. Maximum use also was made of basic mill shapes—tubular steel, bar stock, and specially rolled sections. Bonded steel sandwiches (two layers of steel separated by a steel core designed to give a high strength-to-weight ratio) were produced as standard stock and used on roof panels, front and rear panels, and floors. Seat frames were assembled from steel bars. A single stainless-steel grill module was used in different combinations for front, rear, and side functional and visual effects. Component design was based upon inexpensive metal-forming techniques requiring minimum capital investment in tooling. Thus, matched metal dies, which normally require long production runs to amortize, were purposely avoided. Body elements were designed to be formed on less expensive press brakes, blanking equipment, and roll-form lines.

In the processing of raw materials, certain adjustments can be made for markets that are small by international standards. For example, oil refining can be undertaken at reasonable economic costs, provided the range of petroleum products is limited and domestic supplies are mixed with imported crudes. This may necessitate international trade in raw materials and end products to avoid balance of payment deficits. Certain refineries could import crude oils rich in middle distillates and mix them with locally available heavy crudes to produce the major range of less sophisticated products for domestic consumers. The more abundant heavy crudes can then be exported to earn the foreign exchange needed to import the complementary crude oils and the remaining minor range of more sophisticated petroleum products, such as high-octane gasoline and jet fuel.

In designing a plastics industry for a developing economy with a small internal market, plant size, product range, and the factor mix of domestic and imported materials can be adjusted to minimize the added cost of small-scale production. Economies may be realized by limiting the color range and variety of grades in basic plastic compounds. Products and techniques can be adjusted to an abundant raw material such as natural gas with supplementary imports of an item such as chlorine.

The foregoing examples of technical adjustments in industrial design are indicative of the potential role engineers can play in helping newly industrializing countries adapt to their economic structure and utilize available resources more effectively at emerging levels of productive capabilities. Engineers employed by international firms are in a particularly advantageous position to assist manufacturing affiliates in developing countries. Design parameters drawn from the home and regional markets could be included in a global market strategy and the developing country given a share in this marketing and manufacturing complex. An American manufacturer recently designed a light-weight diesel engine with a fuel economy feature and low-initial cost for three different world markets in mind—the small truck and bus market in Latin America, the stop-and-go delivery truck of North America, and a line of passenger cars and light trucks in Europe. Engineers need to join with development economists in formulating design parameters for industrial systems, if the products and systems are to reflect existing conditions and respond to emerging opportunities.

THE DIALOG BETWEEN ECONOMISTS
AND ENGINEERS

Commentary by Walter A. Chudson

IT WOULD BE misleading to say that in the outpouring of literature on economic development during the past two decades the technological dimension has been neglected. One has but to recall the vast documentation prepared for the United Nations Conference on the Application of Science and Technology for the Benefit of the Less Developed Areas held in 1963.

Nor would it be accurate to say that there has been a gross failure of communication between economists and engineers in regard to the problems of selection, adaptation, innovation, and implantation of technology for the promotion of economic development. There has been no lack of exhortation by development economists to their engineering confreres to aid in selecting from the spectrum of existing technologies those which are most efficient economically in terms of factor proportions. And there also has been a fair amount of pressure on the part of economists to encourage engineers to widen the spectrum of technologies available to the developing countries, including new technologies that permit a better exploitation of existing factor proportions and technologies that facilitate the better exploitation of some known natural resources or overcome structural limitations imposed, for example, by the restricted size of markets or, more generally, increase the physical efficiency with which available resources can be utilized.

Yet, as demonstrated by the convening of this Conference, there remains some uneasiness as to whether the dialog between economists and engineers has been as fruitful as it might be and whether the economic structure and policies of both the developing and industrialized countries have fostered reasonably effective progress on the technological front of economic development.

Perhaps the most insistent call in this context from the economists has been to urge the developing countries and those advising, assisting, or undertaking production in them to adopt technologies that economize on the relatively scarce factor of capital and utilize a high proportion of the abundant factors, especially unskilled labor. The call usually has not ignored the fact that the correct economic criterion is the utilization of all available factors in such a way as to maximize total output and that to follow the rule of optimal factor allocation by no means implies that some goods and services should not be produced by more capital-intensive processes than others. Yet it has apparently led to considerable feelings of frustration among many economists and some engineers, particularly as regards technology in the industrial sector. After a considerable time, few dramatic breakthroughs of this type can be cited either in the form of striking gains from adopting labor-intensive methods in manufacturing from the existing stock of techniques or from devising new labor-intensive technological opportunities foregone. Isolated cases of the adoption of excessively capital-intensive techniques (for example, Soviet metal-working in the 1930s cited by Granick) are balanced by some notable failures in labor-intensive procedures (for example, the backyard iron smelters of mainland China).

This sense of frustration does not mean that there is something wrong with the theory. As the economists have moved from abstract theorizing to quantitative and empirical examination of alternative production techniques, they have gained a considerably better understanding of the reasons for the frustration.

Economists, as Raymond Vernon has recently written, are very fond of conceptual repackaging. Thus, in the light of experience, one can repackage the factor proportions theorem by saying that the tendency to characterize the less-developed countries as having a relative abundance of labor has ignored the fact that this is an abundance of unskilled labor and that increasing the supply of skilled labor is, in economic terms, no different from the production of capital goods. Seen in this light, the resource endowment of many developing countries appears less amenable to the application of truly economically superior technical alternatives in the form of labor-intensive production functions. In reality there appears to be less flexibility in the system—always given the test of maximizing output with a given input—than theorizing about the logic of labor-intensive methods of production seemed to suggest.[1]

Closer study of industrial processes has suggested a number of reasons. The effective use of relatively abundant unskilled manpower often depends on the availability of other scarce factors, both material resources and skilled human resources needed to organize and control production. Thus, the economic utilization of abundant unskilled labor in labor-intensive, small-scale operations frequently depends on the capacity to organize such production and to standardize output so as to make it usable in complementary large-scale production, as in Japanese subcontracting.

Further, in many industrial processes, particularly those of the "continuous-flow" variety, the more capital-intensive processes are simply the more physically efficient beyond a minimum scale of output; they use less of all productive inputs per unit of output, or, at least, less of some inputs, while keeping all other inputs the same.

Still another constraint is that, for certain types of output, quality and precision requirements limit the effective substitution of human skills for machine capabilities. Indirect costs to utilize abundant factors also may be excessive. Thus, the real cost of recruiting, training, and supervising labor has tended to be underestimated. As noted, one may generalize this by describing it as a form of capital scarcity—scarcity of human capital—but it remains real nonetheless.[2]

Although, for the reasons indicated above, there has been a general feeling of frustration about the adoption of labor-intensive technology in industrial processes in the developing countries, there have been numerous instances of efficient technological adaptation and innovation during the past several decades. Some adaptations have been the result of deliberate changes in the design of products and of production systems. Others have been essentially an unintended spin-off from technological developments in the industrialized countries which happen to possess great value in view of the resource availabilities of the developing countries. Everyone can cite his favorite examples of both categories and it might well pay to make a more systematic inventory of such adaptations and applications *pour encourager les autres*. In their respective fields, the United Nations Industrial Development Organization (UNIDO) and the Food and Agriculture Organization (FAO) are doing this to some extent, but still more could be done.

One example which I find intriguing is the recent development of the processing of cashew nuts in Tanzania. While hardly of the dimensions of the petroleum industry, for example, the humble cashew nut has a big future in the dynamic market represented by the affluent cocktail circuits of the industrial world. With favorable growing conditions, Tanzania had developed a thriving industry producing raw cashew nuts. But, oddly, until recently the economics of production was such that the nuts were not exported directly to the markets of the industrial world, their ultimate destination, but instead were shipped across the Indian Ocean to Bombay and other places for shelling, processing, and subsequent shipment to London and other world markets.

The reason? Mainly that labor costs in Africa were so much higher than in India where child labor was prevalent and where, difficult to believe, the alternative employment was even less promising for unskilled labor than in Africa, where a retreat to subsistence agriculture was evidently more attractive than the tedious and skin-searing cracking of one nut at a time, each with its corrosive (if industrially valuable) layer of oil. Experts also attribute the superior Indian productivity to higher level of skill in hand-processing operations and to superior managerial skills within the framework of a very labor-intensive cottage industry.

Under the United Kingdom mandate in Tanganyika (as it was named then) this anomalous situation did not go unnoticed. Numerous efforts were made over a period of years to develop a mechanical decortication system and the problem was regularly referred to the appropriate Ministry in London and from there to an official engineering unit, all with inconclusive results. Meanwhile the prospect for a viable hand-processing industry in Tanganyika was worsened by the enactment of minimum-wage legislation.

In 1962 the problem came to the attention of a visiting Italian industrial firm which has some experience in food processing and specifically in the shelling of nuts.[3] It was not long before the firm had, as it were, cracked the problem. After numerous difficulties, largely of an administrative and political nature, were overcome, the venture produced its first shipment in December, 1965, and is now one of the country's larger manufacturing employers. The Indian producers, despite their almost incredibly low labor costs, are now unable to compete in the world market with the costs of the mechanized process in Tanzania and the structure of world trade in cashew nuts has thus been transformed.

The initial referral of the problem to London occurred at least as early as

1955 or 1956. And it took four years from the day when the project was assigned top priority in the Tanzanian Ministry of Industry to the day when cashew products were shipped from the factory.

Among the major techno-economic problems in Tanzania still awaiting solution is the loss of 20 per cent of the cashew crop owing to inadequate storage and drying facilities. As might be expected, the industry has developed numerous backward and forward linkages with the local economy, including the upgrading of cashew shell liquid for use in the manufacture of paints, resins, and lacquers.

For present purposes perhaps the most interesting feature of this tale is the displacement of a labor-intensive technology by an economically superior capital-intensive technology even in countries with such an abundance of labor as India and Tanzania (and allowing for the effect of a possibly inappropriate minimum wage).

Moving from random anecdotes and impressions to generalizations with a quantitative content, I feel that the following propositions will stand up.

1. Despite the greater awareness of economists and engineers of the needs of the developing countries, the technological innovations of greatest economic significance to the developing countries in the past few decades, actually or potentially, have been, as before, largely the unintended spin-off of research aimed at solving the pressing problems of the developed countries: for example, the desalination of water, the birth-control pill, the L-D (oxygen blast) process for steel production, educational TV hardware and satellite communications, short take-off and landing airplanes, improved lubrication of automobiles, and the like. It could be rejoined that the greater awareness has hardly been matched by greater commitment of resources for research, development, and communication of information, and that such commitment would have yielded greater results. Certainly the importance of the goal and the limited cost of such efforts justify testing this proposition.

2. Apart from the dramatic new strains of rice and wheat, and possibly other botanical breakthroughs with which I am unfamiliar, the chief exceptions to the above generalization have been the result of research designed to utilize infraeconomic raw materials or other natural resources hitherto too costly to exploit or even technically unexploitable: protein derivatives such as fish-meal products, paper from various fibres such as bagasse, the whole coconut, natural fibres, cashew nuts. In the most general sense these cases (and the examples cited in the preceding paragraph) can be described as adaptations of technology to factor proportions (the utilization of relatively abundant natural resources), but they are not examples of the textbook case of relatively labor-intensive technology. In many cases they are either neutral in this respect (as in the L-D process) or more capital-intensive than the processes they have displaced or than those in use in the most advanced countries.

3. There has been some progress in scaling down production processes with no increase, and perhaps some decrease, in unit costs, particularly if transport

costs of bulky products are taken into account. Examples are new processes in the production of cement and petroleum products. There also are significant potential gains to be realized from the modular design of machinery to overcome diseconomies of scale. But there are contrary examples as well of economically superior technology with larger scale operations, for example in the production of synthetic fertilizers. Further, the scaled-down technology is not generally more labor intensive.

4. There is a class of products, as Baranson has shown, of which the automobile is the leading species, which illustrates the case of a vicious circle in which faulty economic policies (mostly, though not entirely, in the developing countries themselves) lead to production for small and sheltered domestic markets, causing technological retardation and disincentives to technological advance and adaptation, leading to high costs, limited markets, and so on around the circle. Market size limitations are much more important than technological or managerial constraints in determining the real cost of production of automobiles, tractors, and similar products in developing countries, even though the process of technological transfer and adaptation could no doubt be made more efficient. Put in another way, in these industries the potential gains from a transformed system of large-scale specialized production of components and international interchange far exceed gains from the substitution of any conceivable, more labor-intensive, methods of production.[4]

5. The most promising area for adaptation and innovation employing more labor-intensive methods appears to be in the agricultural sector and the initial processing of foodstuffs and agricultural raw materials. It is not without significance, I think, that the Intermediate Technology Group of London has moved in this direction, undertaking useful compilations of available agricultural equipment for small rural workshops for the production of simple consumer goods and fostering research in new production processes and product designs. The production techniques involved are less capital-intensive than those used in the advanced countries, but more capital-intensive than those currently used in primitive peasant agriculture and handicrafts.

6. It is regrettable that a "dialog of the deaf" has been permitted to develop between the partisans of "intermediate technology" and the bulk of development economists. This is all the more unfortunate since the economists are, in fact, used to thinking about development problems in terms of a dual economy consisting, on the one hand, of an urban, modern, technologically and administratively complex sector and, on the other, of a rural, technologically primitive sector. It is unrealistic to think of technological transfer and adaptation without keeping in mind the requirements and possibilities of these two distinct sectors. The job of the economist (and the collaborating engineer) is to keep in mind the different economic and technical conditions and possibilities of these two sectors. And it is the job of the economist, in close collaboration with his engineering confreres, to analyze the trade-off in the allocation of scarce resources (including resources for technological research and development) between the two sectors.

There can be little doubt that a "systems analysis" of the rural sector undertaken in collaboration by economists and engineers, not to mention sociologists and other professionals, would yield substantial dividends in many countries. In addition to development of new labor-intensive production techniques for use in agriculture and rural industry, attention should be given to product design, housing, storage facilities, and training techniques. Thinking of this problem in terms of an entire system or set of relationships is certainly the best hope for dealing with the problem of surplus labor and premature high-cost urbanization.

In approaching the technological problems of the advanced sector it will be useful for engineers and economists to focus attention more on the framework of economic policy and institutions in which relatively sophisticated technological transfer, adaptation, and innovation may take place most effectively and on such questions as optimum institution building for national technological capability, the formulation of skill requirements for modern industry and the related strategy of training, and the role of the large multinational corporation in technological transfer.

NOTES

1. This does not necessarily negate the general validity of the proposition that developing countries should be expected to have a comparative advantage in the production of relatively labor-intensive goods, provided that the technological alternatives available (production functions) in the industrial countries do not offset this in particular cases. The recent comprehensive research by Hal Lary (1968) of the National Bureau of Economic Research suggests that, in fact, the ranking of industries according to labor-intensity is roughly the same in both the industrial and the developing countries—thus supporting the proposition that a comparative advantage exists in the production of standardized relatively labor-intensive products in the developing countries (such as textiles, footwear, cheaper clothing, and many simpler consumer goods). A pattern of mostly temporary exceptions to this in certain "high technology" products has been noted and analyzed by R. Vernon in "International investment and international trade in the product cycle," *Quarterly Journal of Economics,* May 1966, and S. Hirsch in "The United States electronics industry in international trade," *Economic Review,* National Institute of Economic and Social Research, London, November 1965.

2. The foregoing are all valid "real" limitations on the substitution of labor for capital according to the test of optimal use of available resources. There are, in addition, the well-known structural friction that prevent optimal combinations of labor and capital from the point of view of the economy as a whole: factor-price distortion (overpriced wage rates, underpriced interest rates, and overvalued exchanges rates) and a variety of social, psychological, and institutional factors inhibiting the substitution of labor for capital. The case for appropriate subsidies or equivalent policies to overcome such frictions is clear and limited only by the very real and practical problems of implementation. The introduction of dynamic elements such as the effort to technological choice on income distribution and capital formation (Galenson-Leibenstein) and of non economic objectives such as provision of employment for social welfare reasons further complicate the picture.

3. The details of this phase of the project are described by J. J. Voci and J. A. F. Stoner in "The reality of technical assistance," *International Development Review* (Washington, D.C.), Dec. 1967, Vol. 9, No. 4.

4. The cost of the present inefficient system to the developing countries is measured in terms of the larger output from a given input of resources that could be obtained from a reorganization of the

industry based on producing a smaller portion of the value of the entire product in a given country. It must be admitted that the attainment of this technologically and economically superior alternative may be beyond the control of a single country, as it involves international cooperation in the form of a system of interchange of parts and components, each produced on a larger scale than presently.

THE ECONOMIC STRUCTURE AND TECHNOLOGY: SUBSTITUTES FOR CAPITAL-LABOR SUBSTITUTION

Commentary by W. Paul Strassmann

FOR MANY YEARS the engineer's job has been virtually synonymous with designing machines to replace workers or, as economists say, as capital-labor substitutions. Since poor countries are poor in capital but not raw manpower, they cannot give high priority to replacing labor with capital. In fact, economists have urged engineers to design in reverse, to find ways of substituting labor for capital. But this task does not appeal to many engineers. Some prefer to apply their analytical talents to the economy as a whole, treating it like a petroleum refinery or an electronic circuit. They create dynamic general systems simulation models.

Unfortunately, these models are a waste of effort. Economists already have much experience with sophisticated macro-modeling. They have made numerous mistakes and been sobered by the limitations of such efforts. There is no need for engineers to prove that they are simultaneously ingenious and naive by repeating these mistakes and discovering the limitations. Let them consider Arthur Lewis' *Development Planning* (1966) and Harvey Leibenstein's "What can we expect of a theory of development?" (*Kyklos,* 1966) as labor-saving devices before proceeding. Even in fairly stable developed economies like the Netherlands, input-output coefficients have to be re-estimated every three years or models become useless for policy decisions. In the social sciences, completely determined systems are impossible if people make up the system. The human ability to learn and plan is inconsistent with predetermined patterns. Moreover, economic aggregates are not like homogeneous electronic components but heterogeneous conglomerates. Assumptions about their characteristics simply cannot be substituted for data: the variety of options and substitution possibilities is simply too great. As logical exercises or heuristic tools, these models are most likely to duplicate previous, often misleading, efforts.

Nor should they follow the economists' advice and look for labor-using methods in the simplest price-theory textbook terms. Economists usually consider factor substitution at given volumes and for value-added alone, hence omitting materials. At the plant level, adapting to volume and materials comes ahead of adjusting to different wage-capital cost ratios. Engineers have made and continue to make valuable contributions by designing machines which save capital without necessarily lowering the capital-labor ratio. Underdeveloped countries need simpler but more versatile machines. In this way each machine can be used for a greater variety of tasks and be amortized over a larger volume of tasks. While designing such machines, engineers also can change the design of products through simplification and standardization of products and components. Can axles or transmissions be made with fewer machines? Can they be redesigned for use in a greater variety of (also redesigned) cars and trucks?

Redesign is easiest where governments can prod the branch plants of technically sophisticated international corporations. But standardization and multipurpose machines also could be developed for many other branches of industry that are small-scale and untouched by international investments: bricks, tiles, window fixtures, furniture, kitchen utensils, paper products, shoes, publishing, and many others. Technical assistance in these branches has consisted largely of making available standard plans from advanced countries. This is good, but it does not show what might be developed if a special effort were made to redesign product and process in terms of, not local conditions, but conditions widely prevalent in poor, small-market countries. Outside engineering help would be most useful in these industrial branches since the plants at present often lack all access to such talent. Their information comes from salesmen who handle too many lines of equipment for much proficiency at even off-the-shelf recommendations. The problem is identifying a place to begin. How can one bring entrepreneurs and engineers together before an inadequate plant has been set up and losses begin? It is not likely that the costs of establishing contact can be recovered in early experiments, but at least the communications network should not cost more than the savings or increased output generated, no matter to whom they accrue.

REPORT OF WORKSHOP 2

Arnold Kroner, Rapporteur

THE INTERNATIONAL Conference's basic objective was to develop new understanding on the transmission of technology. Despite the trend toward increased specialization in the sciences, there is an intensified need for marrying the worlds of engineering and economics. The workshop sessions pointed clearly to the necessity for engineers to join with development economists in formulating the parameters for new industrial systems if they are to respond to the emerging opportunities of tomorrow. There also was relatively little doubt that a "systems analysis" of the existing, as well as newly emerging, industries undertaken jointly by economists and engineers, not to mention sociologists and other professionals, would yield substantial benefits in many countries, both developed and developing. The need for cooperation does not mean that engineers must become economists or social scientists. For example, macro-economic model building should be left to economists thoroughly familiar with the many limitations of such models. But, in order to develop appropriate technologies and product designs for the less developed countries, engineers must consider economic factors. At the same time, they should familiarize themselves with the technological implications of development problems.

Economic variables cover a wide range of conditions—market size which determines the scale of production, income levels which influence product design, and factor prices and the availability of foreign exchange which have a direct bearing upon the choice of production techniques. For example, industrialization programs based upon protection and import substitution nurture small scale, poor quality, and generally inefficient industry.

INTERMEDIATE TECHNOLOGY

Although most participants agreed on the importance of the general question of "intermediate technology," there was widespread disagreement on a definition of the term. Some defined intermediate technology as less advanced than technology used in large-scale industrial economies. Others related the term to the use of low-cost tools and equipment. Low-cost equipment can be designed by stripping a machine of its labor-saving content while maintaining the functional content which is often a small fraction of the cost of a machine. There is considerable misunderstanding over what "low cost" means. According to one definition, it is the cost of tooling any equipment per workplace. An example was cited where equipment costs ran between £1500–3000 in Great Britain for an advanced technical process as compared to only £100–300 for an intermediate technology in a less developed country. This is characteristic of small-scale production which entail high costs per unit of output.

This concept of intermediate technology leads to a maximization of the employment of labor—the abundant factor of production in most underdeveloped countries—irrespective of total economic costs. But the overriding economic criterion is the utilization of all available factors in such a way as to maximize total output and the rule of optimal factor allocation does not imply that some products should not be produced by capital-intensive and very advanced techniques. In most industrial processes, capital intensity is associated with optimal efficiency in total resource utilization.

A third definition viewed intermediate technology as a stage in the industrialization process. In this perspective, intermediate technology is seen as an opportunity for social accomodations, such as cottage industries which utilize village labor, and as a means for introducing modern techniques in gradual stages. For example, in the production of simple pottery, workers at home are first provided with mechanical wheels. Later they are brought to a common work place where quality control and the newest glazing techniques can be adopted. Still later, modern marketing methods and techniques can be introduced and, ultimately, as production becomes more competitive, the more capital-intensive technologies can be used.

It was pointed out in the discussion of Dr. Baranson's paper that, in developing countries, there is no economic justification for a high level of expenditure on advertising. A developing country needs to concern itself with determining the kind of demand generated in the marketplace and the kind of social demand generated by government budgeting. These both are the leading edge which will bring forth production systems and the engineering inputs that go into production systems. In the United States there are vast expenditures for space and defense. In developing countries there is a great need for such things as educational television, communication software, and water desalination. This very important need is a matter of policy, of indirectly inducing efficient uses of resources through transfer adaptation. Therefore, the policy concerned with social and market demand has a very social aspect.

The workshop session revealed a conflict between the above-mentioned economic and social considerations. Some argued that the appropriateness of technologies should be evaluated in terms of social compatibility and social change leading to modernization and industrialization, but that it should be recognized that this approach involves a sacrifice or trade-off with respect to the achievable economic growth rate. As long as it is understood that the nation is paying for a way of life, the economist need not quarrel with this approach.

There was substantial consensus on the need for adapting technologies to the particular stage of development, simply because the products and technologies of advanced industrialized countries often were ill suited to the needs and environments of the developing nations. Generally speaking, intermediate technologies, using more of the abundant factors such as unskilled labor, and economizing on the relatively scarce factors, such as capital and foreign exchange, have scored relatively few dramatic breakthroughs. One of the reasons seems to be less flexibility for adjustment in the production process than the theory implies, since the effective use of relatively abundant unskilled labor depends also upon the availability of the other scarce factors, such as foreign exchange and the skilled labor needed to organize and control production. Another factor is that quality and precision requirements frequently limit the substitutability of machine capabilities with human skills. Moreover, factor price distortions generally overprice unskilled labor and underprice capital resources relative to their productivity.

Despite all these obstacles, there seem to be promising areas for adaptation and innovations employing more labor-intensive methods, particularly in the agricultural sector and the initial processing of foodstuffs and agricultural raw materials. Engineers have made and can continue to make valuable contributions by designing machines that economize on scarce capital or foreign exchange. The less-developed nations also need more multipurpose equipment and standardized design to help

65

overcome the scale problem. Systems analysis of rural sectors in underdeveloped countries, as a collaborative effort between economists and engineers, should prove useful in adapting design of product and service systems (pack and transport) to town development.

POTENTIAL ROLES FOR MULTINATIONAL CORPORATIONS

Because of the acknowledged limits of import substitution programs in markets of limited size, an increasing emphasis is being placed on national specialization serving large regional or global markets. Multinational corporations assume a key role in this regard. They can address themselves to the following issues and dilemmas:

1. Maximizing national product versus national selfsufficiency
2. Employment maximization versus maximized physical output
3. Implanting of a research and development capability versus the importing of technical innovation
4. Foreign ownership and control of production facilities versus economic sovereignty of less-developed countries.

At first glance, multinational corporations are in a unique position to help newly industrializing areas to benefit from the potential gains from international specialization. Multinational marketing and manufacturing groups are able to take full advantage of economies of scale by producing for the much larger international markets. But such hopes are in conflict with national goals of broad industrialization with limited dependence upon foreign imports. Greater specialization would require fuller access to the markets of all nations. Industrialized countries generally have been reluctant to give developing countries preferential access to their markets for manufactured goods.

The fact is that chronic foreign exchange shortages in developing countries have led them to policies of extensive import substitution. These efforts to save foreign exchange generally have resulted in inefficient production for domestic markets of limited size and scope. Pressure for increasing local content of finished products contributes to high cost and inefficiency. Multinational firms also are in a unique position to help implant research and development capabilities in the developing country. Nationals from less-developed countries could be trained to work as engineers and technicians in overseas facilities. Such education and experienced direction would contribute to indigenous technological development.

There is an understandable concern over the loss of human resources (the so-called brain drain) to foreign corporations. Furthermore, newly industrializing nations tend to be suspicious of private foreign investment because they fear economic imperialism. Licensing or joint ventures can help alleviate such legitimate concerns for economic and technological sovereignty.

REFERENCES CITED

Hirsch, S., "The United States electronics industry in international trade," *Economic Review*, November 1965. London: National Institute of Economic and Social Research.

Lary, H. *Imports of Manufactures for Less Developed Countries*. National Bureau of Economic Research, 1968.

Vernon, R., "Conflict and resolution between foreign direct investors and less developed countries," *Public Policy*, Vol. 17, 1968.

————, "International investment and international trade in the Product Circle," *Quarterly Journal of Economics*, May, 1966.

Voci, J. J., and J. A. F. Stoner, "The reality of technical assistance," *International Development Review*, Vol. 9, No. 4 (December, 1967).

5

HUMAN RESOURCES
Principal Paper—K. N. Rao
Commentary—Maximo Halty-Carrère
Commentary—Robert W. Iversen
Commentary—Logan C. Osterndorf
Report of Workshop 3—Carmelo Mesa-Lago,
Rapporteur

Economic and social development, as well as technological development, ultimately must depend on the efforts of interested and qualified people. The
human resources of a nation will strongly influence its potentials for development. This chapter is concerned with the availability of human resources to
the development process.

The Editors

68

THE INFLUENCE OF THE AVAILABILITY OF HUMAN RESOURCES

Principal Paper by K. N. Rao

THE CREATION of employment opportunities for larger and larger propor-tions of the work force is an important goal of all developmental efforts. Entre-preneurs, managers, engineers, technicians, and skilled workers form a small but a critically important part of the total work force of a nation. Their availa-bility in sufficient quantity and at levels of high quality is essential to develop-ment. In this paper, the pyramidal manpower situation of developing countries is first placed in the context of recent demographic findings and the prospects and techniques of increasing employment in the traditional, intermediate, and modern sectors of a country's economy are discussed. The second half of the paper is devoted to a discussion of engineers, technicians, and skilled workers, their formation and utilization in the modern sector, and their roles in initiating and managing change. More intensive application of job analysis and training techniques, so profitably used in the industrial sector, to the analysis of agricul-tural and service occupations is recommended.

HUMAN RESOURCES IN THE DEMOGRAPHIC CONTEXT

In a recent study (1966) of resources and requirements for highly trained per-sonnel, the Colombian Institute for Advanced Training Abroad (ICETEX) summarized Colombia's human resources problems as follows:

Colombia presently has 18 million people, and its annual rate of population growth, 3.2%, is one of the highest in Latin America. Characteristic of rapidly expanding populations, half of all Colom-bians are under age 15. This implies a potentially large future work force, but it also means that a great number of unproductive people must be supported by those who work. Unemployment is high; while over half of the population is potentially capable of working (ages 15–64). Only 35% are actually economically active.

The composition of Colombia's work force shows a notable lack of technical personnel and preponderance of untrained labor. 8.9 per cent of all people covered in a 1963 employment poll were engaged in administrative, professional or technical capacities; 24.6% were office clerks or sales personnel; 66.5%—the overwhelming majority—were laborers. This bottom heavy occupa-tional structure represents an underutilization of Colombia's human resources and is a serious obstacle to economic development.

With quantitative differences, this description fits the present condition of many developing countries and underscores the present concern with the quant-ity, quality, and utilization of human resources in both the developed and underdeveloped parts of the world. Rapid technological change and competition among developed countries in scientific endeavors and the belief that science and technology can elevate standards of living have accelerated the demand for highly trained persons in the scientific and technical occupations. These very forces, however, have tended to further widen the several gaps—economic, sci-entific, technological, managerial—between the developed and underdeveloped countries and between the traditional and modern sectors within many develop-ing countries.

Demographers (International Manpower Institute, 1966) have put the problems of employment generation for the rapidly expanding work forces of underdeveloped countries in the frightening perspective of a vastly increased total world population of seven billion by the year 2000 A.D. These estimates show that both in absolute numbers and in proportions, the underdeveloped countries will need to support the bulk of the population increases in the world over the next 35 years.

Assuming the present 3.2-percent rate of population increase, Colombia's population of 18 million will contribute approximately an additional 18 million to the projected population of 5.4 billion of the developing countries in 2000 A.D. Whether Colombia, with its known natural resources and presently known and future technology, can support a population of this size at a reasonable standard of living is the layman's way of putting in the form of a question what economists have taught us—that to increase income per capita, aggregate output must increase more rapidly than population. While science and technology have contributed to decreases in mortality and increases in standards of living, they are once again challenged to come up with methods to achieve a better balance between population and resources.

TABLE 1.—Population in billions.

	1965	2000	Increase
Advanced Countries	1.1	1.6	0.5
Developing Countries	2.2	5.4	3.2
Total	3.3	7.0	3.7

Population Factors Affecting Economic Development—Economic development is slowed down by several population factors; chiefly, *the high rate of growth.* The absolute value of the rate itself is unimportant except that, for economic development, this rate must be exceeded by the rates of development and utilization of technology in its broadest sense, the rate of capital accumulation, and by the speed with which human resources are developed, properly allocated, and used.

A second population factor detrimental to economic development is the *age structure.* It is characteristic of most developing societies that their population contains a high percentage of youngsters who are unproductive and to whose nourishment and education much of the country's resources will need to be committed. This reduces the capital available for investment in economic growth. In such a circular problem, the larger the proportion of young people, the smaller the possible investment in education per child and in over-all human resources development at an effective level.

Population distribution is yet another crucial factor in economic development. The migration of the illiterate population from the rural to urban areas leaves the rural areas deficient in leadership. This, in turn, aggravates the problem of the cities. Historically, urban development took place in the presently advanced countries through large accumulation of capital from increases in agricultural productivity which were then invested in industrial development of urban centers.

In developing countries, however, the present urban centers began as commercial or governmental centers. With population increases, these centers have become "over-urbanized" with disproportionately large concentrations of people in the cities relative to employment opportunities available. There now is the danger that, with further mechanization of agriculture but without necessary incentives for "people to stay on the farm," the urban-rural imbalance will become worse. In many a developing country anxious for quick results from industrialization, investment in the rural sector unfortunately has lagged. Thus, the city has tended not only to drain the country of its human resources, but also to divert needed investment away from it.

In a slightly different context, a well-known educator (Ward, 1967) has made the point that we need to be concerned with *"mankind* and not just *manpower."* Applied to the population of a nation, this may be interpreted to mean *the quality of manpower,* particularly of high-level manpower which, as classified by Harbison and Myers, includes: (a) entrepreneurial, managerial, and administrative personnel; (b) professionals of all kinds such as scientists, engineers, and agriculturalists; (c) teachers; (d) sub-professionals and technicians; and (e) representatives of political, labor, legal, and military professions. While the Harbison-Myers' composite index based on educational statistics may be helpful for comparative international measurement, the quality of a national population is more elusive of measurement. Even among the "elite" of the work force identified above, there appears to be a smaller number of individuals and groups who, as "modernizers," contribute uniquely to economic and social development. They often create and sustain an atmosphere for both sociological and technological innovation, whose rate of generation and assimilation determine the rate of development. The population quality factor is thus of great significance to educational and economic development.

These demographic considerations have been discussed at length not only because of their implication to educational planning, employment generation, and allocation of economic and human resources and their utilization, but also because it is believed that some of these present issues and problems should form the central concern of the engineer or the technologist of the future.

Application of Systems Analysis—It has been suggested that concepts of systems analysis be applied to relate several elements of human resources development and utilization. A rudimentary diagram of a manpower-generation-utilization system is attempted in Fig. 1. The diagram shows how the work force is part of the total population (usually about one-third) and how the "technical" part of the work force is but a small proportion of the work force in most developing countries. We saw earlier that only 8.9 per cent of the economically

71

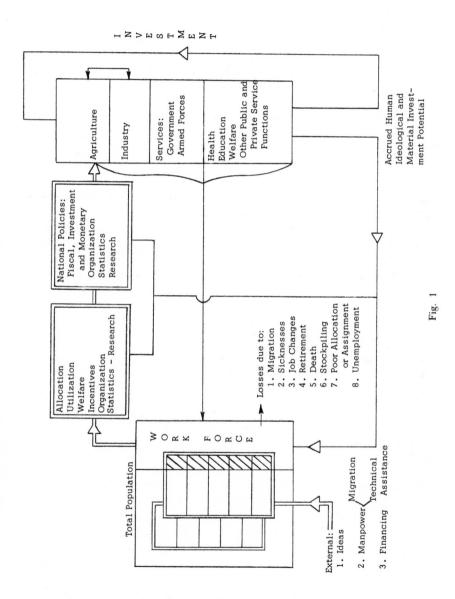

Fig. 1

active population of Colombia are active in administrative, professional, and technical capacities. In the United States in 1968, the professional, technical, and kindred workers formed 13.3 per cent of the work force and an equal percentage were craftsmen, foremen, and kindred workers. Figure 1 shows that, for the work force to be productively employed in agriculture, industry, and the service sectors, policies for their allocation and utilization must be developed and incentives provided. Reliable statistical information and research are indispensable for sound manpower resource planning and utilization. Reference to Fig. 1 will aid in studying the major issues in this field.

Population, GNP, and Employment—The manpower economist takes the population factors cited above, relates them to the gross national product, the contributions of the industrial, agricultural, and service sectors to this product, and the rate of new job creation, and thus comes to judgments on how growth and employment are related in a particular economy. Such analyses of the performance of developing countries have led to the startling conclusion that "economic progress generates unemployment"! (International Manpower Seminar, USAID, 1966.) As already mentioned, education seems to have an unsettling effect on rural youth. In advanced and developing societies alike, rural areas export people to the cities, but industries concentrated in the urban areas cannot always absorb them. Furthermore, when modern industries are established in underdeveloped countries, "employment frequently does not increase because the new industries are capital intensive and not labor intensive." Professor Harbison, a frequent participant in USAID's International Manpower Seminars, explains further:

In the modern sector of the economy of the developing countries, the increase of the labor force is greater than the increase of population. If the population increases 2.5 percent per year, the labor force will increase about three percent. Also in the modern sector, the rate of new job creation is slower than the rate of increase in national income. If G. N. P. grows about five percent per year, then the rate of new job creation will be around 2.5 percent. Moreover, the increase in labor force will be three percent. Though the economy may be growing, unemployment will rise.

This is a problem for which the obvious long-range solution is a drastic reduction in the rate of population growth.

Automation and Employment—In the process of new job creation, one process of technological change called "automation" has been hailed as the harbinger of the manpower revolution, creating in the modern sector a large number of new jobs. "On the other hand, antagonists of automation have blamed it for every rise in unemployment and have even suggested that turning back the clock and checking technological progress might be necessary if full employment is to be achieved. The threat of automation may tempt developing countries to promulgate policies to prohibit importation of capital-intensive new technology. Except that the employment-generating capacity of industrialization traditionally has been overestimated, recent studies indicate that the bizarre or the beneficial effects of automation on employment have not been as significant as the protagonists of either cause have made them to be." In their recent book, *Technology and Jobs,* Jaffe and Froomkin further show that recent efficiencies or increases in productivity are part of a century-long growth and that countries such as Italy, West Germany, and Japan have experienced higher rates of productivity than the United States during the 1950s. The net result of this controversy is that innovations, of which automation is but one form, still will be required. Such innovations will need to be both sociological and technological in the broadest senses if human resources of the developing countries are to be optimally formed and profitably used.

Employment in the Service Sector—Table 2, depicting changes from 1950 to 1960 in the distribution by activity of population aged ten years and over in Brazil, illustrates some of the above trends and the developing impor-

TABLE 2

Field of Activity	Distribution		Change 1950 to 1960
	1950	1960	
Agriculture	27.04	23.99	−3.05
Mining and Quarrying	1.32	1.18	−0.14
Manufacturing	4.40	4.25	−0.15
Construction	1.60	1.61	+0.01
Retail Trading	2.62	3.12	+0.50
Sub-Total	36.98	34.15	
Transportation, Storage, and Communications	1.91	2.23	+0.32
Services	4.58	5.60	+1.02
Others	3.35	4.48	+1.13
Active Population	46.82	46.46	−0.36
Economically inactive population—school children and unremunerated domestic workers	53.18	53.54	+0.36
Total	100.00	100.00	

tance of the service or tertiary sector of an economy (Dannemann, 1966). This tendency for the increase in service occupations is observed in both the developed and developing countries. The computer is said to have "bleached the blue collar" and created many more service jobs at the technician and "customer-engineer level." In the traditional sector of agriculture, there is accumulating evidence that, with the increase in production brought about by the application of new technologies, many more service jobs related to production, distribution, and processing of agricultural products could be created. Education itself is a highly labor-intensive service industry. However, the creation of jobs in the service sector requires greater investments by the developing countries in education and welfare activities. The underdeveloped countries already are beginning to commit significant percentages of their budgets for education and, in the case of several countries, it is doubtful if additional funds could be squeezed out of other sectors for investment in education.

To summarize the foregoing, those involved in the development, allocation, and utilization of human resources are faced with several dilemmas. The mere raising of the gross national product might produce greater imbalances between the urban and rural sectors. A rapid rise of GNP through capital-intensive industrialization may benefit the few at the expense of the many. Because of the historically low investments in agriculture, wage differentials between agriculture and industry, and other causes, the rural-to-urban migration has become a serious problem. Although rural modernization is an extremely important goal that must be pursued, it is naive to think that significant reductions in the rate of rural-to-urban migration are likely to occur in the foreseeable future. If increased food production is accepted as a major priority goal, then reduction of unemployment, raising of GNP, and, above all, sharp reductions in the rate of population growth are the other goals which the underdeveloped countries must pursue with equal dedication if balanced growth is to be achieved. Among these, recent studies identify the rate of population growth as the critical factor to be kept under close surveillance. But the effects of population delimitation policies, initiated now, begin to produce the intended results many years later. It is, therefore, necessary for the short run to take additional steps to redress imbalances in manpower allocation and to create additional employment opportunities in all the three sectors—industrial, agricultural, and service.

THE ROLE OF HIGH-LEVEL HUMAN RESOURCES IN INITIATING AND MANAGING CHANGE

It is against this background that one will need to examine the part played by science and technology in the transformation of traditional societies and the role high-level human resources can play in the initiation and management of change. The discussion heretofore has revealed the interdisciplinary nature of the problem and suggests that, in the spirit of the theme of the Conference, the attack will need to muster the services of many other disciplines in addition to the techniques that science and engineering may bring. The frame of reference will need to include cultural and political factors. Also, in many a developing country, the division of the economy into a traditional sector and a modern sector is an oversimplification. An intermediate sector of productivity has been discerned in several countries and this sector can be used as the springboard for modernization of the agricultural sector (*Education and World Affairs,* 1967).

MISALLOCATION AND POOR UTILIZATION OF ENGINEERING MANPOWER

The roles of the scientist and engineer are traditionally related to the activities of the modern sector. Much of the early manpower surveys in the developing countries started out with the counting of scientists and engineers in industries and government establishments, and rather exaggerated estimates of the numbers of engineers and scientists needed were put forward by planning groups. This flurry of activity was most useful in calling the needs of high-level manpower to the attention of governments of developing countries. Subsequent careful analyses have revealed that, in many a developing country, the urgent need may not be to increase the rate of production of engineers sharply, but to use the employed engineering manpower and the output of present institutions more efficiently. The application of the so-called rate-of-return approach and cost-benefit principles has had sobering effects on the earlier forecasts of needs of high-level manpower. Simply stated, how much high-level manpower can the national budget afford?

The ICETEX study of Colombian manpower referred to earlier concludes that, generally speaking, enough engineers are being produced by Colombian

TABLE 3.—Firms and engineers employed in Mexico, 1963.

Firm	Number of Employees	Number of Engineers			
		Production	Sales	Management	Total
Chemical	240	15	5	3	23
Chemical	1200	98	43	25	166
Electrical	2800	65	25	13	103
Pharmaceutical	700	140	0	3	143
Textile Fibers	820	16	1	2	19
Metal Fabrication	300	18	3	2	23
Construction	15 000	370	0	30	400
Chemical Construction	2500	95	2	35	132
Metal Fabrication	400	10	3	0	13
Metal Fabrication	2500	44	0	6	50
Total	26 460	871	82	119	1072

universities to meet future development needs, but their proper utilization will be a serious problem. Eighty per cent of Colombia's agricultural engineers are working outside the field of agriculture. In a study of high-level manpower in the economic development of Argentina, Morris A. Horowitz shows that, although engineering is the third largest profession (following medicine and law) and is growing at the fastest rate, many engineers are not employed in the engineering field but are in politics, executive and administrative jobs in industry, and even serve as economists. Although these might be important gains for the engineering profession, they point up problems in educational resource allocation and in the structure of incentives of engineers. Table 3 for Mexico shows that over 20 per cent of the engineers trained by Mexican universities work in sales and management positions rather than in engineering positions.

Recent reports from countries such as Nigeria and India speak of surpluses in

76

engineering manpower. This is surprising in view of the development needs of these two countries and the universal disquietude about short falls in engineering manpower. With the limited size of the modern sector comprised of packaged technology imported from abroad, with upper engineering management positions occupied by foreign technicians and engineers, and with advancement to senior management positions blocked by "partially educated entrepreneurs" and their sons, the engineer often is confined in his job to routine tasks which could be more easily performed by the technician. Inflexible and outdated curricula make training of the engineer somewhat unrelated to the tasks to be done in the modern sector of the economy and do not prepare him well for the larger developmental tasks of the nation. These causes lead to unemployment, poor utilization when employed, and to migration, while the problems both in the modern and the traditional sectors of the economy remain unresolved for want of competent engineering talent.

DEMAND FOR NEWER ENGINEERING SPECIALTIES

Although countries such as Nigeria and India are, in general, reasonably well supplied with engineering manpower for the present, some are experiencing shortages in the new fields of engineering, such as chemical engineering, electronic engineering, and in the interdisciplinary fields of material science. Also, engineers skilled in the use of systems analysis techniques for infrastructural development are in short supply. Improving the quality of engineering education and giving it a development orientation are questions of high priority. Of course, government policies in regard to investments in the modern sector will influence the rates of absorption of engineering manpower in this sector and could stimulate the universities to move in the direction of modernizing curricula to include the newer fields, concepts, and techniques of engineering education. In several countries, duplication of faculties of engineering with expensive facilities and staff represents a misuse of scarce resources, which could otherwise be applied to develop new engineering specialties.

The modern sector of the economies of developing countries is likely to be reasonably well served by a gradually increasing supply of engineers; the real challenges of the future exist in the traditional sector to which engineering faculties have, until now, given too little attention. The education of an engineer in most developing countries does not include technical and engineering problems in the traditional sectors of the economy. The principles of industrial engineering, which have brought the modern industrial sector to high levels of efficiency, would appear to hold important lessons for the modernization of agriculture. The further development of small-scale industry and service enterprises in the traditional sector is frequently held back, more for a lack of management expertise than for a lack of technology. Would it be desirable to think of insisting that engineering students write their senior papers and Master's theses on an engineering problem of local or national importance? What about courses on agricultural modernization for engineers? In many Latin American countries, there are service requirements for graduates of medical schools. Should one think of rural internships for engineering students?

GRADUATE EDUCATION IN ENGINEERING

One of the critical shortages in the engineering sector is of professors of engineering. A method of relieving this shortage and of starting national centers of engineering innovation is through graduate education. Such a local resource would, in the long run, help reduce dependence on expatriate technical personnel and would have the following additional benefits:

1. These graduate-level programs would act as the breeding ground for ideas and leadership.

2. They are needed to prepare the large number of science and engineering teachers for undergraduate programs.

3. They help to prepare high-level scientists and technologists who can understand, manipulate, assimilate, and/or adapt new technology as it flows from the developed to the developing countries, and ultimately develop the indigenous technologies to solve problems peculiar to the country or region.

However, graduate education in science and engineering, and indeed in other fields, is an expensive, long, and low-yield operation. Not every country can afford to have extensive programs at this level and, even in a single country, duplication of effort is a great danger. The costs of preparing leaders for graduate education are high and the problem of retaining these leaders in the countries, or at least in the region, requires significant changes in governmental policies and procedures with respect to high-level manpower. But, when carefully planned, graduate education would provide a mechanism to set up a regenerative cycle within the educational system to provide the high-level manpower for the entire educational system and, in turn, to be enriched by it. Properly supported and managed, it can in the long run provide "feedback with amplification" that might help offset the numbers lost through migration. The development of graduate education is inextricably tied to national policies for higher education in science and engineering.

It is inadvisable to start graduate programs in every country of a region, but a good first step would be to identify national programs in selected countries of the region and, with careful inputs of internal and external resources, elevate their capability for graduate-level training and research. A high degree of coordination among national, regional, and international agencies would be required in such an undertaking. Such a program in science, technology, and education is beginning to take shape in Latin America. Such national institutions and programs, with carefully developed international linkages, are likely to retard the flow of high-level talent away from the region and might even become poles of attraction for "brain-drainees" and thus lead to qualitative improvement of the high-level manpower resources of a nation or a region.

"APPROPRIATE" TECHNOLOGY AND
ITS EFFECT ON EMPLOYMENT

In the modern industrial sector, a variety of employment-expanding approaches have been suggested. Many of them, however, go against the definitions of efficiency or profitability that engineers and entrepreneurs have come to accept. When underdeveloped countries buy processes from the developed countries where labor is expensive and has, therefore, been reduced to the minimum as a factor of production, such processes and equipment become unrealistic for economies of underdeveloped countries. The importation of labor-intensive new processes and secondhand equipment has been tried, but not with great success. In the author's experience in Indonesia (1956) in a program of mechanization and modernization of small-scale industry, Japanese equipment and processes were found to be more suitable, not only because of the minimum disruption they caused in the rudimentary labor markets, but also because of their simplicity of maintenance. Similar experiments are being conducted in India by the prototype design centers established by the Indian Government. While the transfer of technology from the highly developed to the underdeveloped countries is a much-researched topic, the nature of the flow of technology from the intermediate-level countries to the less-developed ones is still a very much under-researched area. Hudson Institute's "sidewise technology" concepts, proposals of the Intermediate Technology Development Group, Ltd., of London, and activities of VITA are new initiatives which can revive and improve approaches to small-scale industry development in the less developed countries.

In the developing countries, institutes of industrial and scientific research which often atrophy into mere testing centers for the government or engage solely in scientific activities should re-examine their structure and activities, take on a development orientation, and begin to experiment with types of technologies which would aid in the gradual growth of the low productivity, small industries into medium-size undertakings, and then into the larger industries that characterize the modern sector. This is an evolutionary process and one can only hope that governmental policies can hasten the rate of this process.

Several other approaches relating the modern high-productivity sector to the intermediate sector of industries through subcontracting for parts, finishing, and distribution can create additional jobs. Enlightened managers of large industries in the modern sector, prodded by government policies, can see the advantages of such relationships. Geographical proximity to highly developed countries, such as that of Mexico and the Caribbean nations to the United States, and of Greece, Italy, and Turkey to Europe, can be a highly advantageous factor in encouraging first-phase industrial development through subassembly of equipment, partial processing of raw materials, or finishing operations. The beginnings of this phenomenon in Mexico and the Caribbean are worth watching from the point of view of their application to similar situations elsewhere in the world. The policies of industrial autarky by national governments can, however, prove inimical to such development.

A NEW TECHNOLOGY OF TROPICAL AGRICULTURE

Working backwards from the high-productivity, through the intermediate or medium-size enterprise, one finds that the small enterprise, located physically close to a rural market, has the potentialities for acting as a kind of surge tank, absorbing some of the outflow of labor from the rural area and providing goods and services that agriculture needs, but which are not provided directly by the urban large-scale industry or the government. The recent upsurge of interest in agri-business is based on the realization that many of the problems of rural proverty, rural-to-urban migration, and even the further development of the modern industrial sector in the developing countries may, in part, be attacked by applying the resources and techniques of the modern industrial enterprise to agriculture. The critical element is the development of a new technology of tropical agriculture, including new strains of seed, harvesting, processing, and marketing techniques, which would then set up a chain reaction beginning with increased production, better health and wellbeing of the farmer, savings, re-investments in agriculture and in expanding the consumer market with its resulting benefits to the high-productivity sector of modern industry. These techniques provide interesting projects for the systems analyst or his cousin, the operations researcher, and his half-brother, the industrial engineer, all of whom have contributed so much to improving the productivity of the modern sector.

SUBPROFESSIONAL ENGINEERING EDUCATION

Subprofessional technical education is usually one of the underinvested and underinvestigated areas of education in the developing countries. It also is one of the more controversial educational developments even in the advanced countries. Most technical manpower studies of the less-developed countries indicate major needs for middle-level development manpower. Literature on this subject reflects the problems of defining technician occupations but it is generally agreed that there is an upper- and a lower-level technician, each differing from the other in the proportions of skill and knowledge in their training and the relation in their work to persons in other parts of the manpower spectrum. These can be called, respectively, the engineering technician, who is a member of the engineering team, and the industrial technician, who, as the most highly trained member of the skilled worker category of the work force, performs some very highly specialized functions in industry.

The development of well-planned programs for the training of engineering technicians yields many advantages to the developing countries. It helps relieve the shortages of engineering manpower faced by some countries by adding engineering technicians to the work force and thus relieving professional engineers for more creative functions. The cost of training engineering technicians is somewhat lower than that for engineers, particularly because of the shorter duration of training. A recent study in Brazil showed that the cost of training engineering technicians are 40 per cent of those for an engineer. Engineering technician programs are a method of diversifying systems of higher education and providing differing pathways to those aspiring to technical careers. Specialization in industry requires technicians whose training has involved a ratio of skill to knowledge different from that of an engineer. Recent approaches in engineering education have emphasized the need for a more generalized form of education and training, but many of the tasks in industry are specific and require specific skills. At the earlier stages of industrialization in the developing countries, these skills in the work force become even more critical than in the case of the advanced countries, which have the advantages of a better developed human resource infrastructure. Carefully planned technician training programs are also a source of (1) supervisory personnel and teachers of technical subjects for industry and the vocational schools and (2) technical support personnel for research programs.

When resources are committed for the enlargement of university-level engineering programs, on the one hand, and for expensive programs of vocational and technical education at the high school level, on the other, subprofessional technician training programs usually have to make do with what is left. Often that is not very much. The competition for funds for junior college development in the various states of the United States is a symptom of this condition. In the developing countries, where the technician has yet to find his niche in the occupational hierarchy, support for technician education is hard to come by. Wherever technician programs have been initiated, they have been subjected to a "pincer" movement by the engineering programs, on the one hand, and the vocational technical programs, on the other, each feeling itself threatened by imagined encroachment of its domain. Certification procedures for engineers in several developing countries put up artifical barriers for the acceptance by industry of the technician.

In the Commonwealth Conference on the Education and Training of technicians, held in October, 1966, and attended by representatives of more than 20 Commonwealth countries, the recurring theme was that, unless the technician was accorded the "status" that is legitimately his in the occupational structure, the ranks of the technician would be filled by the "failed engineer." Unfortunately, many technician programs attempt to acquire social and educational respectability by violating their curricular integrity and devising technician curricula to meet professional engineering requirements. Also, this level of education, which is an innovation in many a developing country, suffers from a serious lack of teachers.

Manpower specialists and educational planners have suggested a variety of ratios of technicians to engineers, but studies of requirements by industry have revealed wide divergencies of needs. It is most difficult to suggest a universal ratio in forecasting needs in developing countries. Table 4 shows ratios of technicians to professionally qualified manpower in various sectors of employment in Britain. These ratios are indicative and suggest changes in emphasis needed in educational planning in the developing countries.

The teachers of technician programs require a unique combination of skills, technical knowledge, and teaching competence. University teacher training programs most often are directed toward the preparation of secondary-level vocational teachers. On the other hand, engineers tend to teach the way they were taught. They also lack the skills that the technician is expected to have. The result has been an *ad hoc* attempt to hire teachers from industry and the universities. The development of degree-granting, four-year technician programs in the United States universities is an attempt to meet the shortage of teachers for technician programs. The development of colleges of technology, under the stimulus of the Industrial Training Boards to integrate courses in technology, commerce, domestic science, and technical teacher training, is an

TABLE 4—Ratios of technicians to professionally qualified manpower in various sections of employment in the United Kingdom, 1965.

Universities and Higher Education	Roughly 1:1
Industry	
Food, Drink, Tobacco, Etc.	2.8:1
Chemicals and Allied Industries	1.8:1
Mineral Oil Refining	1.1:1
Metal Manufacture	3.8:1
Mechanical Engineering	5.5:1
Electrical Engineering	3.9:1
Electronics	3.4:1
Motor Vehicles	6.5:1
Aircraft	6.0:1
Textiles	5.4:1
Other Manufactures	4.7:1
Construction	6.5:1
Nationalized Industries and Public Corporations	3.7:1
Government	
Central Government	3.5:1
Atomic Energy Authority	1.4:1
Local Government	2.2:1

Source: Education and Training of Technicians, London, 1967.

important innovation in British education. Such institutional forms may have application in the developing countries. The British practice of "sandwich" (co-op) courses and "block release" arrangements have the unique advantage of bringing industry and education together. In Latin America, possible cooperative arrangements among industry, engineering, and teacher training departments of universities, and training agencies such as SENA (Colombia) or SENAI (Brazil) would be more economical and expeditious for teacher training than the establishment of new institutions for this purpose.

Although attempts have been made to delineate the work of the technician in industry, similar analyses of the role of the agricultural technician pose difficulties because of the diversity of the conditions in the industry and the relative lack of specialization in many areas. "If a farmer can be likened to a tradesman, a technician in agriculture would, in many of his roles, be the communicator of modern agricultural techniques to the farming community." Several developing countries do have two- to three-year diploma courses in such fields as dairy technology, food technology, horticulture, poultry farming, irrigation, fruiticulture, farm mechanization, wood technology, forestry, and extension services. These courses are undersubscribed and employment in the sector does not yet provide the satisfactions and the emoluments necessary to be competitive with industry in the modern sector. To achieve the necessary change in attitudes and techniques, it is necessary to train and compensate agricultural technicians on terms competitive with all other major industries. Detailed occupational analysis of agricultural occupations of the kind used in trade and industry would be

TABLE 5—Distribution according to educational level of
the 1965 Nigerian Educational System's contribution to
the labor force.

Educational Level	Number	Percent of Labor Force Entrants
Primary	420 644	88.5
Dropouts	274 149	57.6
Completers	146 495	30.9
Junior Secondary	30 874	6.6
Dropouts	8 652	1.8
Completers	22 222	4.8
Senior Secondary	19 546	4.1
Dropouts	5 335	1.1
Completers (with & without cert.)	14 211	3.0
Tertiary: Non-University, Dropouts and Completers	2 114	0.4
Tertiary: University	2 114	0.4
Total	475 292	100.0

Source: *Nigerian Human Resource Development and Utilization*, New York, 1967.

needed to determine at what level these programs should be established. It is possible that several functions now assigned to agricultural technicians could, by careful analysis and work simplification procedures, be assigned to others with lower skill and education levels. The task is important in view of the urgent need to increase world food production.

NONFORMAL METHODS OF SKILL TRAINING

Since one of the charcteristics of a developing society is that only a very small proportion of the population completes formal education at the different levels, it must be concluded that much occupational training takes place outside the formal education system. Statistics on those served by the educational system are not reliable because they often do not include migrants into the urban centers and those in farming areas where youngsters supply much of the needed labor on the farm. Table 5 on the Nigerian educational system's contribution to the labor force is illustrative. Table 5 emphasizes the magnitude of the job of upgrading those who obtain employment in the traditional and the modern sectors, and of the immensity of the needs of the marginal populations from the point of view of education and training preparatory to their entering gainful employment.

Because of lack of data on migration from the rural to the urban sector, many projections of training needs in the developing countries are based on urban population statistics. A recent OECD study (1968) attempts to take into account the addition to the work force from agriculture to production in the modern sector to calculate manpower requirements under different assumed rates of economic growth. Similar studies are needed for other developing countries to bring forecasts more into line with reality. The OECD study refers to a French study (*Etudes et Conjonctures,* October 10, 1966, Table 14, page 31) in which it was found that, between 1959 and 1964, the change from agriculture to urban industry employment was as follows: 9 per cent became office workers; 14 per cent became transport drivers; and 70 per cent went into the "craftsman and operatives category" of which 20 per cent were in building occupations and 30 per cent were unskilled workers. While it is unrealistic to think that similar "proportionation" from agriculture to urban occupations takes place in the developing societies, these statistics show the need for analysis of the "marginal" populations and the types of occupations through which they become integrated into urban society. Such analyses could then form the basis for training or retraining programs.

The skilled worker in the modern sector acquires his skills and knowledge by a variety of methods: formal schooling, on-the-job training, and apprenticeship. Most recent discussions of the subject have revolved around how best to share the responsibility and costs of training between the formal training institutions and employers.

VOCATIONAL TRAINING: ITS COST, RELEVANCE, AND MANAGEMENT

Vocational schools and technical training centers are expensive to establish and operate and can only deal with a small proportion of those who need to be trained. The regulations under which they operate make them inflexible and unresponsive to the needs of industry. After all, so the argument goes, industry is the ultimate user of the product and must bear the cost of training. The most serious objection is that the training centers often become schools of general education in disguise and offer, at best, a second-quality general education.

Some of these criticisms of vocational schools are justified, but the schools still have an important role to play in modernizing economies. Revitalized programs of the vocational schools in the developing countries can be most helpful in the preparation of industrial and lower-level technicians. Such schools could act as feeders to technician training programs and even to some types of engineering programs. Vocational programs, when carefully integrated with general education as in "comprehensive" schools proposed for some countries, could give a practical bias to education generally. One should not forget, however, that industrialization requires a variety of *specific* skills and that "overgeneralization" of education tends to dilute this emphasis. "Area-vocational" programs, as in the United States, provide for specialization based on local needs and for combination of programs of training for agriculture and industry.

In response to the needs of development, many developing countries have embarked on ambitious programs of technical training at the skilled worker level, but mostly for employment in the industrial sector. Agriculture and other service sectors have pressing needs at this level which remain unmet. The author's review of these efforts leads him to identify the following urgent needs if the programs are to improve in quality and expand their services to other sectors of the economy:

1. Extension of techniques developed in demonstration centers to the point of national adoption.

2. Coordination and integration of programs now conducted under different auspices, such as the ministries of industry, labor, education, and the universities.

3. Sharing of ideas, techniques, and instructional materials developed in one country with other countries in the same region with similar development goals.

4. Investment of loan and grant funds for the purchase of equipment made locally wherever possible; local industries have yet to appreciate the potentialities of the local education market for products and services.

5. Initiation of programs for teacher education using existing physical facilities; there is no reason why a single facility cannot serve many purposes: teacher education, pre-employment training, evening programs for employed workers, skill training for rural migrants.

6. Management for the expanding programs of vocational and technical education; strained are the present thin cadres of leaders available for directing these programs. Many programs are developed without adequate research because research competence often is lacking. Directorates of vocational education of ministries of education, training offices of industry, and program and research staffs of manpower offices need to be strengthened with well-qualified professionals if these programs are to be well managed.

Cooperation between industry and vocational education programs is essential to match employment requirements and training needs. Industry knows that it needs skilled people, but industrialists in the developing countries still feel distant from educational concerns and do not quite know how best to relate themselves to these programs. Strassman (1968) has summarized industry's feelings:

Comments by managers shed little light on the effectiveness of the program (vocational education). Where productivity is good, managers take the credit; where it is poor, they call for more and better vocational schools as the solution. Where high skills are needed, managers want schools to create them. Where work is simple and repetitive, managers fear that vocational training gets workers into slow habits and makes them think they know enough to argue. If industrialization moves from task simplification to mechanization and instrumentation, therefore, the need for vocational education will rise.

In Latin America, employer participation in industrial training has aided the development of some very innovative organizations for industrial training that are worthy of close study by other developing regions. In Brazil, the SENAI (the National Service of Industrial Apprenticeship) has organized, in close cooperation with industry, training programs in over 200 training centers. These schools are outside the formal vocational-technical school programs of the Ministry of Education and the whole operation is financed by a 1 per cent industrial payroll tax. Similar organizations in Colombia (SENA), Peru (SENATI), Chile (INACAP), and Venezuela (INEC) perform a unique role in industrial training. SENAC in Brazil is SENAI's counterpart for training in commercial and service occupations.

In Colombia, the operations of SENA extend into the agricultural sector and provide training services for a variety of agricultural occupations. This experiment is worth watching as it might yield techniques of more universal applicability for training community development workers, small-scale rural entrepreneurs, rural teachers, and persons with specific skills in irrigation, insecticide and fertilizer application, food technology, and the other skills needed for rural modernization.

Apprenticeship and on-the-job training are two other methods of training skilled workers, but in those countries where employers are assessed a tax to support training programs, the employer naturally tends to shy away from elaborate training programs on his own, as he is afraid of "poaching" by other employers of the persons he has trained.

While such industry-related and industry-financed programs serve the needs of this sector, they are not the answer to the larger needs of unemployed workers displaced as a result of technological changes or rural migration. The variety of programs for the training and retraining of such persons now in progress in the United States might provide lessons for the developing countries. Particularly relevant are those programs which provide incentives, including reimbursement of costs to employers who train people under these arrangements and ultimately absorb them into their work force.

SUMMARY

In summary, this paper has attempted to suggest the following major issues and approaches in human resource development generally, and in the formation and

86

utilization of high-level manpower, specifically engineers, technicians, and skilled workers.

The initiation by the developing countries of national programs for demographic research and population control is extremely urgent. This conclusion is inescapable in the face of mounting evidence that the present rates of economic growth in the developing countries cannot provide the large number of jobs needed by the expanding work forces resulting from high rates of population growth.

Manpower forecasters and governmental planners have necessarily taken greater interest in the modern industrial sector of the economies of developing nations. If an important goal of development is the creation of employment for larger and larger segments of the work force, *urgent attention should be given to the rural sector.* This will require changes in policies on investment and organization. In this task of rural modernization, technology has a very important role to play.

In the modern sector itself, the developing countries have not yet exhausted the potentialities of a variety of employment-generating forms of technology and industrial organization. Indigenous institutes of research and the universities have a unique role to play in the generation of new technology. The intermediate sector of the economies containing small- and medium-scale industry and service enterprises can serve as the springboard for action in rejuvenating the rural sector. The agri-business sector can be a fruitful field for the interplay of agricultural and engineering principles and techniques.

If engineering is to play a role in rural modernization, the emphasis in the training and education of the engineer must change. The present reported shortages in engineering manpower in several countries are attributable to poor utilization and lack of incentives. On a regional basis, graduate education programs offer one of the methods of increasing the availability of engineering professors. Graduate education in engineering is an expensive undertaking; a desirable first-stage action would be to identify strong national programs at the undergraduate level and, with well-planned inputs of external and domestic resources, elevate them to graduate-level programs to serve the region. This might also be one of the methods of repatriating "brain drainees."

There is an urgent need to develop programs at the technician level to diversify higher education programs, provide the spread of skills and knowledge required by modern industry, and relieve shortages of engineering manpower. It would appear that the techniques of trade and job analysis so useful in rationalizing industrial occupations could be employed with profit for analyzing technician training needs in agriculture and service occupations.

The biggest challenges for human resource planners lie in the allocation of resources and development of organizations for training skilled and semiskilled workers for both industrial and agricultural occupations. In tackling this immense task, financial and organizational participation by industry would be important. Forecasting training needs and arranging training programs for the large numbers who migrate from rural to urban areas in search of employment poses special problems. Developing countries already burdened with the problems of providing education and training to the literate urban populations are, at present, unable to make the large additional investments necessary to incorporate the "marginal" populations into the modern sector. Urgent action is necessary in this regard to avert and prepare the way for orderly development.*

---

*For a discussion of the paper by K. N. Rao, see p. 111.

HUMAN RESOURCES AND TECHNICAL CHANGE
Commentary by Maximo Halty-Carrère

TECHNICAL CHANGE is defined as a continuous process involving the creation of new knowledge through research, the diffusion of knowledge through the transfer of technology, and the application of knowledge through technical innovation. The task at present is to analyze the problems involved in utilizing knowledge without being directly concerned with its development and dissemination.

It is obvious, and therefore easily agreed upon, that entrepreneurs, managers, engineers, technicians, skilled, and semiskilled labor are indeed essential for the successful application of technology to the industrialization of any country. This paper will concentrate on the first two categories, entrepreneurs and managers, because their role is crucial in the process of technical innovation, and to a lesser extent on engineers and technicians.

THE ROLE OF ENTREPRENEURS AND MANAGERS

Although all listed categories are required inputs for the process of technological innovation, the role of entrepreneurs and managers is crucial because these individuals, as well as engineers, are dynamic agents of that same process; all categories are necessary requirements for the application of technical knowledge to the industrialization process, but the first two are the decision-makers in technological innovation. Their strategic role is further enhanced if it is realized that, for the process of technical change to be completed, a continuous link between the development, diffusion, and utilization of new knowledge is essential. If utilization, or technological innovation, does not occur, then all previous efforts are of no economic validity, whatever inherent value research and diffusion might have in the context of technical development per se. By definition, technological innovation—which, in the present scientific revolution, is the major factor behind economic progress—materializes only when new knowledge is effectively incorporated into the system of production and distribution of goods and services, through developing new products, new materials, new equipment and new processes. In other words, technical innovation is a complex process by which a creative act—such as an invention—is matched with the vision and managerial expertise of an entrepreneur to meet the present or potential social demands of public or private needs. Therefore, technological innovation is a decision-making process which takes place at the enterprise level, and entrepreneurs and managers—the key decision makers—constitute the direct agents of technical change.

These considerations, by presenting the fact that technological innovation essentially is a management responsibility, introduce the relative importance of the "managerial gap" as compared to that of the "technological gap." In the author's opinion, most of what has been defined as a "technological gap" is essentially a "managerial gap." The success of United States firms operating in

European markets, as well as the relatively sizable investments in research made by European countries, tend to prove that the existing gap lies not so much at the stage of development of new knowledge as at the stage of incorporating that knowledge into the production system. Thus, entrepreneurs and managers are the most critical and strategic human resource categories involved in the process of technological innovation. Engineers and technicians constitute equally crucial categories insofar as they act as decision makers in translating scientific and technological knowledge into technical innovation.

CURRENT RESEARCH ON THE AVAILABILITY OF HUMAN RESOURCES FOR DEVELOPMENT

Analyzing the present state of knowledge on the availability of human resources for development is an almost impossible task. In a recent study on scientific and

TABLE 1.—Average productivity and the percentage of professionals and technicians in the labor force in various Latin American countries.

Country	Productivity US$—1960	% of Professionals & Technicians in the Labor Force
Venezuela*	2.878	5.0
Argentina	1.508	6.3
Uruguay	1.293	6.1
Costa Rica	1.257	5.0
Chile	1.240	5.0
Mexico	1.127	3.6
Colombia	0.925	4.1
Guatemala	0.878	2.5
Nicaragua	0.846	2.6
Brazil	0.816	3.2
El Salvador	0.760	2.5
Peru	0.659	3.6
Ecuador	0.653	3.1
Honduras	0.652	2.7
Paraguay	0.513	3.2

Source: "Profesionales y Técnicos en América Latina," by Mariano Ramírez and Elvidio Parra, Unit of Technological Development, Department of Scientific Affairs, O.A.S.

*The distortion of the correlations in the case of Venezuela is due mainly to the influence of the oil sector.

technical personnel, the OAS made a correlation analysis of the ratio of professionals and technicians to the total labor force in several Latin American nations with respect to the average productivity of the labor force, in accordance with the results of the 1960 census (Table 1). The correlation was relatively satisfactory (0.84), but it proves only that the occupational categories of professionals and technicians—which include all of the first categories of the human resources listed earlier—follow a pattern similar to that of the labor productivity index, which might be taken as a reasonably good indicator of technical progress. It does not prove at all that the availability of a higher proportion of these occupational categories is the cause of a higher level of technical change, but at least it implies a certain correlation of both phenomena.

On a different but closely related subject, the OAS conducted a survey to analyze the educational level, experience, and motivation of entrepreneurs establishing an industrial firm for the first time. The survey, made in various Latin American countries (Mexico, Colombia, Ecuador, and Central America), showed that 50 per cent of the new industrialists had previous working experience as merchants in closely related fields and that 30 per cent were professionals, mainly in the technical fields. The last figure tends to prove the importance of the availability of high-level personnel in establishing new businesses. This is a different activity, but one closely connected to technical innovation in the sense that it requires a dynamic attitude and a willingness for promoting change.

RECOMMENDATIONS FOR FURTHER STUDY

Two basic lines for further investigation are recommended:

1. *A comprehensive research project on the total process of technological innovation.* The facts related to the problems of the process of technological innovation must be determined, the associated parameters and constraints found and the strategies outlined.

Research is needed to acquire a better understanding of the process and then to serve as a basis for operational programs. As part of the research program, specific studies should be undertaken on a worldwide basis to analyze the favorable or unfavorable climate for innovation, to determine the obstacles preventing an effective demand for knowledge, and to assess the economic, social, technical, psychological and cultural variables associated with knowledge. The aim of such studies should be to appraise the receptivity of the national environment to technical innovation and determine the possible incentives for it.

Case studies should be developed in various countries at different levels of development in some representative sectors of low, average, and high intensity levels of technical change in order to analyze, evaluate, and compare concrete examples of successes and failures of technical innovation, and to describe the obstacles encountered and practicable solutions for overcoming these. These case studies should explicitly include the experiences of international firms.

2. *A parallel investigation of the possibility of changing the usual basic methodologies for human resources studies.* The basic approach in manpower assessment studies of most international organizations (OECD, OAS, ILO) up to now has been, with no exceptions to my knowledge, fundamentally a demand approach: the requirements of human resources were determined for specific targets of output and technical change, the latter through productivity estimates. In order to learn about the influence of the availability of specific human resources categories in causing technical change, it will be necessary to change the "demand" approach to a "supply" approach and to utilize new analytical tools.

Finally, in analyzing the requirements for availability of "desirable human resources," the public sector officials and the development banking officials should be included within this phraseology. Both are deeply connected with the problem of creating a suitable environment for technological change in the industrialization process and are essential to that process.

TWO PROMISING WAYS TO DEVELOP HUMAN RESOURCES

Commentary by Robert W. Iversen

IT IS ASSUMED that a major factor in economic development is the availability of human skills. It also is assumed that a developing country cannot rely indefinitely on external assistance in obtaining its talent. Every effort must be directed at the maximum utilization and development of indigenous talent and, toward this end, I would like to suggest two approaches which are becoming increasingly important in the United States but which are not widely known around the world: "job redesign" and "work-study" schooling. I hope that their adaptibility to the needs of developing countries will be quickly apparent.

JOB REDESIGN

The principles of job engineering and design have long been used to achieve greater efficiency and economy but, recently, it has been recognized that these principles might be applied to the achievement of newer social purposes while still fulfilling some of the criteria of efficiency. The problem was recently pinpointed by Dr. William H. Stewart, Surgeon General of the U.S. Public Health Service, when he observed:

> Year by year, our top professional personnel are being trained to perform still more complex tasks. How long can each profession afford to hang on to its simpler functions—the routine filling of a tooth, for example, or the several easily automated steps in a medical examination? How can we train the physician or dentist to make full use of the skills available in other people, freeing himself to perform only those duties for which he is uniquely qualified?

Similar questions should be asked of all administrative, professional, and technical personnel for, if development is being hampered by an apparent shortage of top talent, it also is being slowed by the indifference, underutilization, or hostility of the uninvolved. Nothing less than the maximum utilization and involvement of all the nation's skills and talent will be required for its fullest development.

One attack on this problem is underway in the federal government's project MUST (Maximum Utilization of Skills and Training). One of the social purposes of the project is the greater employment of minority and disadvantaged people and the central factor in MUST is "job redesign." It is believed that an analysis of most of the jobs done by highly trained professionals would reveal ingredients which could be performed by workers with considerably less training. One manager, for example, found that "one so-called technical job out of three is not truly a technical job" and believed such jobs could be performed by persons with less training. What is called for is a redesign of jobs which would, on the one hand, retain for the professional those tasks which only he was qualified to do and, on the othe hand, reveal and define simpler jobs which would permit the employment of people with lesser training and skills. This would permit the maximum utilization of scarce top talent, but it would also permit a portion of the population that has not previously shared in the development effort to enter the world of work. This, coupled with postentry training, could add tremendously to a nation's pool of talent. Job redesign also suggests possible uses for the frequently underutilized liberal arts graduates who often are alienated from a nation's development process.

It is important to accompany any MUST-type program with the opportunity for continued personal growth. A portion of any new work assignment should be devoted to training. At one end of the talent spectrum, this might well involve the assignment of courses in basic education: reading, writing, arithmetic, and speaking. At the other end of the spectrum, individuals placed in paraprofessional or subtechnical positions might well reveal motivations and aptitudes that would warrant encouraging them to develop more sophisticated skills. The important point is that, by job redesign, one frees the hands of the rare professional from demanding, though relatively trivial, tasks: at the same time, one brings into the world of work, people who had previously been shut out. Once such people are employed, their potentialities can be ascertained and developed.

WORK-STUDY PROGRAMS

For over fifty years, a work-study or "cooperative education" format has provided the framework in which large numbers of students in the United States have simultaneously achieved professional education and practical experience. The format has been particularly prominent in engineering education, although it has achieved renown at more general institutions such as Antioch College. The advantages of the program are many, particularly in these times which see an increasing student alienation from the mainstream of national life and a widespread feeling that education is irrelevant or divorced from the real world and its multitude of problems and needs. By designing education which carefully articulates the classroom and the job, much of this feeling can be overcome. The work-study format usually has been applied at the college level, but there is certainly no inherent reason why it is not adaptable to secondary education as well.

To describe work-study programs very briefly, the student alternates periods of study with periods of work. It may take five years to achieve the customary four-year college degree, but the work-study student will emerge with at least two years of practical experience in his field and will be immediately useful at a higher level than his traditionally educated classmate.

The work-study approach, however, is not to be confused with part-time work. The job and the curriculum are closely integrated so that they reinforce one another. If this is well done, the program assures greater educational relevance, a more realistic view of the world of work, and a personal commitment to service. The latter is very important in undercutting the widespread estrangement of youth from society, for it calls on the fullest development and use of his talent.

There are a wide range of work-study models and experiences. The private sector has been deeply involved in these programs since the graduates constitute highly desirable recruits. The industries frequently play a role in the curriculum as well as in providing the work assignments which constitute almost half the program. The work-study idea may see greater growth in the coming decade. The Escuela de Administration y Finanzas e Instituto Tecnologico at Medellin, Colombia, may well have the first successful work-study experiment in Latin America. The School is devoted to preparing technical experts with supervisory and middle-management responsibilities. In 1967, the Ford Foundation granted $1 million to several schools to broaden the work-study concept as a means of bringing lower-income and minority students into the educational mainstream. Certainly some of the lessons learned in this effort will be applicable to developing countries. Finally, it has been widely observed that the education commonly offered in developing countries rarely prepares the student for a role in his country's modernization. It is suggested that the work-study approach might well be a way of assuring the emergence of students with needed skills, practical experience, and a positive drive for service and achievement.

CONCLUSIONS

Both of these approaches require the close cooperation of the public and private sectors. The existing associations of administrative, professional, and technical personnel must recognize the professional and social desirability of projects such as MUST. The existing schools and universities, as well as public and private industry, must recognize the cooperation required for the successful work-study programming. But, above all, there must be a clear statement of national policy to the effect that the development of a country requires the maximum utilization and development of its people's skills. No stable development can long remain dependent upon outside talent and no developing country can attain its fullest potential if large numbers of its people must remain outside the system. Beyond such policy and leadership pronouncements must come the administrative and managerial contexts for actually implementing those programs. The virtue of both the MUST program and the work-study program is that the job is identified and the individual is trained for that job simultaneously, eliminating the frustration of people being trained for nonexistent jobs or of jobs being opened up for people who cannot fill them.

THE AVAILABILITY OF DESIRED HUMAN RESOURCES THROUGH EDUCATION

Commentary by Logan C. Osterndorf

IN CONSIDERING HUMAN resources, we are, on the one hand, dealing with two of the factors of production—labor and the entrepreneur—and, the other hand, with human beings, their aspirations, shortcomings, and need for basic necessities of life, irrespective of the forces of supply and demand. And, while we are involving the human being as a factor of production, we are, or should be, at the same time, directing that production for the benefit of humanity.

Industrialization in most developing countries will be influenced by the lack of available human resources. Trained engineers, technicians, entrepreneurs, skilled, and even semiskilled people simply are not available on the scale needed to bring about any degree of industrialization. Unskilled labor in large numbers appears to be the normal condition for most developing countries.

If a country is to develop, what should its development objective be? Keeping in mind the application of engineering technology, perhaps the definition given by Barend de Vries (1968) of the World Bank will be appropriate: "Let the objective be a society in which all are employed in activities in which the most productive methods known to man are used." This is in sharp contrast to the typical country in which the least productive methods are only too often being used.

Industrialization presupposes trained manpower; therefore, top priority must be given to assuring that needed skills are available. In discussing all sectors of the labor force, from the highly trained technologist to the semiskilled laborer, it is necessary to look at the prospects for overall education and training in the less-developed countries.

Educational planning is the heart of a sound education program. To be effective, it must be consistent with the stated national goals and have official governmental support. Effective implementation must follow planning. It is encouraging that approximately two-thirds of UNESCO member countries presently are committed to a policy of educational planning. Of these, about one-half are actually involved in planning, even if only on a limited scale. The remainder are still in the process of getting started.

Unfortunately, all is not as well as appears. Education is in a state of crisis which has been brought about by an ever-widening gap between the educational system and its environment. Only too often education simply is not meeting the needs of a new society.

Education is not easily adapted to change, but change it must, both quantitatively and qualitatively. Faced with population explosion, the revolution of rising expectations, and a recognition of education as the key to the better life, the number of persons being educated is falling percentagewise in many countries despite increased efforts and expenditures for education. Furthermore, the actual number of persons being educated is inadequate. In many countries, only one-third to one-fourth of the young are receiving a full primary education. One-tenth of that number may benefit from a secondary education and approximately one-tenth of those with a secondary education are fortunate enough to earn a college degree. Although efforts should be made to increase the number of persons being educated, it is a delicate task to gearing that increase to the general level of economic expansion. To upset the balance can bring about not only an economic, but also a political crisis, thereby jeopardizing stable government, a necessary ingredient for sound development.

Qualitatively, education has only too often been the wrong kind, thereby limiting the contribution to development in terms of the investment involved in human resources.

Another factor in the crisis, and a problem which can be expected to worsen before improving, is the "brutal economic squeeze," as Philip Coombs (1968) puts it, "between the rising costs per student on the one hand, and a slowdown in the growth of their financial resources on the other." Increased costs will come about not only through inflation, but also through (1) higher salaries for teachers without a corresponding increase in productivity and (2) the additional costs of higher levels of education.

To complicate matters, there will be added demands for funds to meet other needs within the society—food, health, military, and so on. At the same time, the rate of economic growth will no doubt be low for some time to come. Inevitably, the squeeze will intensify and education *can* be the victim.

Despite the problems, cures must be found and changes made. Among areas needing attention are facilities, curriculum, teacher training, educational management, and the direction of universities. Personnel from all disciplines and specialties—the social scientist, the engineer, the business administration expert, as well as the educationalist—should be called upon to assist, using the analytical tools available to science and engineering. The effort should be directed not only towards formal education, but towards adult education and on-the-job training as well.

The task is monumental when the local resources are so limited. Outside assistance must be sought. One approach has been the enrollment of teachers and students in foreign institutions. Frequently, the results have been wanting; many students majoring in science and technology return overqualified or trained in fields unrelated to the manpower needs of the society. Unemployment or inadequate employment follows. Other graduates become candidates for the brain drain. To improve the program, better screening methods for choosing the prospective student might be adopted when other than his or her personal funds are used. Greater selectivity might be exercised in choosing the institution in terms of its ability to offer courses and guidance necessary to meet the needs of the society as well as of the individual.

Paralleling the export of students has been the import of specialists and skills, the "doers" and the "demonstrators." The "doers" can be expected to "get things moving" in the short run, but essential development can become a reality only when a country has its own training and educational institutions using its own trained staff to educate its people to meet its needs. Hence, the need for the "demonstrator," on a long-term basis working within the framework of well-defined objectives which might include training manpower, building organizations, developing decision-makers, and building for future growth.

Beginning with President Truman's Point-Four Program, the world embarked on a program of technical assistance of a scope never before witnessed by mankind. Bilateral and multilateral approaches have been used. Without discussing the advantages and disadvantages of the two approaches, it should be stressed that there is a need for better coordination between the two types when they exist in a given country.

UNESCO today represents the single largest multilateral approach to technical assistance in the education and training of human resources. Over 1500 professional persons serve on international teams in approximately 100 countries. In the Special Fund program, 87 projects should have become active by the end of 1968—51 projects in the field of the natural sciences and their application to development, and 36 in education. Twenty-eight new projects are planned for 1969–70 in the science and technology area, and 22 in education. A 13-percent increase in expenditures over those of 1967–68 is estimated for 1969–70. The average annual increase in personnel is estimated to be 10 per cent with an approximate annual turnover of 30 per cent.

A profile of UNESCO experts serving in the education section in the field shows that 65 per cent have a master's degree and 35 per cent have a doctoral degree. Sixty per cent have had more than 10 years of experience in their field of specialization and 5 per cent have had less than 5 years of experience. Experts are required to possess greater skills than in the past; a larger number of specialties also are required. Not only are the experts expected to contribute in their field of competence, they also are expected to change and encourage innovation in the educational system itself.

What about the contribution of the United States to the program? Financially, the United States is doing well; it contributes approximately one-third of the UNESCO budget. Americans are serving in staff positions in the Secretariat in Paris, but on a limited scale. As to the important contribution of United States experts serving with UNESCO in the developing countries, working on a day-to-day basis with educational problems, the report is dismal. Approximately 6 per cent of all the professional field positions are occupied by Americans. Numerous factors help explain this deplorable situation: (1) international competition for positions, (2) political attitudes of the requesting governments, (3) emphasis on bilateral programs in the United States, (4) unavailability of United States professors during the academic year, (5) negative professional attitudes regarding service with international teams, (6) affluent living conditions in the United States, and (7) salaries.

With the apparent decline in the United States' participation in the bilateral programs, added support must be given to the multilateral approach if the United States is to continue to share its wealth in science and technology with the less fortunate nations of the world. The task however, is not to find reasons for the poor representation, but to find answers as to how more can be done. Some of the problems are beyond the realm of this Conference, but many can be considered and several recommendations made. Since colleges and universities are the primary source of supply for experts in the UNESCO program, I would suggest these institutions consider the following recommendations to better support the United States' effort in multilateral programs, particularly those of UNESCO:

Give valid and meaningful recognition to the multilateral approach. This is not always done. Developing countries are seeking ways and means to solve their problems based on their culture, potentials, and goals. An international approach provides greater options.

Recognize the value of service with an international team in terms of professional as well as personal improvement. While technology is advancing rapidly in the United States and the technical problems of a developing country are less sophisticated, there can be much in an overseas experience to challenge a person professionally. The expert sought by UNESCO is one who will keep abreast of developments in his field, provided he is not absent for an extended period of time.

Develop an institutional or professional program to enable an expert to be informed of progress in his field during his overseas service. Such a program might include a research project related to the UNESCO assignment or attendance at an international professional meeting. Much can be learned through dialogue with the international members of the team.

Encourage staff members to serve abroad through pay incentives, promotion, tenure, and fringe benefits, and utilize the specialist's overseas experiences upon his return to campus and community.

Train potential specialists for international service. Technology cannot be transferred nor superimposed on a society. It must be integrated into that society and persons having not only technical skills but knowledge and understanding of other cultures as well are needed. The International Education Act passed by the 89th Congress would help accomplish this on the graduate and undergraduate level.

Provide means whereby an expert can be released during the academic year. School years begin and end at different times throughout the world and experts are needed during the entire calendar year. Yet, United States professors normally can be considered for programs beginning during the months of June, July, and August.

Industrialization cannot become a national goal unless the human resources are trained and available at the time and place needed. Hence, an educational program becomes part and parcel of any development plan. The immediate prospects for an effective educational program appear limited. I would like, therefore, to add another dimension to this Conference by suggesting that engineering technology, with its analytic techniques, be applied to the educational programs of the less-developed countries as they seek to achieve their goal of industrialization.

Note—The views expressed in this paper are those of the author and do not necessarily reflect the thinking of the U.S. Office of Education.

REPORT OF WORKSHOP 3

Carmelo Mesa-Lago, Rapporteur

BECAUSE OF HISTORICALLY low investments in agriculture, wage differences between agriculture and industry, and the limitations of the modern sector in generating the number of new jobs for an expanding work force resulting from uncontrolled population growth, developing countries are facing acute problems of unemployment and underemployment. Sociological and technological innovations are needed in the industrial, agricultural, and service sectors to increase the number of jobs in each of these sectors, but most particularly in the agricultural sector. An action program for the generation and utilization of the engineer, the technician, and the skilled and the semi-skilled worker in the broad human-resource strategy should include the following considerations.

—*The initiation by the developing countries of national programs for demographic research and population control.*

—*Urgent attention to the rural sector.* This is crucial and if an important goal of development is the creation of employment for larger and larger segments of work force require changes in policies on investment and organization. In the task of rural modernization, technology has an important role to play.

—*The generation of indigenous or appropriate technology by indigenous institutes of research and the universities.* In the modern sector itself, the developing countries have not yet exhausted the potentialities of a variety of employment-generating forms of technology and industrial organization. The intermediate sector of the economies containing small and medium-scale industries and service enterprises can serve as the spring-board for action in rejuvenating the rural sector. The agri-business sector can be a fruitful field for the interplay of agricultural and engineering principles and techniques.

—*A change in emphasis in the training and education of the engineer if engineering is to play a role in rural modernization.* The present reported shortages in engineering manpower in several countries often are attributable to poor utilization and lack of incentives. On a regional basis, graduate education programs offer one method of increasing the availability of engineering professors. Graduate education in engineering is an expensive undertaking and a desirable first-stage action would be to identify strong national programs at the undergraduate level and well-planned inputs of external and domestic resources to elevate them to graduate-level status to serve the region. This also might be one of the methods of repatriating "brain drainees" back to the region from which they emigrated.

—*Develop programs at the technician level* to diversify higher-education programs, provide the spread of skills and knowledge required by modern industry, and relieve shortages of engineering manpower. It would appear that the techniques of trade and job analysis so useful in rationalizing industrial occupations could be used with profit for analyzing technician training needs in agriculture and service occupations.

—*Allocation of resources and development of organizations for training skilled and semiskilled workers for both industrial and agricultural occupations.* In tackling this immense task, financial and organizational participation by industry would be important. Forecasting training needs and arranging training programs for the large numbers who migrate from rural to urban areas in search

100

of employment pose special problems. Developing countries already burdened with the problems of providing education and training to the literate urban populations are at present unable to make the large additional investments necessary to incorporate the "marginal" populations into the modern sector. Urgent action is necessary in this regard to avert conflict and prepare the way for orderly development.

—*Adaptation of two specific United States approaches for use in developing human resources abroad.* One approach is job redesigning as exemplified in the United States government program, MUST (Maximum Utilization of Skill and Training). This approach has two advantages: it enables better utilization of scarce high-level skills and generates new jobs at lower levels. A second approach is work-study programs at both secondary and college levels, combining and integrating jobs with relevant curricula so that students are prepared for needed jobs while they get actual work experience. Work-study makes education relevant to the practical work and supplies the country with trained manpower with some experience. Both approaches have the advantage of encouraging broader involvement of indigenous talent in the country's development effort.

—*Provision of assistance to students and trainees from the developing countries prepared in the developed countries in acquiring specific skills and techniques to cope with concrete problems in the developmental programs of their own countries.* The educational institution in the developed country should be selected on the basis of its teaching resources for and specialization in dealing with the concrete problems of development in the student's country. The long-range solution is the strengthening of institutions in the developing countries and giving programs a development focus. The impact of the training received should be measured by two indices: application of the learned techniques in solving concrete problems and transmission of the acquired knowledge from the trainee to others in the native population.

Colleges and universities in the developed nations are an important source of supply of experts who can be sent to the developing countries. Such a supply could be increased by greater commitment to international service on the part of the institution as evidenced by the incentives it provides for members of its staff to participate in international development programs. The feedback of this accumulated experience to the home campus is essential. Arrangements for sharing the accumulated knowledge and development experience with other developing countries are yet to be perfected.

—*Encouragement of experts from the developed countries to work in interdisciplinary international teams.* The usefulness of such teams is measured not only in terms of the success of the project assigned to them, but also by the legacy of skills and knowledge left by them in the form of trained indigenous human resources.

—*More effective use of managers and entrepreneurs.* Dynamic factors or direct agents of technological change are managers and entrepreneurs, the decision makers who play an important role in incorporating innovation into the production process. Statistics on managerial resources in developing countries are scarce as are the available techniques for developing new entrepreneurial talent. Research is needed in this area to improve current knowledge. In many developing and developed countries engineers and technicians are used in management positions, most often without any formal managerial preparation. Management principles and techniques should be incorporated into engineering curricula. Two types of high-level manpower needed for development are managers of research and development for industry and government, and highly qualified public-sector officials concerned with national planning and development banking.

—*Elimination of labor immobility in developing countries, and especially in Latin America, as an obstacle to the mobilization of human resources for development.* Illiteracy, lack of skills, negative social attitudes, and, in some countries, cultural dualism impede labor mobility. Trade unions protect their members from competition with the unemployed by raising artificial barriers to entry into the trades. Labor legislation in many countries introduces legal stratification by regulating labor conditions of professionals and of white and blue collar workers. The multiplicity of social insurance funds and the lack of mechanisms for transferring contributions chain the workers to their trades and jobs. Race and sex discrimination are additional barriers. Institutional changes supporting greater labor mobility are agrarian reform, increases in budget allocations for both the urban and rural disadvantaged sectors, and the consolidation of social insurance funds.

BIBLIOGRAPHY

Agency for International Development. *Manpower in Economic and Social Growth.* Proceedings of the Sixth International Manpower Seminar, June 1–August 13, 1966. Washington, D.C.: Agency for International Development, U.S. Department of State, Office of Labor Affairs.

Commonwealth Education Liaison Committee. *Education and Training of Technicians.* Report of an Expert Conference of Education (Technical) at Huddersfield, England, October 1966. London: Commonwealth Education Liaison Committee, 1967.

Coombs, Philip H., "The challenge of educational planning," *International Development Review,* Vol. 10, No. 2, June, 1968.

Dannemann, Robert N., "Problems of human resources in Brazil," *International Labor Review,* Vol. 94, No. 6, December, 1966.

Davis, Russell G., *Scientific Engineering and Technical Education in Mexico.* New York: Education and World Affairs, Occasional Reports.

De Vries, Barend A., "New perspectives on international development," *Finance and Development,* No. 3, 1968.

Education and World Affairs. *Nigerian Human Resource Development and Utilization.* New York: Education and World Affairs, December, 1967.

Hieronymus, George H., *Job Design: Meeting the Manpower Challenge.* Washington, D.C.: Society for Personnel Administration, 1958.

Horowitz, Morris A., *High Level Manpower in the Economic Development of Argentina.* Boston: Bureau of Business and Economic Research, Northeastern University. Reprinted from *Manpower Education* by Harbison and Myers. Reprint Series I–31.

ICETEX. *Resources and Requirements for Highly Trained Personnel, 1964–1975.* ICETEX (Colombian Institute for Advanced Training Abroad), Human Resources Department, 1966.

Journal of Cooperative Education. Philadelphia: Drexel Institute of Technology.

Larke, Alfred G., "Getting technologists out of nowhere," *Dun's Review and Modern Industry,* Vol. 67, No. 6, June, 1956.

Leuba, Clarence., *Effective Learning and Cooperative Education.* New York: National Commission for Cooperative Education, 1964.

McVoy, Edgar C., Relevance of U.S. Experience in Manpower Programs for Developing Countries. *Proceedings of the Industrial Relations Research Association.* Winter, 1967.

OECD. *Education, Human Resources and Development in Argentina, Methodological Problems and Statistical Data.* Paris: OECD, 1968.

Pearl, Arthur, and Frank Riessman, *New Careers for the Poor.* New York: The Free Press, 1965.

Rao, K. N., "Small scale industry and economic development in Indonesia," *Economic Development and Cultural Change, Vol. 6, No. 2, January, 1956.*

Rao, K. N., *Technical Education in the Developing Countries.* Ford Foundation Reprint, SR–16.

Strassman, W. Paul, *Technological Change and Economic Development.* Ithaca: Cornell University Press, 1968.

U.S. Department of the Air Force. *Solving Skills Shortages by Job Rearrangement.* Washington, D.C.: U.S. Government Printing Office, 1951.

U.S. Department of the Army. *Job Engineering: Modification of Jobs for Better Utilization of Manpower.* Washington, D.C.: U.S. Government Printing Office, 1954.

Ward, F. Champion, *From Manpower to Mankind.* Ford Foundation Reprint, 1967.

Wilson, James W., and Edward H. Lyons., *Work-Study College Programs.* New York: Harper, 1961.

Wooldridge, Roy L., *Cooperative Education and the Community Colleges of New Jersey.* New York: National Committee of Cooperative Education, 1966.

6

THE INFLUENCE OF SOCIAL AND CULTURAL ENVIRONMENTS

Principal Paper—Bert F. Hoselitz

Discussion of the Papers by K. N. Rao
and Bert F. Hoselitz

Report of Workshop 4—Roland Robertson,
Rapporteur

All men are social animals with concerns, at various levels of their existence,
with their cultural environment which influence them in their professional
efforts and must, hence, be of concern in the development process.

The Editors

THE INFLUENCE OF SOCIAL AND CULTURAL ENVIRONMENTS

Principal Paper by Bert F. Hoselitz

THE HUMAN RACE has spent several tens of thousands of years on the surface of this earth, but our concern is with the last ten thousand years—from the beginning of the Agricultural Revolution which took place about 6000 or 7000 B.C. and can be considered the very first major step in the evolution of the productive man. Many simple tools, fire, and housing had been discovered or developed earlier, but the Agricultural Revolution was the first change in production which affected all mankind. It began in the Middle East and, from there, in three or four thousand years, had spread throughout the entire inhabited world.

Agriculture was revolutionized by the planting and harvesting of seed crops. Seed for the following year was produced and since that time mankind has continued to produce seeds every year and has never been without seed for the following year. In the four thousand years or so during which the Agricultural Revolution was taking place, mankind lived in villages. Probably less than 1 per cent lived in the few existing cities which were primarily religious centers and the homes of monarchs.

At the time of the Agricultural Revolution, mankind also began, and made slow progress in, some of the so-called industrial occupations. Ships were built and used for exploring so that, by 100 or 200 A.D., all of Europe, North Africa, and much of Asia, including India, was known. The Agricultural Revolution is generally thought of as the first economic revolution; about 1700, the second economic revolution began—the Industrial Revolution. From 2000 B.C. until 1700 A.D. mankind developed primarily in agriculture; the progress in industrial work was slow because each individual person was still part of the feudal social system. Though many branches of industry were highly productive compared with agriculture, industry was carried on in artisan shops and increased production could not develop rapidly under the prevailing feudal system. The Industrial Revolution might have taken place in 1500 A.D. if man could have abolished the feudal system then and instituted the capitalist system. But this did not occur for another 200–250 years. Therefore, the Industrial Revolution did not begin in 1500 but took place in England in approximately 1700.

The Industrial Revolution and the simultaneous advent of capitalism were of very profound significance to most of the Western world. The conditions of industrial workers were completely changed under the capitalist system. The non-Western world, with the possible exception of Japan, did not experience the Industrial Revolution at the same time and its only connection with capitalism came through its contacts with Europe.

Capitalism was introduced to underdeveloped countries principally through the raw-material industries. Exploitation of oil wells, copper and tin mines, and the agricultural production of a few commodities such as coffee, bananas, and tea by foreign enterprises occurred and was capitalistic in application, but these mines, oil fields, and plantations employed very few people and, by the end of World War II, the world in general was still divided into the industrialized capitalistic countries of the West, with predominantly white inhabitants, and the economically underdeveloped countries with predominantly nonwhite inhabitants.

Economic development is considered the force that will make underdeveloped countries capitalistic, raise their incomes, and make them as industrially oriented as the Western world, and tremendous pressure is being exerted to bring about this change. However, such a change is a long and slow process, and it is doubtful whether it will be achieved by 2000 or 2100.

At the end of World War II, it was obvious that a third revolution was taking place—the Scientific Revolution. It has reached its highest level in the United States but the scientific achievements of the Western European countries are close to those of the United States. Professor Glenn T. Seaborg (1965) was one of the first American scientists to speak about the third, or scientific revolution. He feels that, with the advent of the third revolution, science has become so important to our national welfare, not only in terms of national defense but also for economic growth and social wellbeing, that the relationship between science and man is, for us in our day, a matter of profound significance. We shall, therefore, discuss briefly the history of the Scientific Revolution in the United States in the last 20 years in an effort to determine the meaning of this scientific revolution to us.

In 1920 the United States had an official expenditure of $48 million for scientific investment. This was 0.05 per cent of our total national income. Scientific work accounted for the employment of 7367 persons out of a total civilian labor force of 40 282 000 in 1920. Compare this with the figures for 1964, the last year for which statistics for other countries are available: the total expenditure for research and development was $21 075 million, 3.4 per cent of the national income; roughly 700 000 people out of a civilian labor force of 74 000 000 were employed in science (Hoselitz, 1967). When we spend between 3 and 4 per cent of our national income for scientific purposes, one may ask, "How much more can the United States spend? Can we, for example, spend 10 or 20 per cent of our national income for scientific purposes and, if so, what would result?"

I feel it is important to analyze how the 3.4 per cent of our national income was actually spent because I am reasonably certain that spending in years subsequent to 1964 has followed the same pattern. The largest portion was spent for raw materials and investigation of various physical and chemical problems. Although the physicists, chemists, and engineers are paid very well, it is questionable whether a sufficiently large number will develop into the kind of research staff personnel which is progressive, creative, and inventive in the various scientific fields. Even though the United States, to dwell on the most successful country, has increased its labor force in scientific activities devoted to research 100 times in the 44 years between 1920 and 1964, it cannot increase the working force from now on by a similar factor. In the years from 1950 to 1960, about 3000 Ph.D. degrees were awarded each year to physicists, chemists, and engineers in the United States (Holloman, 1965). We assume that the number has increased to about 4000 since then. In addition, in the period from 1956 to 1961, 4869 scientists and engineers immigrated to the United States each year (OECD Observer). An estimated 500 to 1000 of these had Ph.D. degrees and most of the others had B.S. degrees. A large number of these immigrants were absorbed by private industry. Thus, the total of new doctorates granted to those engaged in these scientific fields has risen to 4500 to 5000 annually in the United States. Of these, many do not go into research but teach in universities or accept jobs in industry which involve no scientific research. In other words, in order to increase greatly the number of graduates going into scientific research, we would have to spend relatively more money than we are spending now. It is doubtful whether we could bring such an expenditure to a level at which there would be even twice as many scientific Ph.D. degrees awarded every year as are earned now.

In addition, in the 1960s our scientific accomplishments decreased. At that time, A. Weinberg, Director of the Oak Ridge National Laboratory, said,

Our operating budget for science has increased since 1950 by a factor of almost 5, whereas the number of Ph.D.'s in science and engineering has increased by only a factor of 2. I know of no evidence to show that our people are smarter now than they were a decade ago. We merely heap more money on them and therefore we use each dollar less efficiently.

In a similar vein, Paul Weiss of the Rockefeller Institute said about biologically trained scientists,

Biological experimentation at the height of success is beginning to drift into habits that threaten to place bulk ahead of brains and routine exercises ahead of thought. As research has grown in volume it also has grown softer by loss of self-restraint, lowered selectivity, and blurring of research targets.

And a pertinent comment on the nature of physics in the last 50 years was made by Hans Bethe:

The pace of basic discoveries in physics was far greater in the first thirty years of this century that it has been in the second thirty years. Many very important details have been discovered in this second period but it is all a lot of important detail but nothing you cannot summarize in one or two sentences.

Obviously, the doubling or even the tripling of our research and development budget would not be likely to lead to a doubling or tripling of scientific accomplishment (Orleans, 1965).

As to scientific research and development, there are two other points which must be discussed. The first concerns the distribution of funds between different fields of scientific research and the second concerns the use of scientific personnel in various firms in the United States.

DISTRIBUTION OF FUNDS

Regarding the first point, approximately 63 per cent of all research and development funds in the United States are allotted to atomic research, space research, and defense industries. This is a very large amount and very little from this expenditure is of benefit to other industries. It is generally said that an invention in one field is, after more or less time, also of importance to other fields. But it is very difficult to see how expenditures on the needs for war or on space exploration will prove significant for the so-called private field. Even though expenditures for investigation of certain aspects of the use of atomic power could, of course, be of peaceful benefit, unfortunately most of the expenditures for atomic research are made for research on improvement of atomic bombs and not on research for the utilization of atomic power for nondefense needs. Since it is clear that 63 per cent of the research and development funds are used for defense and space research, only 36 per cent of the funds are left for research for the benefit of the balance of the economy. Of this, 28 per cent are in economically motivated sciences and only 9 per cent devoted to research in welfare and health. This division of research and development expenditures in the United States needs no further comment.

USE OF SCIENTIFIC PERSONNEL IN DIFFERENT FIRMS

The United States has approximately 300 000 firms. Only 300 very large ones, including the government, employ about 80 per cent of the total employees in the scientific research and development field. These employees are not assigned exclusively to scientific work. Some of them are administrators or their services are used for indirectly scientific work, and others often are away at universities or on assignment in other countries. Although the budgeted funds are spent on research and development in the 300 large firms, there is a very loose interpretation of the term "research and development" for the kinds of work which fall into this classification. These large firms, including those handling the major research work in atomic science, space science, and defense, have their own structures for research activities. They set up their own strict organizations; they have their own goals in research. The most natural consequence of this system is that the only research done is usually for the purpose of achieving the limited goals which have been set. Therefore, many scientists do less independent research than they did in the 1920s and 1930s, engaging instead in very formal types of research. The employment of more scientists is likely to accentuate this tendency at twice the cost with less than twice the output.

SCIENTIFIC RESEARCH AND DEVELOPMENT IN EUROPE

So far I have discussed only the United States, but Europe is following in its footpath. To report the figures for various European countries would be boring; furthermore, they are easily available. The expenditure for scientific research and development in European countries is about 2.5 per cent or less of national income. It has not yet reached the United States level, but there is little doubt that, in about 10 to 15 years, many European countries will spend as large a percentage of their national income on scientific research as the United States.

In 1964 all the Western European countries together, instead of spending $21 billion and employing 700 000 persons as did the United States, spent $6260 million and employed 470 000 people. However, both figures are increasing rather swiftly. Scientific research in the Union of Soviet Socialist Republics is officially an enigma because we know, at least publicly, nothing about personnel employment, the breakdown between research for peaceful and military use, or the total amount of money spent on scientific research and development. Nevertheless, some attempts have been made to estimate the extent of Soviet personnel, and even the Soviet expenditures, engaged in research and development. In 1962 the number of Soviet scientists and engineers engaged in research and development was estimated to be between 416 000 and 487 000, and total personnel from 1 039 000 to 1 472 00. The larger number is based on "project" assumption, the lesser number on "conservative" estimate. Soviet expenditures on research and development were assumed to be $4300 billion; however a comparison in terms of official exchange rates has little meaning since it takes no account of differences in research costs in various countries. The salaries of research workers are much higher in the United States than in the USSR. Therefore, it is of greater advantage to compare the expenditures in terms of the general cost of living. Such "research exchange rates" were calculated with regard to the cost of labor and raw materials; it was found that the cost of research in the United States is about three times that in the Soviet Union (OECD Observer).

My general personal opinion is that the United States will never spend much more than 5 per cent of its national income for research. I think it will spend more on applied research than on basic research, partly because the progress of basic research is always slow, partly because, as more is accomplished in basic research, the field for additional new discoveries is narrowed and proposals for carrying on such research are fewer; partly because basic research that really makes a valuable contribution to world knowledge is usually done by a few very gifted people whose talents are often and increasingly used elsewhere; and partly because there is a tendency to grant research funds to large institutions for applied research rather than to small ones devoted to basic research.

EFFECTS OF SOCIETY

In general terms, the form of a society has a very great effect on the rate of invention. However, a society which encourages technical progress in its formative years can, as a result of the very inventions it engenders, eventually retard further progress until a new social structure replaces it. I do not question that the total industrial progress which is typical of the Western countries can eventually be adapted to the underdeveloped countries, but I seriously question whether the scientists' inventive streak can continue with the same velocity it had during the first quarter of this century.

Many people believe that, because of the population explosion, the percentage of physicists, chemists, and engineers will increase, but I personally do not believe that the number of people capable of being scientists will increase in the same proportion as the general population. I foresee the future of scientific invention in the advanced countries concentrated on the improvement of living standards and on the adaptation of industrialization to the underdeveloped countries for the purpose of improving the living conditions there.

I believe that there is a great difference between the reality of the future and its depiction by our movies and short stories. According to movies and fiction, in a very few years we shall be floating around in space, all our living habits will be different, and the whole universe will be our domain. This certainly will not be true in 2000 or 25 000; it may *never* be. Perhaps in the advanced countries we shall have fewer work hours, but the population explosion will create an increasingly larger dependent group so that we shall still need to keep a large percentage of the world's inhabitants fully occupied, especially as long as methods of production remain comparatively primitive in most parts of the world.

I think scientific research will progress primarily in molecular biology, high-energy physics, nuclear energy, space exploration, and the behavioral sciences. While achievements in molecular biology will be considered important, in my opinion, those in space exploration will not. In other words, we shall welcome all the medical advances as benefitting all humans, but it is doubtful that we shall want to expend the funds and research efforts necessary for successful travel to the moon. I think the groundwork for progress to come was laid in the first quarter of this century and the achievement of that progress will be merely a very profitable implementation of the theories already established. In other words, there will be a sort of subrevolution. I do not know whether there is much general agreement with this opinion; I do know that it is shared by many scientists whose work I have read.

RECOMMENDED EXPENDITURES ON RESEARCH AND DEVELOPMENT

One of the great differences between developed and underdeveloped countries is the absence of research in the underdeveloped countries. At the conclusion of the 1968 UNESCO Conference in Delhi on The Application of Science and Technology to the Development of Asia, it was resolved that the participating governments of Asia should endeavor to reach a minimum level of total national expenditures on research and development amounting to 1 per cent of their gross national product as soon as possible, but not later than 1980, this figure to be reached by both government and private sources. To carry out this resolution, the Conference stipulated the following priority areas of action (UNESCO, 1968):

1. Full use of modern communication techniques and science clubs and fairs; cooperation with appropriate organizations to promote the appreciation of science with special emphasis on rural populations.

2. Improvement and expansion of science education at all levels by increasing

the number and raising the qualifications of teachers with a parallel improvement of curricula and teaching materials.

3. Improvement of career prospects and possibilities of upgrading middle-level technicians.

4. Expansion of agricultural education and application of agricultural research programs, both basic and problem oriented.

5. Strengthening of existing information and documentation centers.

6. Collaboration between universities and laboratories; creation of institutes for advanced studies to foster scientific research and technological development.

7. Promotion of international and regional cooperation through the exchange of information and scientific personnel, in this way cooperating with the transfer of appropriate technology.

All of this sounds very fine but is extremely difficult to implement since some of these countries are very far from expending as much as 1 per cent for science in any of its forms. India and, on a smaller scale, Pakistan possibly come closest to following this recommendation, although their expenditures are still considerably below the 1-percent figure. But, since the other Asian countries, especially those of Southeast Asia, make practically no expenditures for scientific research and development, it certainly will be difficult for them to live up to the resolution. Even if they should achieve this aim on the technical level, the large masses of their present populations would probably be very little affected. Approximately the same can be said about Latin America. And it is certainly true that none of the countries of Africa, with the possible exception of South Africa and Southern Rhodesia, is spending anywhere near the 1-percent figure.

In practical terms, this percentage means that the countries would be sufficiently theoretically adapted and practically advanced to accept industrialization. They would be practicably adapted to the idea of scientific agriculture. They would be, at least in some ways, capable of advancing the scientific adaptation of those processes most suitable for their countries. This is true in theory; whether these processes can be utilized in practice would depend upon the industrial enterprises and, even more significantly, on the sizes of land holdings.

It is much easier to put these demands on paper than actually to achieve them. Even if this 1-percent demand is met, the backwardness of the countries still will exist, but at least the theoretical conquest by modern technique will be guaranteed. This is an important point. The factor limiting development of needed changes in underdeveloped countries is the social organization to insure it. In countries such as India or Pakistan, a long period would be required. It is common to ignore the tremendous difference in economic development in the United States and economic development, if any, in the underdeveloped countries, and also to ignore the fact that raising the standard of living for the inhabitants of the underdeveloped countries should be the first objective of our social efforts.

The progress of the last several thousand years from the Stone Age to the recent Scientific Revolution has given us the means of providing plenty for all.

Although many benefits from early and recent inventions are now taken for granted, let us remember several examples: one man with a threshing machine replaces 135 men with hinged flails, and even a flail is a comparatively advanced threshing tool. In 1830 it took 58 man-hours to produce a bushel of wheat with sickle and flail, whereas in 1930 it took only 3 man-hours with a combined harvester. Achievements in industry are far greater. It has been reckoned that, if the equipment of the United States were upgraded to the highest technical standards available in the postwar years, present production could be multiplied six-fold so that six times the commodities now available would be obtained.

I think the important thing for the future of the world is the distribution of the present level of scientific inquiry to the entire world rather than its concentration in a few countries. Only if this is accomplished will the application of the scientific knowledge we now have materialize and its full benefits be realized by all the human race.

DISCUSSION OF THE PAPERS BY K. N. RAO AND BERT F. HOSELITZ

POINTS BROUGHT OUT during discussion of the papers by Dr. Rao and by Dr. Hoselitz were:

1. There is a considerable waste of scientists' time if they must also serve as administrators or managers, performing certain routine tasks and raising funds. The present system of using a scientist as an administrator should be revamped.

2. The invasion of the engineer into management and into the social and political aspects of life is certainly a gain for engineering. But, in terms of the larger tasks to be performed in a developing society, in attempts to interconnect varieties of institutional forms for the development of human resources, this new role should not be overly extended. Engineers still have important specific tasks to fulfill. An engineer may not always be able to handle the role of philosopher or planner.

3. If income for those in developing countries, such as India, increased four times, there would be fewer pauses in the country's politics than there are now.

4. Two ways were suggested for working out practical forms to associate developing countries in the research work of the developed countries without risking loss of the resource man from the developed country: (1) establishment of a mutual agreement between governments on projects for scientific research; and (2) increase cooperative agreements between different universities and, specifically, between schools of engineering.

5. There is a lack of agreement about the causes and cure for the "brain drain" from both developed and developing nations. It was felt that a superior intellectual background of universities in a nation, such as Britain, would prevent scientists and engineers from emigrating, whereas in the different intellectual atmosphere in a developing nation, such as Mexico and Argentina, they do not have the same identification with the university and are, thus, more likely to emigrate.

A counter argument maintained that Britain does, in fact, lose a very large number of good brains, so much that there are many discussions there on how to stop it. It was agreed that implementing the idea of different developing countries cooperating to form one excellent regional university would provide an asset for the region.

A third view was that perhaps in Britain the proportion of high-level talent in relation to the total availability of such resources in the country is such that it can afford to lose some of its people to other countries but, in the case of developing countries, the problem is more serious because a number of people at this level of qualification and interest and knowledge is very small in comparison with the total pool available for development purposes.

Concern with high-level manpower and its migration all over the world is a salutary thing for developing countries. Economic talent moves in response to supply and demand. The only rational way to prevent brain drain in a developing country is to give high-level manpower the required status in the country.

A study on the motivation for Chileans emigrating from Chile and remaining in the United States was brought up. Conclusions from the study indicated that the problem of salaries is only one part of the whole picture, accounting for only approximately 30 per cent of the emigration; 40 per cent was due to better opportunities for work in technical fields and the possibilities of doing research and meaningful work. The main problem seemed to be the need for a proper environment in terms of work, status, and opportunities for research, a much more complicated problem to solve. The O.A.S. is trying to build up the necessary infrastructure by developing centers of excellence in Latin America. Groups at several institutions of various countries are trying to make a joint effort to build up a center that will be of the highest level possible in that field. By upgrading institutions to a level that will offer all personnel the possibility for the highest level of satisfaction in their work is one way in which a multinational corporation could try to solve the problem.

Development of a multinational system of education was also suggested as a solution in both developed and developing nations. Some programs in international studies have been successful because funds have been made available. The United States must demonstrate that this is an intrinsic part of education. Meaningful relationships must be developed between institutions. Personnel in educational institutions need to be involved in on-going programs through which they can identify what they are teaching as relevant to the development of a nation.

A further problem brought out was the "oversupply of brains" in a developing nation. For instance, in India there are between 25 000 and 30 000 unemployed engineers and scientists. By 1972 there may be between 50 000 and 150 000. Thus, hiring Indians in any other country can hardly be referred to as a brain drain.

The discussion on the problem of the brain drain was summarized as follows: We have been told to have better universities and then we shall not have the problem of brain drain or to have a better policy for human resources or better planning and we shall be able to overcome the problem. This is only a part of the answer. In order to have better universities, we need our best professors and, in order to keep our best professors, we cannot compete with universities in the United States. It is not only a matter of higher salaries; it is a matter of institutions for research which Western universities can provide and which, at least at this stage, we cannot provide. Therefore, I think this problem has to be approached much more on an international level than on only the level of the policy in each of the developing countries.

REPORT OF WORKSHOP 4

Roland Robertson, Rapporteur

THREE MAIN THEMES emerged from the opening statements: (1) the category, developing countries, is far too gross to capture the sociological problems involved in comprehending receptivity to technological change; (2) there is a pressing need for more adequate understanding of the range of factors which constitute obstacles to modernization and technological change; and (3) there is an ever-present problem of why and under what conditions attempts to change indigenous attitudes toward work, technology, and industrialization should be made.

Initial discussion about the resistance to modern technology covered such issues as the nature of thought patterns in primitive societies; distinctions between magic and science; and the moral and practical problems of inducing modern forms of discipline in work and attitudes toward technology. One of the points most strongly emphasized was that industrial societies vary greatly among themselves in work orientations and attitudes toward technology and that it is, therefore, necessary to be aware of similar variability in pre-industrial and embryonically industrial societies. Opinions differed as to whether it is practically and politically worthwhile to encourage the development of generalizations applicable to all "developing societies," when detailed experience of and familiarity with local cultural, social, political, and economic circumstances is so vital to the effective upgrading of indigenous disposition to engage in economic and technological modernization. Something approaching a compromise position was reached in the recommendation that social scientists should try to establish more detailed models of factors relevant to the comprehension of social and cultural change.

Two central problems were raised: (1) identifying the most salient factors in inducing acceptance of technological change, and (2) matching general strategies of change conceived in a Western society to the unique social and cultural circumstances of a given deprived society. It was agreed that the first problem had, in one sense, received a great deal of attention. Sociologists, in particular, have written extensively about such phenomena as competing loyalties to tribe, region, religion, and so on; the impact of such traditional loyalties on work discipline; and traditional forms of the division of labor. But the larger problem of estimating in these factors have received much less attention. Thus, there should be a move from gross generalizations about the nature of social relations in pre-industrial or embryonically industrial societies to firmer knowledge of the pivotal institutions and minutiae of social relationships. Only in such terms can information become available adequate to the task of policy implementation for economic and technological change. Ideally, there should be, not only a greater and richer comprehension of societies in terms of critical social and cultural variables, but also a sophisticated elaboration of the types of strategy of change-promotion most appropriate to the kind of society under focus.

In the light of such considerations it was frequently stressed that there was far too much naive optimism based on Western, especially American, experience often leading to disastrous results. It was suggested that, insofar as a sense of urgency and considerable financial effort had, to date, produced relatively little concrete change in the economic condition of deprived societies, much more reflective attention should be paid to the actual processes of planning for economic and technological change. In this connection it was emphasized that evaluative mechanisms need to be built into all programs directed at such change. Moreover, one of the most urgent priorities is to establish more sophisticated and knowledgeable attitudes among the policy-makers, decision-makers, and responsible personnel of privileged societies—attitudes which realize and are willing to integrate the contributions of specialists, such as the engineer.

BIBLIOGRAPHY

Friedwald, E. M., "The research effort of Western Europe, the USA, and the USSR," *OECD Observer*, Special Issue on Science, Feb., 1966.

Holloman, J. Herbert, "Science, technology and economic growth," *Science and Society*, Norman Kaplan, ed., Chicago, 1965.

Hoselitz, Bert F., "The socio-economic variables," *The Transfer of Technology to Developing Countries*, Daniel L. Spencer and Alexander Woroniak, eds. New York, 1967.

OECD Observer, October, 1967.

Orleans, Harold, "Federal expenditures and the quality of education," *Science and Society*, Norman Kaplan, ed., Chicago, 1965.

Seaborg, Glenn T., "Science and the general welfare in a democracy," *Science and Society*, Norman Kaplan, ed. Chicago, 1965.

UNESCO. *Conference on the Application of Science and Technology to the Development of Asia, New Delhi*. Paris: United Nations, August 21, 1968. Press Release.

7

THE INFLUENCE OF THE LEGAL STRUCTURE

Principal Paper—Paul Henri David

Discussion of the Paper by Paul Henri David

Commentary—Tom J. Farer

Report of Workshop 5—David Cohen, Rapporteur

The legal structures vary dramatically from one country to another. Industrial development obviously is strongly affected by the laws which govern the corporate entity. The influence of these legal structures is the subject of Chapter 7.

The Editors

THE INFLUENCE OF THE LEGAL STRUCTURE
Principal Paper by Paul Henri David

THE LEGAL STRUCTURES of the developing countries are complex, uncertain, and evolutionary. They do not always correspond with the views of industrialists seeking plant locations or ways to meet the needs of foreign investors, resulting in problems, even conflicts which hinder industrialization.

This virtual discrepancy between the legal system of developing countries and the needs of their industrialization programs is as evident in the field of national regulation as it is in the area of international contracts.

NATIONAL REGULATIONS

National laws and rules able to influence to some degree the industrial development of a country are countless. But prospective industrialists are likely to be more sensitive to juridical rules which are of direct concern to them. Their new plants must be located inside the chosen country, in a specific region. Their final decision, influenced by all the previous ones, will stem from the solution of the problem of location.

Industrial location problems are perhaps more important in developing than in developed countries. In the developing nations, economic activity is heavily concentrated in very few cities. Industrialists seem to need the opportunities of an urban environment, where, however, public authorities also are located. And these public authorities have their own views about location policies. For social and political reasons, they try to balance regional incomes. Furthermore, these authorities have established multilevel legal systems, the top level of which is planning.

The General Legal System: National and Regional Planning. The large majority of developing countries have established and are implementing a national plan. In most of these plans, chapters or paragraphs concern the territorial or regional aspects of development. As it is not possible to equalize regional per capita incomes rapidly, areas most fitted to development in the near future are those where governments are trying to attract industry by both incentives and restraints.

Incentives and Restraints. All developing countries seem to try to orient industrial locations to their own advantage by using a range of incentives, mainly in the area of taxation. Often these inducements apply to the whole country, beginning with income tax. For instance in Mexico, this exoneration lasts ten years for basic industries which make production goods, seven years for industries of economic importance which contribute to satisfaction of the essential needs of people, and five years for other industries.

Besides these nationwide measures, there are other incentives applicable only to selected areas. For example, in Argentina tax exemptions are granted for industrial investments in Patagonia and in the northwestern and northeastern areas of the country. Grants-in-aid are more rare. In Morocco, they reduce by 20 per cent the cost of industrial investments.

When all these juridical tools do not suffice, public authorities still have at their disposal traditional means of restraint. When they are forbidden plant locations in developed regions, industrialists are indirectly obliged to locate in lagging areas.

However, the effects of all these measures, positive or negative, seem rather limited. Restraints cannot, by themselves, direct industries towards regions to be developed and tax incentives can have only marginal influence, particularly in international decisions.

Beyond National Frontiers. It would be best if developing countries did not compete unwisely in inducing prospective industrialists. As long as all countries grant the same benefits, they cancel each other out and encourage higher levels of inducement. Such escalation, in countries where the financial situation is generally not good, can lead only to jeopardization of the general economy and of new industrial ventures in particular. Thus, it would seem highly desirable to reach an international agreement defining standards and bringing some order into the still wild domains of national regulation and international contracts.

INTERNATIONAL CONTRACTS

International contracts, in our field, are the second main source of law. Their practical importance is growing. More and more international commerical contracts are taking over direct investments so that property and machinery remain in the developing country and are less subject to unilateral measures such as nationalization. Profits are more limited but safer. Moreover, all the difficulties are not suppressed: the possibility of contest between foreign investor and public authorities has been replaced by the possibility of argument between the parties.

Contestation Problems. It is largely agreed that difficulties linked to the implementation of international commerical contracts can be settled legally by an arbitration freely accepted by the parties. But the problem often is to designate the arbitrators. The European Convention for International Commerical Arbitration concluded in Geneva in 1961 has set up a special committee for that purpose. It surely would be useful to create such an organism for contests arising from investment contracts in developing countries.

But it would be necessary to establish, at the same time as the arbitration procedure, a set of legal norms or standards which arbitrators would have to enforce. Otherwise arbitrators would have, because of the legal gap, a discretionary power that would jeopardize transaction security. This is a very important question for the future of relations between industrialized countries and developing nations.

118

These legal norms are established by national legislation or international conventions but, especially in our field, by codification of customs. This procedure has been used by the Economic Commission for Europe of the United Nations. The Commission has prepared model forms or general conditions of contracts for many types of transactions related to international sales and investments. These forms are due largely to the work of Kopelmanas who for many years was legal consultant to the United Nations Economic Commission for Europe and whose thoughts have deeply influenced the Commission's present work.

Model Forms of Contracts and Their Advantages. Model forms of contracts offer so many advantages that it is surprising to see them utilized still relatively rarely. In the first place, these models avoid difficulties in implementing contracts since they must define with extreme precision the obligations of each of the parties.

A second advantage of such model contrasts is that they accelerate negotiations which will be limited to the specific character of each transaction— technical details and price. It is essential, however, that model forms used without any discussion be equitable for both parties. This is of great importance: the success of model contracts stems from their impartiality. In Geneva, conventions have been arranged by working groups on which were represented importer and exporter countries as well as centrally planned and free-market nations. And these agreements have been approved by all the delegations after many long and difficult dicussions.

Sometimes the complexity and the diversity of problems prevent the use of model contract forms and the Economic Commission of Europe must limit itself to writing a practical guide, for instance for the transfer of technology.

Guidelines in Technology. The guidelines for the international transfer of technology laid down by the Secretariat of the U.N. Economic Commission for Europe are of great interest for industrializing countries, owing to the importance and the complexity of technology. The guidelines present real situations which can be met, analyzes legal problems, and details the benefits and drawbacks of choices the parties can make. Finally, the guidelines analyze difficult questions such as preliminary negotiations, secrecy, guaranty, exclusivity, patents, responsibilities, and arbitration.

CONCLUSION

The legal system which is the framework of industrialization in developing countries seems characterized at the same time by an excess of regulations and a lack of legal norms. The network of multilevel planning inducements and restraints often seems excessive, almost ineffective, and rather risky because of the unhealthy competition it can provoke between developing countries. Moreover, international commercial contracts, common in the industrialization field, must be based upon a system of legal norms which now is largely lacking.

Perhaps there is a single remedy to both of these defects: international discussions sponsored by an impartial organism such as UNIDO. Two types of meetings would be organized: (1) a meeting on conditions under which developing countries could avoid excessive competition, mainly in a given regional context, on the type of preliminary research necessary for limiting restraints that can be economically justified; and (2) a meeting on international commercial contracts with working groups similar to those gathered in Geneva by the Economic Commission for Europe, but including representatives from other continents and from developing countries. Such meetings accomplish a very useful task by setting up model forms of contracts and guidelines which would fit the real conditions in developing countries.

DISCUSSION OF THE PAPER BY PAUL HENRI DAVID

INTERNATIONAL LAW FOR DEVELOPMENT

The legalistic approach so far has constituted a hindrance to development, rather than a stimulus. This is an area in which stimuli are needed. Yet, because international law has been very slow in adapting itself to the new situation, to the new relationships created by agreements on development, lawyers in the field are called upon to pioneer in a new branch in international law—international law for development.

Until now, for many (mainly political and sociological) reasons, the men who have been making the laws have not had exactly the same viewpoints as the men who have been industrializing the developing countries. Now it is necessary to improve and accelerate the evolution of the legal system, not in the national context, but within an international framework. UNIDO or a similar international organization could be of great help, because in an international framework there is less a spirit of competition and more a spirit of cooperation.

PRECEDENT AND EQUITY

The U.S. Agency for International Development has worked around the world, particularly in the construction field. There is a group in Switzerland named FIDIC which combines engineers and contractors. One of the principal strengths of such a group is the equity between parties; another is arbitration. However, it is quite common for governments not to believe in equity between the parties, because of the issue of sovereignty. It is, therefore, important to create norms to begin to regulate and perhaps to establish precedent, ending arguments over what fits that precedent or some precedent other than the equity between the parties.

Norms are important because arbitration can be done in two ways. Arbitrators can have freedom to choose the best solution in their personal view, based on technical and equity considerations; or the arbitrator can be obliged to enforce certain prefixed norms. In the second way, the freedom of the arbitrator is more limited. It has been agreed generally that the implementation of the pre-established norm is better for facilitating the transaction.

AGREEMENTS TO AVOID UNHEALTHY COMPETITION

In their desire to attract the best possible and highest number of new industries, the developing countries are prone to give uneconomical inducements for attracting these firms. A public financial institution can be put in a very poor position because the taxation yield can be very low; this situation is aggravated by the increase in public expenses which are necessary to the industry, such as roads, an industrial district, and social structures such as schools and housing. These expenses can be very substantial for a developing country. Thus, at least in the short term, the economic situation of the host country can be worse than before the establishment of the new industry. Perhaps in the long term, the situation will improve but, even then, other difficulties may arise.

On the other hand, inducement can be economically justified when granted to stimulate the placement of industry in less-developed areas of a given country. It is, therefore, necessary to distinguish between economically justified inducements and those which are purely arbitary and responsive only to some wild and irrational competition between poor countries. The dividing line between these two kinds of inducements could be made more precise by research. International organizations could be very useful in undertaking such work.

GUARANTEE OF CREDIT

Nigeria has had difficulty with the guarantee of credit. Often after credits have been guaranteed by the host government for an industrial investment, it is discovered that the investment should never have been made and that, sometimes, the investment credit guarantee resulted from a case of fraud involving members of the government. Also, the contracted project often does not generate any of the results which were proposed in the original agreement. However, the government has signed an agreement and guaranteed the credits; there is nothing it can do.

In Nigeria's case 90 per cent of the credit came from one country; when that country refuses to negotiate behind the cloak of multilateral conventions, there is a host of legal problems which touch a great deal on the equities. Inasmuch as Nigeria has foreigners as consultants, credit is a kind of contingent liability even if the national government guarantees it.

If a government, such as Nigeria's, is obliged to guarantee the credits, "obliged" means that the government could turn down the whole idea of guarantee if it wishes. At the same time, however, the government is interested in these investments.

CONCLUSION

Only with international agreements and international institutions can any kind of solution be found because, when there is no fixed framework, experience seems to show that the difficulties are almost insurmountable. It is only with a structure, a specific structure established by international agreement, that there could be a practical means of solution.

LAW AND ECONOMIC DEVELOPMENT: A DEFINITION AND POTPOURRI OF SPECULATIONS

Commentary by Tom J. Farer

THE KNOWN AND THE UNKNOWN

IT CANNOT BE entirely mysterious that, in a nation which worships expertise and where the lawyer is the only technician regarded as an all-purpose expert, law and economic development have become modish subjects. Despite spreading enthusiasm for this phenomenon as the core of a course, the object of research, or bait for foundation dollars, parts of the subject area are about as well charted as the interior of Africa in the 18th century. Until very recently, scholarly concern settled on the intellectual coastline of international law and international institutions which affect trade, aid, and investment. Scholars have thrust a multitude of reasonably well-constructed shafts into this rich vein of legal problems. Trade preferences, regional economic arrangements, commodity agreements, the law of expropriation, economic development contracts, and procedures for the settlement of investment disputes all have received substantial treatment in the burgeoning literature and are increasingly included in the law-school curriculum.

The acceptance, at least in the United States, of lawyers as central participants in the transnational processes affecting third-world development may have distorted, in some measure, the perceptions of the nonlegal participants and, consequently, deflected their necessarily limited energies. While operating unabashedly in the traditional domains of other technicians (for example, economists and financiers), the lawyer is shrewd enough to seek justification for his omnipresence. He may be inclined, therefore, to grasp the legal tail of a financial or political problem and proceed to shake it fiercely until all eyes shift from the head and body to the agitated rear extremity.

One striking manifestation of this tendency is the remarkable quantity of energy expended in the struggle to shape the international law of expropriation, remarkable in terms of the value of alien property actually expropriated by less-developed countries. My own impression is that potential investors are far more concerned about this contingency than precedents warrant. I suspect that their hypersensitivity is partially a consequence of the legal profession's apparently unquenchable interest in the problem. One wonders whether, if all the lawyers had at some point decided that there was no international law on the subject which was terribly useful and that there was not likely to be any in the foreseeable future, the great investors would have promoted at an earlier date a comprehensive insurance scheme which would have sensibly and definitely removed the problem from the investment equations and the overburdened tables of international negotiations.

Although there may be justification for contemplating waspishly the legal mind's excessive interest in matters concerning which a monopoly of knowledge

122

can reasonably be claimed, one must nevertheless concede its utility for converting a concordance of national views on some matter of economic or financial policy into a formal instrument which clarifies the agreement, not only with respect to existing problems but also with respect to those which are now latent. Lawyers from the United States may be peculiarly well equipped for this task because of their sustained creative involvement in the commercial and financial processes of American society.

A second segment of the broad subject area which has been carefully, even finically mapped, is inhabited by domestic laws designed to encourage foreign investment—primarily investment-incentive statutes. While one can only admire the meticulous care with which these statutes have been analyzed and compared, one is impressed by the dubious relevance of these scholarly operations to the main, gritty problem of encouraging an accelerated flow of investment funds to the less-developed countries. At least one highly regarded study of the foreign investment decision process suggests that neither investment-incentive laws nor, for that matter, any other facet of the legal structure appears to affect entrepreneurial calculations; investors' concern does not appear to reach beyond market size and political risk. Of course, after the investment decision is made, the lawyers are called in to evaluate the legal structure (company laws, labor laws, and so on) and to assure full exploitation of whatever benefit arrangements are available. If this is an accurate sequential picture of investor behavior, the utility of incentive statutes to host countries is clearly subject to doubt, and such doubts are increasingly voiced.

The relatively unexplored sector of law and economic development is the impact of domestic law on locally generated economic activity. In theory, at least, there should be important differences between the interaction of law and economic growth in technologically advanced Western nations and in less-developed countries. In the former, most substantive law is shaped by well-organized and informed interest groups. It is the response at the society's political pinnacle to the felt needs of those groups. In this context, then, law may be said to play a relatively passive role. It is not part of an elitist strategy to create new social and economic patterns; rather it mirrors the dialectical processes at work beneath the political level, although simultaneously participating in those processes. In other words, substantive statutory law in the West is not primarily an expression of a unified vision of the society's ideal future condition. For example, I assume that corporate charters ceased to be a legislative prerogative in the United States because an already powerful and selfconscious class of entrepreneurs were able to influence the political process, not because legislators concluded, in a spasm of illumination, that standardized corporation laws would facilitate capital formation.

In some less-developed countries, on the other hand, a law will frequently antedate the economic phenomenon to which it is applicable. This is so because there is a political class with a considerable degree of autonomy in policy selection and because economic development frequently is this class's conscious *rai-*

son d'être. In such societies, then, the opportunities for the purposive use of law to promote economic growth should prove greater than in the West, until the role differentiation, increased education, and more elaborate network of national communications which coincide with economic development seriously erode elite automony.

THE VIRTUES OF PREDICTABILITY

One function of law in the West which is frequently assumed to have a positive impact on economic growth is its enhancement of predictability in economic relations. Law enhances predictability both by clarifying the theoretical consequences of a given act and by specifying the means for assuring that those consequences actually occur. For instance, in each of our states, law defines both the measure of damages for breach of contract and the procedures for compelling payment of those damages in case of breach. Where the formal procedures are onerous, the measure of damages would probably prove functionally irrelevant unless social, economic, ideological (including religious) or other nonlegal pressures would normally compel compliance with the norm of compensation. Unless the breach were inadvertent, it is a little difficult to visualize the context in which extralegal compulsion would not prevent breach but would compel compensation for breach.

Predictability is deemed relevant to economic growth on the basis of an assumed positive relationship between it and the inclination to save and invest. Obviously that positive relationship exists only in cases where the predictable consequences of entrepreneurial behavior are remunerative. Hence, from a growth prospective, there is nothing intrinsically benefical about predictability. Where the elite is hostile to entrepreneurship generally or, as is not infrequently the case, to a particular class of entrepreneurs, there probably is an inverse relationship between entrepreneurial activity and predictability defined in terms of formally promulgated substantive and procedural rules. To put it roughly, corruption may be the required handmaiden for economic growth.

As Professor Nye of Harvard pointed out recently in an extremely shrewd article, "In East Africa, for instance, corruption may be prolonging the effective life of an important economic asset—the Asian minority entrepreneur—beyond what political conditions would otherwise allow."

One might argue, I suppose, that a juxtaposition of law and growth disincentives in this context is misleading, that only the formal law is a disincentive and that the pattern of "baksheesh" is really an alternative normative system. "The living law triumphs over statutory abstractions." This is a perfectly acceptable and possibly even useful conceptualization of the process where corruption is virtually institutionalized and hence predictable. But even where it is random, it may be preferable to economic strangulation by a morally scrupulous bureaucracy.

In states governed by elites sympathetic to entrepreneurial activity, one can develop a compelling theoretical case for a positive predictability-growth rela-

124

tionship: the greater the predictability that the postponement of consumption will permit substantially greater consumption in the future, the greater, in some degree, will be the propensity to save. Similarly, the inclination to invest savings in capital-enhancing ventures should vary, though again not necessarily in any regular way, with the predictability of profit. But does law have very much to do with those predictabilities? Or to phrase the question in operational terms, what types of law reform can buttress the confidence of savers and investors? Can saving and investment activities be induced by piecemeal change in the legal milieu? Or does the legal strategist have a role only after financiers or entrepreneurs, responding to social, economic, and political conditions, decide it is desirable to establish merchant banks or stock markets, for example, and then turn to the legal technicians to draft appropriate private agreements and legislation?

There are those who may feel that I have sketched an illusory dichotomy, that this is a classic chicken-egg problem, and that any effort to discover causal sequences is destined for frustration. Investigation might substantiate the accuracy of this view, but the necessary research can be undertaken only if scholars accept the possibility of identifiable causal relationships. This is hardly a matter of purely academic interest. It goes to the optimal deployment of scarce human and material resources. It could affect content of aid and foundation programs and the shape of graduate education in less-developed countries.

Among at least some of the scholars currently studying the law-growth relationship, there appears to be a heady confidence that the legal environment can either induce or frustrate savings, investment, and entrepreneurial activity. For instance, the preliminary report of an elaborate study of law and economic development in Latin America states flatly that "Laws or regulations which make possible and control institutions and media for savings, banking laws, insurance laws, commercial laws affecting the fiduciary duties of controlling shareholders or management, laws imposing duties on other fiduciaries, and the like—are relevant to the levels of capital formation."

That is a terribly plausible proposition, but is it, in fact, consistent with the sparse historical evidence? Was the level of capital formation in the United States during the post-Civil War sprint to economic preeminence adversely affected by the rampant disregard of fiduciary obligation, even where such obligations were deemed to exist? Perhaps the economy would have grown even faster if savers could have invested funds with less fear of being victimized by the financial paladins. On the other hand, perhaps the era's entrepreneurial ecstasy was heightened by the sense that means, both fair and foul, for the pursuit of profit were available to all men of energy and imagination, however larcenous. But even if the absence of effective fiduciary obligations did not affect capital growth adversely, there may be no historical lesson here for societies not blessed with a frontier, prodigious resources, and Calvinistic passion.

The point I have been toying with unsatisfactorily might be clarified through the following illustration. In country X there are no publicly owned corporations. There is a rudimentary general corporation law which does not impose fiduciary duties on controlling shareholders or management. Nor does the legal structure of country X contain any concept equivalent to the common-law trustee with his fiduciary responsibilities. With the assistance of two United States law professors hired by AID, the government of X amends its corporation law and adopts a trust code which imposes fiduciary duties comparable to those applicable under the law of the State of New York. Is there any reason to believe that this action, this essentially exogamous phenomenon, will hasten the appearance of publicly held corporations or a securities market? If its efficacy is measured in terms of its impact on investor confidence, a negative answer would seem inevitable except when one of the following conditions is met:

1. for cultural reasons, entrepreneurs respond positively to changes in the formal norms governing their behavior; or

2. trial procedures are reasonably expeditious, judges relatively incorruptible, collection mechanisms normally effective, and resort to the courts is a culturally accepted means for vindicating rights.

Both conditions are likely to prove exceptional. In less-developed countries, those likely to feel most liberated from general community norms are entrepreneurs. In countries where they are members of a selfconscious ethnic or religious minority, they presumably are endemically unresponsive to norms originating in the political culture of the majority. Nor in such cases is it likely that they would resort to the majority's dispute-resolving mechanism to vindicate rights against each other.

Entrepreneurs who spring from the majority should prove equally unresponsive to norms which inhibit the pursuit of profit. Their very participation in individualistic entrepreneurship evidences a break with the historical community. Moreover, the contemporary glorification of economic growth provides a comforting justification for commercial rapacity, just as an embourgeoised Calvinism did for an earlier generation of capitalists.

The prospect of vindication of rights through the courts is bleak. Old communities implicated in the processes of development are coincidentally communities in process of dissolution. The new thrusting market economy provides a glacial climate for the venerable pieties of an intimate collectivity. During the consequential moral interregnum, corruption should flourish. Even if a state can create a cadre of highly professional and reasonably honest judges, can the meager human and material resources of the developing society provide adequate sheriffs, marshals, bailiffs, clerks, and the other essential participants in an effective judicial system?

The critical word, of course, is "system." In the absence of the institutional and attitudinal infrastruture of mature capitalist states, law reform in the guise of additions to or subtractions from the corpus of formal law has the impact of a pebble tossed into the sea. It is an intellectual exercise analogous to medieval Realism which assumed a true substantive existence for the world of ideas.

LEGAL TACTICS FOR AN ELITIST STRATEGY

In order to develop, whether by means of a free market or one dominated by the political apparatus, the technologically retarded states must revolutionize whole systems of thought and behavior. Law can be a useful instrument, one among several, for carrying out this revolution. And it is as one integrated element of a coordinated strategy of systemic change that law will find its vocation in the third world.

As I have just suggested, some measure of social dissolution is a necessary concomitant of the adventure of modernization, but dissolution can proceed to the point where the minimum conditions of order required for economic growth cannot be satisfied. The political kingdom may collapse into anarchy or civil war. Dissolution is experienced as the loss of a sense of identity and purpose. Law can serve as a vehicle for conveying to the surging, confused mass a new sense of who and where they are, and where they are going.

The elite's ultimate aspirations for the society can be announced and shared with the bulk of the population by the incorporation of those aspirations in a constitutional document. Immediate economic goals may be recorded in legislation implementing development plans. In technologically retarded societies, law's primary role may be educational and, perhaps, inspirational, rather than the role assigned to it by that once and (one hopes) future legal scholar Eugene Rostow, as "the means through which social policies become social action." Some governments may simply not have the power to translate social policies into action. They are limited to defining the new relationships and collective hopes of the society, and they must rely for the most part on private initiative.

Paradoxically, at least from a W. W. Rostowian perspective, law is more likely to serve as a mechanism for translating policy into social action in states governed by radical elites or what David Apter calls "mobilization societies." In the first place, these policies are directed by an integrated socio-economic philosophy which seeks to alter decisively the traditional structure of society. The political elite cannot, therefore, leave social change and economic growth to the play of diverse and invariably conflicting social forces. Of necessity they must formulate and seek to implement a wide-ranging set of specific social policies. The more innovative the social policies, the greater the need for their articulation in legal form: first, in order to endow the new policies with the maximum aura of legitimacy and permanence; and second, to assist administrative cadres by providing authoritative and detailed instructions for the mass by providing a yardstick for measuring the propriety of orders from local officials. Although the bureaucrats of an ideologically fired mobilization society are more likely to be faithful and zealous in carrying out their duties and to have a superior sense of direction than their colleagues in laissez-faire ("reconciliation") societies, they coincidentally bear greater burdens because of the elite's commitment to dismantling traditional arrangements. They must struggle with the inertia and conventional wisdom of the governed and, as the progeny of that same society, they also may have to struggle with themselves. Moreover, the reservoir of adequately trained men in small third-world states is very limited. Indeed, we are discovering in our own society with proportionately the largest college-trained population in the world how difficult it is to find effective administrators.

COMMUNICATION AND LEGAL PROCEDURES

A potentially valuable function of law in a mobilization society is as a channel for the movement of information concerning the perceptions and preferences of the mass to the presidential palace. Perhaps the principal functional cost of the totalitarian approach to development is in the communications field. Information about the attitudes of different social and economic groups is free in a democratic society. In the single-minded, one-party state, it becomes a scarce commodity. But it remains essential. The governmental resources required for repression would have to be withdrawn from the development sector and repression itself will debilitate the mass, thus compounding the blow to the leadership's developmental ambitions. Physical coercion, then, should be the last resort of rational leadership in a mobilization society.

Ideally, the mass should be carried along as enthusiastic participants by means of education and moral suasion. But when the normal political channels for two-way communication have been closed, the flow of critical data relating to the mass's subjectivities can decline to a useless (and often deceptive) trickle. Then the government may inadvertently pursue intolerable policies and discover its error only after a collective distemper has assumed the shape of rebellion. At that point, the elite is confronted with the stark alternatives of repression or defeat. This apparently is what occurred in North Vietnam's Nghe'-An Province shortly after Ho Chi Minh's accession to formal power. Local Communist Party officials attempted suddenly, and with the maximum crudity, to collectivize the peasants' land. News of the peasants' intense antagonism apparently did not reach Ho and his circle until the very guns which had decimated the French Expeditionary Force were turned on the local cadre. It is estimated that six thousand farmers died in this heartland of the anti-French struggle before the rebellion was crushed. At a subsequent Party meeting, General Giap unequivocally confessed gross errors of judgment in the entire affair.

In a one-party state, the cost of information can be reduced by strengthening the legal system and encouraging resort to it for vindication of rights infringed by local officials of the party or the state. Claims made through the legal system could provide the leadership with valuable information about the humor of the mass and the fealty and capability of the administrative apparatus without exposing it to political threats. Indeed, the availability of an effective, formal means for the redress of grievances against petty officialdom would enhance the legitimacy of powerholders at the center.

An effective legal system in a mobilization society must have these attributes: (1) a widely promulgated set of codes defining with reasonable clarity the respective rights and responsibilities of citizens and officials; (2) the development

128

of simply and widely understood procedures—courts of first instance must be conveniently located and rules of evidence must correspond to the probabilities accepted in the dealings of ordinary men; and (3) a judicial system constituting a hierarchy competitive with the administrative hierarchy, although members of both hierarchies might be linked through the party and both would, of course, ascend to the unified authority of the highest political leadership. The failure of one-party states to recognize the costs they must currently pay for useful information and to construct legal channels along the lines just described is an index of political ineptitude.

CODA

Sustained development can occur only within a reasonably ordered community imbued with some sense of continuity and permanence. Regardless of the political superstructure, the law is always a primary means for the construction of such a community. As Eric Erickson notes in his magisterial work, *Young Man Luther,*

> Established law tries to formulate obligations and privileges, restraints and freedoms, in such a way that man can submit to law and order with a minimum of doubt and with little loss of face, and as an autonomous agent of order can teach the rudiments of discipline to his young.

What some are inclined to forget is that law is excluded from the high vocation in societies where balance of obligation and privileges, and of restraints and freedoms is perceived by the subject of law to be unjust.

REPORT OF WORKSHOP 5

David Cohen, Rapporteur

IN CONSIDERING the influence of the legal structure on the application of engineering technology to the industrialization of developing countries, the group first noted that law is an articulation of the social policies of a society. Therefore, if law is a hindrance to development, it is most likely that the hindrance is the result either of conflicting social policies or of the failure to articulate social policy.

The group agreed that a legal structure could serve as a hindrance to development if the legal structure did not reflect the needs of a country at its particular stage of development. For example, when a country reaches the stage of development at which the importation of technology is more important than the importation of capital, the legal structure must include some form of patent system if it is not to impede the fulfillment of the country's needs. In contrast, if a country is at a stage of development where the importation of capital is of more importance than the importation of technology, the absence of a patent system in the legal structure does not constitute an extremely important hindrance to the process of development. It thus appeared to the group that the legal structure can be a hindrance to development if a country fails to determine its needs and thus fails to articulate those needs in the form of the requisite legal structure.

The group agreed that there were few developing countries which did not require the importation of capital. It was recognized that the sources of capital for importation must be either private or public. Where the source of capital is public, whether the public body is national or international in character, the structure of the legal system of the developing country is, in all probability, of little relevance. All dealings are at the nation-to-nation level or nation-to-international organization level and the specific terms and conditions for the investment of capital are the result of international negotiation. However, when the source of capital is private, direct negotiation usually is not possible and investment will take place under terms and coditions set in a general manner by the legal structure of the country in which the investment is to occur. For this reason, the group further narrowed the scope of its discussion to the influence in developing countries of the legal system on investment by the private sector of the foreign economy.

In considering what types of laws a developing country requires in order to attract foreign investors, the group noted that it is frequently important to distinguish between formally enacted laws and the *de facto* state of the law. The mere enactment of a sophisticated body of law does not mean that either the means or the desire to enforce such laws exists. It was agreed that what is important to the would-be investor is a clear manifestation on the part of the developing country of its intention to provide fair treatment. The group was of the opinion that private investors would be influenced by the existence of procedures, established prior to the actual investment, which would be available for the settlement of investment disputes. Recognizing that this is lacking in several developing countries, the group felt that the establishment of the Center for the Settlement of Investment Disputes by the International Bank for Reconstruction and Development was a positive step. However, as the Center's panel of arbitrators consists primarily of individuals from the developed countries, it was the opinion of the group that nationals of the developing countries should be trained as arbitrators to be added to this and other panels. If this were to be done, the developing countries might be more willing to utilize the Center's procedures.

The group also considered a proposal for an international contract or agreement between the developing countries of various regions which would obligate the parties to refrain from taking measures which would jeopardize further investment in the area. Such an agreement might be enforced with the cooperation of the United Nations (provided the participants agreed to such at the time of entering into the agreement) in the form of censure or other sanction in the event of a violation.

In considering the problem of expropriation, it was the opinion of the group that ventures resulting from fair negotiation, as opposed to those imposed on a developing country by devious means or by unfair bargaining power, are far less likely to face nationalization or repudiation by the nation at a later date. The group also believed that tension between the desire of a developing country to retain its sense of sovereignty and selfdetermination, and the desire to attract foreign participation in its economy by providing for security of investment could be minimized by increased utilization, if possible, of joint ventures between foreign entrepreneurs and nationals of the host country and by contracts requiring increasing percentages of the final product to be produced in the developing country.

In summary, it was the opinion of the group that, in order for developing countries to attract the capital necessary for the development of technology from private investors, these countries must respond to the reasonable expectation of the investor that his capital can, in due course, be recovered along with a fair profit. This implicitly means that there must be a reasonable degree of predictability as to the future of the venture. This predictability is probably not possible unless the host country makes a commitment of its intention to provide an atmosphere of "fair play." So long as a policy of fair play is articulated, the specific requirements for the legal system will vary from country to country depending upon the stage of development; but at all stages, some means, either judicial or of some other nature, must be provided for the fair settlement of disputes.

8

THE INFLUENCE OF POLITICAL ENVIRONMENTS

Principal Paper—Ward Morehouse

Discussion of the Paper by Ward Morehouse

Commentary—Sidney C. Sufrin

Report of Workshop 6—James Way, Rapporteur

Man is a political animal. He establishes political sturctures to facilitate his efforts toward equality and justice for all his fellows and/or as devices to aid his efforts toward a higher status. Chapter 8 is concerned with the influence of the political environment on science and technology in developing countries.

The Editors

THE KING AS PHILOSOPHER

The Influence of Political Environments on Science and
Technology in Developing Countries

Principal Paper by Ward Morehouse

WE LIVE, Barbara Ward (1968) has observed in her most recent book, in a
"lopsided world." She and many other commentators on the human condition
in the second half of the 20th century consider the gap between the rich and the
poor, between the advantaged and the disadvantaged, to be one of the main
issues of our times. All the evidence we have, furthermore, points to the widening of the gap between the rich and the poor. By the end of this millennium in a
scant 32 years, the world will have become so lopsided as to generate speculation about whether its present orbital course around the sun will not be affected.

We cannot know as much as we should about the social condition of our fellow men, argues another commentator on contemporary society, C. P. Snow
(1963). But we do know, he insists, two most important things.

First we can meet the harsh facts of the flesh, on the level where all of us are, or should be on. We
know that the vast majority, perhaps two-thirds, of our brother humans are living in the immediate
presence of illness and premature death; their expectation of life is half of ours, most are undernour-
ished, many are near to starving, many starve. Each of these lives is afflicted by suffering, different
from that which is intrinsic in the individual condition. But this suffering is unnecessary and can be
lifted. This is the second important thing which we know—of if we don't know it, there is no excuse
or absolution for us.

We cannot avoid the realisation that applied science has made it possible to remove unnecessary
suffering from a billion individual lives—to remove suffering of a kind which, in our own privileged
society, we have largely forgotten, suffering so elementary that it is not genteel to mention it. For
example, we *know* how to heal many of the sick: to prevent children dying in infancy and mothers in
childbirth: to provide enough food to alleviate hunger: to throw up a minimum of shelter: to insure
that there aren't so many births that our other efforts are in vain. All this we *know* how to do.

It does not require one additional scientific discovery, though new scientific discoveries must help
us. It depends on the *spread of the scientific revolution all over the world.* [Author's italics.]

Any kind of human endeavor with this potential payoff, whatever else it may
be, is bound to be political. My thesis, therefore, is a simple one. "Political environments," in the more inclusive sense of "political," are decisive influences on
how developing societies try to cultivate and use modern science and technology.

It is not only the potential payoff to society which causes science and technology to be subject to political influences and control. Science and technology cost
money, frequently big money, and, certainly in many developing countries,
largely public money. The consequences have been well stated by the British
biologist, N. W. Pirie (1964):

The idea that science should be controlled by scientists is therefore erroneous. . . . Working scientists are satisfied that they know what ought to be done in any domain in which their interest has
been aroused, and they have as good a record of humane arousal as any other group of people.
Nevertheless, even the most anarchical realize that someone must pay the bills; this means some
form of civil service control. How do we get controllers who will understand what is going on? The
problem is as old as Plato, who suggested the king should be a philosopher.

Monarchy is not as popular a form of government as it once was, and it may well be that what we now need are not so much philosopher-kings as philosopher-civil servants and philosopher-politicians. But the point is clear, regardless of the form of government. Science and technology are so closely intertwined with the political system in any society where they are pursued on any appreciable scale that the best we can hope for are political leaders and administrative elites who are sensitive to the requirements of science and technology and to the conditions under which payoff to society can be maximized.

Successors of Noah Webster offer the rather traditional view that politics is "the science and art of government." Most students of the subject today would insist that politics is broader than that. Politics involves the institutions and processes through which power is allocated and exercised in society and, as we have increasingly come to recognize in recent decades, the allocation and exercise of power is by no means confined to the formal institutions and processes of government. The influences of the political environment on modern science and technology in a developing country—or anywhere else for that matter—are not, therefore, confined to parliamentary bodies, ministries of industry, technology or scientific research, cabinets, and planning commissions but also include political parties, interest groups of varying sorts lying in part outside the political system but interacting with it, and individuals who nominally occupy nonpolitical roles in society but in fact are very actively involved in the political system from time to time.

It does not follow from my central thesis that what I shall call, for want of a better label, the "political science of science and technology" can provide all the answers to the complex interactions of science, technology, and society. As a defrocked practitioner of an "almost-science," I renounce all claims to the motherhood of political science among the social science disciplines. Other disciplines may subscribe to a suitable paraphrase of George Orwell's (1946) whimsical dictum on equality in *Animal Farm:* "All animals are equal, but some animals are more equal than others,"[1]* but political science is not "more equal."

The political system is clearly influenced by economic and social institutions, by the values and aspirations of a society, and indeed by the changing character of scientific and technological knowledge which is constantly creating new options for the political leadership. What we have, in short, is a "systems problem" which is a fancier formulation of the classic dilemma of the chicken and the egg with a few more variables thrown in for good measure.

But the interrelated and multidisciplinary nature of our concern notwithstanding, the influence of political factors on the role of science and technology in contemporary societies is decisive and fundamental. We are often told that knowledge is power in the modern world. Without the capacity to use scientific knowledge and technology, knowledge itself is of little value and the capacity for

*Notes and references for this section appear at the end of the chapter.

effective use depends on social and economic institutions and the political processes and arrangements that condition the environment in which the social and economic institutions function.

These considerations help to delineate the structure of the problem of assessing the influence of political environments on science and technology. Such an assessment involves analysis and understanding of the interaction of political institutions and processes of society with the institutional structures for science and technology. The analysis can move in two basic directions: (1) looking at these phenomena in less-developed countries and (2) examining them in more developed countries in terms of their relationship with and influence on the status of science and technology in the less-developed nations.

Since it is difficult to generalize about less-developed countries except in very gross ways by use of approximate measures of social, economic and political performance, I shall deal rather, by way of example, with only one less-developed country of the "Third World"—India.

Aside from its sheer quantitative importance in the modern world—one out of every seven human beings is an Indian—India is in many ways a less than ideal choice as a source of my illustrations. It is true that India is a very poor country in terms of per capita income. There is no question about where it belongs in Professor Blackett's (1961) handy division of the contemporary world into the "$100 countries" and the "$1000 countries." But in other respects it does not fit the usual categorizations of less-developed countries so neatly.

India has, in absolute terms, a considerable volume of industrial activity. Depending upon which indicator one chooses, it is among the ten or twelve largest industrial nations in the world. Its political system is characterized, at least thus far at the national level if not in some of the Indian states, by a high degree of governmental stability and orderly transfer of power. Even more immediately germane, India has a sizable scientific and technological community concerned with research and development and a correspondingly complex institutional system for research and development.[2]

The patron saint of modern science and technology in independent India was Jawaharlal Nehru, who dominated national political life in the country until his death in 1964 and who expressed, on more than one occasion, sentiments and convictions such as:

It is science alone that can solve the problems of hunger and poverty, of insanitation and illiteracy, of superstition and deadening custom and tradition, of vast resources running to waste, of a rich country inhabited by starving people. Who indeed can afford to ignore science today? And in return we have to seek its aid. The furture belongs to science and to those who make friends with science.[3]

Cynics within the political elite which grew out of the nationalist struggle for independence, and which has thus far largely dominated the formal institutions of national government, sometimes observe that India is the first to identify a problem but the last to solve it. Among the "first" claimed by India in this context are the first Minister for Science and the Scientific Policy Resolution adopted by the Indian Parliament in 1958 and described by its proposer, Mr. Nehru, to be the first of its kind undertaken by a legislative body anywhere in the world. If the "political environment" for science and technology were primarily determined by declarations of policy by formal institutions of government, it would be hard to imagine a more propitious climate for science and technology than India over the past decade since the adoption of the Scientific Policy Resolution (Government of India, 1958):

The Government of India have accordingly decided (the Resolution concludes) that the aims of their scientific policy will be . . . to foster, promote and sustain by all appropriate means, the cultivation of science and scientific research in all its aspects—pure, allied and educational . . . and in general, to secure for the people of the country all the benefits that can accrue from the acquisition and application of scientific knowledge.

The political environment for science and technology is not, of course, determined by formal declarations of policy although it may be influenced by them. In India's case, there are a host of governmental and quasigovernmental instrumentalities, many with name and formal function similar to those found in scientifically and technologically more advanced countries, which also help to determine the political environment. These instrumentalities might be loosely labeled the "science policy community" and include the Scientific Advisory Committee to the Cabinet (the most elevated structure for providing advice on scientific and technological matters to the political leadership of the national government, which has recently been reorganized as the Committee on Science and Technology or COST), the Planning Commission, the major research councils and similar bodies (such as the Department of Atomic Energy, Council of Scientific and Industrial Research, Indian Council of Agricultural Research, Indian Council of Medical Research, and University Grants Commission), and key elements in different ministries which help to determine and implement technological policy, particularly the Directorate of Technical Development.

But even these instrumentalities do not alone determine the political environment for science and technology. Indeed, it has been said that while Mr. Nehru was alive, policy for science and technology was essentially decided through a series of personal interactions between Nehru as Prime Minister and leading figures in the scientific community, such as Homi Bhabha, the first Chairman of India's Atomic Energy Commission; S.S. Bhatnagar, the first Director-General of the Council of Scientific and Industrial Research; and Professor P. C. Mahalanobis, the doyen of Indian statisticians and a key figure in the Planning Commission for several years. As a consequence of these personal interactions, the institutional arrangements for determining policy in this field to some degree atrophied during Nehru's long tenure as Prime Minister. Thus, one of the critical problems for the present political leadership of the national government is to breathe new life into these instrumentalities or find alternative ways of developing and implementing scientific and technological policies which will serve the economic, social, and political goals of the country more effectively.

Any political system is but a part of a larger social order and is intimate-

136

ly affected by and interacts with that social order. In India's case, there is a complex web of relationships and interactions, well beyond the scope of this discussion, which help to determine the political environment for science and technology. Suffice it to say that there appears to be a process of "Indianization" of the Indian political system, which is based to some degree on the emergence of regional mass cultures as major political forces and which is adapting the formal institutions of government, largely an inheritance of the British period in India, to Indian circumstances. This process involves displacing what one of the leading American students of the Indian political system, Myron Weiner (1965), has called the "elite political culture" by an "emerging mass political culture."

While this process clearly will influence the political environment for science and technology, it should not be assumed that the "emerging mass political culture," which many observers would label as more traditional in origin and outlook, is opposed to modern science and technology. In fact, to assume a fundamental polarity between "traditional" and "modern" oversimplifies and distorts the situation, for the leadership of the emerging mass political culture wants "modern" things. Weiner himself (1965) points out that ". . . there is nothing traditional about the demands for more schools, roads, wells, fertilizers and jobs." He goes on to observe that the elite political culture which has heretofore dominated the government in India, particularly at the center, "though it appears to be extraordinarily modern and is generally characterized as being modern by those who belong to it, is often quite inappropriate and unadaptive to these goals."

This set of circumstances is well demonstrated by the changing posture of the political leadership toward agricultural research. Within the past couple of years, modern agricultural technology, based on high-yielding varieties of crops and on fertilizers and pesticides which are in turn the product of agricultural research, has been introduced on a significant, though still relatively modest, scale in India. The political leadership, particularly in the Indian states where the process of "Indianization" of politics has in general gone farther, can now see the kind of political payoff which comes from the introduction of this technology. The Director of the Indian Agricultural Research Institute in Delhi, which is the leading agricultural research institution in the country and has played an important role in the whole strategy for introducing modern agricultural technology, reports that he is now regularly visited and his views are solicited by chief ministers of various states and their ministers of agriculture. A couple of years ago this would have been most unusual.[4]

Conflict and consensus exist in all political systems, whether in economically and technologically less- or more-developed societies. An important dimension of the political environment for science and technology is the mechanisms or processes for conflict resolution and achievement of consensus. In the industrial field, to use India as a case in point again, the roles to be played by foreign and indigenous technology generate inevitable conflict. Advocates of "technological swaraj," including the sizable research community to which we have already referred and important elements of political leadership, are pitted against the more modern industrial sector of the business community which actively seeks new technology through collaboration with foreign countries, frequently in preference to indigenous technology. The principal mechanism and the administrative level for resolving this conflict is the Directorate of Technical Development. The stated policy, with some qualifications, favors "technological swaraj," or indigenous technology, so the conflict by and large does not manifest itself at the policy level. Here, through a variety of interministerial consultative arrangements and committees on licenses, foreign agreements, capital goods, and similar matters, the Directorate of Technical Development seeks to resolve conflicting demands with not only economic but also political and social implications.[5] Intervention in the decision-making process sometimes occurs from elements in the political leadership, for example, the former Chairman of the Estimates Committee of Parliament, who has sought to block foreign collaboration in favor of indigenous technology in the manufacture or direct importation of such items as television receivers or component parts of other kinds of communication equipment.[6]

Conversely, skills, technical and otherwise, in developing proposals, as well as general reputation and political influence, all play a part when major industrial concerns seek government approval for foreign collaboration and importation of new technology. Consider this comment by the former senior official of one of the industrial groups mentioned:

Among the industrialists in India, there is a high degree of preference among government servants. The Tata group are invariably able to short-circuit the laborious process. . . . The reasons are obvious. Among collaborators, the Tatas, as a single group, have the largest number of successful foreign collaborations in India. Secondly, most of their collaborative project reports are very carefully prepared, anticipating the whole gamut of questions which the Advisory and Consultative Committees of Government demand as the deliberations develop from stage to stage. . . . Tata Fison [one of the Tata group of companies] went through Government at the amazing speed of three weeks. . . .

Birlas also get a favourable treatment, again because of the sophisticated programme recommendations they make. But in some cases, I must say that Birlas achieve some part of their programme by political influence which as a business house, they wield much more than the Tatas. The Kirloskar gróup, although a very enterprising and dynamic industrial complex, is so strongly in favour of private enterprise, that they tend to feel injured when Government demands certain types of information and certain prognoses from them. The Sarabahis do extremely well short-circuiting three or four steps in the chain to its final sanction. The Dalmias are suspect. They take much longer and are unable generally to speed up their programmes. . . .

The Southern industrialists are a very canny lot. Very often, they obtain clearances quicker than the Tatas do in terms of red-tape. But the sizes and commitments they envisage are invaribly more modest than those of the North. . . .

Nowhere is the decisive impact of the political environment on the application of technology to industrialization more evident than in a recent case study of the manufacture of diesel engines in India through collaboration with an American concern. The author, Jack Baranson (1967) of the World Bank, demonstrates how Indian planning, which many observers consider to be a highly politicized process, and the industrialization and technological policies designed to achieve planning targets, can become counterproductive. Comparative costs, he points out, are neglected in favor of "targets and balances." The continuing pressure on increasing domestic content of items manufactured with foreign collaboration may, in fact, as appears to have happened to the Cummins Engine Company collaboration in India, have cost India more in foreign exchange than if the engines had been imported directly![8] In an oblique way, this is a useful reminder that development and industrialization are not synonymous.

This raises, of course, the critical issue for the policy-maker and administrator in the developing country, seeking to advance the process of modernization through the application of science and technology. What is economically rational in formulating or implementing a particular policy may turn out to be highly "irrational" politically or socially. Illustrations of conflicting consequences abound in the Indian context.

Case studies of technological innovation in 19th century Bengal reveal the complex "rationality" of those confronted with these innovations in accepting or rejecting them. Closer analysis reveals that it is by no means a simple case of sentimental and irrational attachment to existing ways of doing things which results in rejection of a technological innovation; cultural and social constraints are generated by the desire of those presented with such options to preserve existing work group relations, social security, and control over primary means of livelihood.[9] In more recent times, we also have come to recognize that significant changes in the economic consequences of adopting or rejecting innovation will produce quite different responses. Indian farmers, whose economic reserves to sustain losses are all too often nonexistent, showed considerable disinterest in increasing their investment by application of fertilizer when the increase in yield promised at best to be 20 or 30 per cent of what they were getting without fertilizer. But with the introduction of high-yielding varieties of crops, where the increase in yield may be 300 per cent, the response is entirely different. In these circumstances, there is nothing quite so innovative as the Indian farmer in pursuit of a hot rupee, and a lively black market in fertilizers and high-yielding seeds has developed within the country in the past few years (Marglin, 1968).[10]

Such social, cultural, and economic factors spill over into the political system and interact with elements in the political process. The present Minister of Food and Agriculture, who often is regarded as representing the interests of the "ex-Untouchables" in the Indian Cabinet, is said to have at first resisted the whole strategy of introducing modern agricultural technology because he recognized that there would be uneven access to the required inputs for such technology in terms of seeds, fertilizers, pesticides, and assured supplies of irrigation water. (Farmers of higher status and greater material means are more likely to be able to secure these inputs than those of lower status and more limited means such as the Untouchables and others near the bottom of the Indian social order.) He, therefore, saw one of the consequences of widespread introduction of this kind of technology to be an increase in social and political tensions within rural Indian society.[11] The parallel is striking with American society where the growing affluence of white middle-class segments of the society has been accompanied by increasing militancy of the disadvantaged cultural and racial minorities who, although possibly better off in absolute terms, are more and more conscious of the widening gap between their condition and that of the middle-class majority.

In the industrial field, similar interactions can be observed. It may well be economically more rational to rely as heavily as possible on imported technology, at least in certain fields where technology has been highly developed elsewhere in the world. Baranson's case study of the Cummins Engine Company in India provides convincing evidence. But this conflicts with a long historical experience with foreign capitalist enterprise which many elements within the political leadership in Indian society would regard as exploitative. Thus, the political movement to boycott foreign—principally British—manufactured goods in favor of domestic or "swadeshi" goods which began in the early years of the 20th century and was such an important part of the nationalist struggle for independence from the British, has been a powerful continuity in the politics of independent India. Virtually all major political leaders and their parties today advocate economic selfreliance, of which "technological swaraj" or selfsufficiency is considered to be an integral part.[12]

Another way of examining analytically the interrelationships between the scientific and engineering community on the one hand and the political system on the other is to look for the consequences of the policy to invest significantly in the training of scientists and engineers, with the subsequent emergence of a sizable research and development community as has occurred in India. These consequences are of two basic kinds. First, a significant research and development community or its leadership is capable of exerting pressure on political and administrative elites. Second, the mere existence of such a community creates policy options for those elites.

In India's case, the heavy emphasis on basic research and atomic energy, rather than on agricultural or medical research, is a reflection of the first kind of consequence. Similar in character has been the development and concentration of resources in public-sector research institutes instead of in the universities or private industry. (Other factors, of course, have also been involved.)

The second type of consequence—creation of new policy options—is found in a number of instances in recent Indian experience. To opt for an import-substitution policy as India has done, for example, is possible only when there is a sizable research and development community. Another instance has been the insistence on substantial Indian technical participation in foreign industrial activities in India. (This has been especially true in defense production and related industrial fields, where concern for national security has dominated government consideration of industrial policy in recent years.) While the policy has been applied unevenly in practice, it would not have been a realistic option without the existence of a substantial scientific and engineering community in the country.

What the policy-maker and administrator require in the complex and conflict-ing circumstances described is something we certainly do not have as yet and perhaps never will possess, given the well-known difficulties of comparing apples, pears, and peaches. The need is, simply stated, a means of measuring the likely economic, social-cultural, and political consequences of a particular policy or decision in *comparable* terms. Taken collectively, these indices would add up to a cost-benefit ratio for public policies and decisions affecting the role of science and technology in the modernization process. Presumably, individuals with intelligence, good will, and the power to exercise meaningful options would fol-low that policy or make that decision which had the best cost-benefit ratio.

This is a large presumption, of course, and the evidence is far from reassuring that, in any political system, whether in a less or more economically and tech-nologically developed country, individuals of intelligence and good will occupy the critical positions of power in the system or that, even if such individuals are strategically placed, the institutions and traditions generated by society will permit them to act according to the dictates of a cost-benefit ratio which seeks to take into account varying social, economic, and political consequences.

Let us take just one example among the more-developed countries to illustrate how influential—and irrational or counterproductive—the environment within the political system of the developed country can be.

However clairvoyant they may have been in other respects, the founding fathers of the United States exhibited a myopic vision of the future on one vital point of major concern in the modern world when they drafted the Constitution almost 200 years ago. They neglected, when they gave the power of the purse to the legislative branch of national government under the separation of powers, to recognize that the long-term character of the development process abroad would conflict with the short-term interests of a significant proportion of the elected members of the legislative branch who, under the federal system, are highly subject to local and regional pressures within the country. To the degree that the foreign economic assistance program of the United States has represented, in the postwar decades, an important means of helping less-developed countries use modern science and technology to achieve economic and social goals, the results of this constitutional arrangement of powers appear to have been significantly counterproductive. (Foreign economic aid has not, of course, been solely directed toward the economic and social needs of developing societies but has also been used to serve short-term political and military goals of the American government—presumably coinciding with long-term political objectives. This "mixing" of purposes has been one of the sources of a certain segment of current Congressional resistance to the foreign program.)

The dramatic changes in Mexican agriculture are persuasive evidence of the need for continuity and long-term commitment in development aid and technical assistance. The Rockefeller Foundation's ability to stay with a problem involv-ing agricultural research and training over the relatively long period of two decades seems to have been a significant factor in the success achieved, although other factors, including the role played by the Mexican Institute of Agricultural Research and the marketing and pricing policies of the Mexican Government, were also involved. Something similar may well be happening, although it is too early to tell, in terms of the role played by American foundations (with relatively small investments of money in comparison with the size of expenditure on foreign aid by the United States Government) in the technological transformation of Indian agriculture, as well as of several other countries in South and Southeast Asia.

But the one most determined effort to give recognition to the long-term character of the development process—by President Kennedy when he sought Congressional authorization for long-term aid in the early 1960s—was unsuccessful, foundering on the shoals of tradition and institutional inertia in the American political system. So jealously did Congress guard its prerogatives through the power of the purse that it refused to acknowledge the economic and social consequences of a policy alternative which, if we could construct a meaningful social-economic-political cost-benefit ratio for it, offered considerable promise of achieving a better ratio than the past and present policy of annual authorizations and appropriations of foreign aid. The critical consideration here is the frequency of Congressional involvement, not the divorcement of Congress from such a vital aspect of government in the modern world.

The current emasculation of the foreign aid program, reflecting in part growing Congressional frustration with lack of quick and highly visible results in the modernization process in developing countries, is another case of chickens coming home to roost. Just as in India, a preoccupation with economic selfreliance and "technological swaraj" may be economically counterproductive even though it is politically palatable, the inability of the American political system to accommodate to the economic and social characteristics of the modernization process in developing countries likewise appears to be counterproductive.

The present state of our knowledge of ways in which the political environment influences the development and utilization of science and technology in societies seeking to modernize themselves is grossly inadequate. This is true, of course, of virtually any problem of substantial interest to the "almost sciences." The "almost sciences" are indeed condemned to a limbo of "near-salvation" in a morass of inexactitude and uncertain predictability by the very nature of the phenomena with which they are concerned and the data with which they must work. The situation is simply more acute in the present instance.

It is easy to see why this is so. The systematic study of science, technology, and public policy—indeed, still more broadly, the scientific study of the character of science and technology and their interaction with society by the social sciences—is of relatively recent origin. Characteristic of American academic entrepreneurship, there has been a rapid growth of what are frequently called "science and public policy programs" in the universities of this country, now numbering somewhere in the neighborhood of 40 institutions. But the vast majority of these programs are predominantly, if not exclusively, concerned with public policies toward science and technology in the United States or, at most, Western European countries as well. The argument is, of course, that it is in these countries where most of the action takes place, where the biggest budgets for research and development exist, where the largest research communities with the most complex institutional systems have grown up. The situation is well reflected in a basic syllabus for the study of science, technology, and public policy produced by one of these university programs, which relegates what is labeled "Developing Science in the New Nations" to the unlucky thirteenth position out of fifteen topics which should be considered in any systematic exploration of the "field" (Caldwell and DeVille, 1968).[13]

The situation is not very much better elsewhere. UNESCO, through its Science Policy Division, has stimulated a number of studies of science policies in less-developed countries and OECD has undertaken studies of several of its less-developed countries in Southern Europe and the Middle East. The Universities of Sussex in England and Lund in Sweden are notable centers of activity. In the developing countries themselves, all too little is being done. In India, for example, which is probably farther along than most other developing countries, the Research, Survey, and Planning Organization of the Council of Scientific and Industrial Research has made a bold beginning in the last few years, although its future is uncertain. Only scattered interest exists in several other institutions in the country.[14]

What is needed to advance the present state of our knowledge is reasonably clear: many more case studies of institutions, industries, and decisions affecting the role of science and technology in developing countries; more extensive and reliable statistical data; better and more extensive survey data on the attitudes, actions, and social and economic circumstances of those whose roles, taken collectively, help to make up the political environment for science and technology— including legislators and other political leaders, senior civil servants, and leading members of the research and development community.

With these kinds of data and analyses, we should then be able to move on to a whole series of interesting and exciting, as well as politically, economically, and socially significant questions about the role of science and technology in developing societies. The list is virtually unlimited and I shall attempt here to pose only a few by way of illustrating the longer catalog which might be developed.

Perhaps the most fundamental question is whether there is a science-based technology. Derek Price (1965, 1968) argues that the reverse is true historically in Western Europe, that artisan-based technology stimulated the scientific revolution by way of scientific instruments and their makers, but he is less convinced of the proposition when it is turned around the other way and applied to the modern world. The question is, of course, of concern to all societies in the world but, given the more limited resources and therefore the more decisive character of policy choices in developing countries, it is critical. Indeed, the general tendency to blur the distinction between science and technology and to argue that the latter is clearly dependent on the former may have already led the political leadership in developing countries to make unfortunate policy choices. In the case of India, there are some who argue that Mr. Nehru's inability to distinguish sharply between the two and to understand the intimate relationship between technology and production has generated some of the difficulties which the research community in that country is now experiencing at the hands of the political leadership.

If it should turn out that there is a science-based technology, what are the implications for developing societies which have not experienced the growth of modern science as it has occurred in Western Europe? Since technology grows out of and is dependent upon a particular social context, is technology based on modern science without extensive adaptation, incompatible with the social, economic, and political circumstances of developing societies?

On the answer to these questions hang answers to other critical questions for developing countries. Is a "self-generating scientific tradition" the proper goal for a developing country, as Caryl Haskins (1964) and Gerald Piel (1964) have in effect argued? Or is the kind of "three-stage" model for achieving this exalted state advanced by George Basalla (1967) of the University of Texas a nice analytical device but quite irrelevant to the policy choices which must be made by political leadership in these societies? Is Blackett (1968) on the right track when he argues that developing countries should aggressively import technology in the most advanced state in which they can find it anywhere in the world and concentrate on its adaptation and further development to fit their own particular economic and social circumstances?

The ability to provide meaningful answers to such questions leads us inevitably to the perplexing problems of measurement. How do we measure scientific or technological performance, beyond the devices we now employ such as counting papers or patents? How do we determine the economic, social, and political consequences of different policies and decisions? Is it a pipe dream to suggest that we may be able to construct meaningful cost-benefit ratios for the policy-makers and administrators which will weigh alternative, and sometimes conflicting, consequences?

Much of the discussion in recent years about criteria for scientific and technological choice has grown out of the circumstances and experiences of scientifically and technologically more advanced societies. The work published by Weinberg (1963, 1964), Williams (1964), Toulmin (1964, 1966), Maddox (1964), and Derek Price (1965) on this subject constitutes an encouraging beginning.[15] But the implications of these criteria need to be pondered with particular reference to developing countries. Are the implications essentially the same or does it make a difference that a particular society is at a different stage on the ladder of scientific and technological growth? If the "research ratio" (ie the percentage of gross national product spent on research and development) is not a satisfactory basis for allocating resources for research and development in a less-developed society, what is? The "research ratio" may not even be a useful criterion in a more developed society, although it is frequently cited as though it were. What criteria should be used in allocating whatever amount a society decides should be spent on research and development as a whole for basic research, applied research in agriculture, industry, medicine and other fields, scientific and technical education, and so on? And what should be the balance between importation of technology from abroad and its development at home?

Answers to such questions will lead us, on the basis of serious and careful comparative studies of relative performance in different developing societies which we sorely lack, to some ideas about the kinds of institutional structures and arrangements which would be most effective in assuring a political environment conducive to maximum social and economic return from science and technology. The tendency, at least in a country such as India, is to borrow institutional forms from other societies at quite different stages of scientific and technological development. Even if these institutions have been working well in the societies from which they are borrowed, the practice would be a questionable one. But there is now some evidence to suggest that the chief source of India's borrowings of institutional forms for science and technology—the United Kingdom—has had rather mixed experiences with its own institutional arrangements and has been struggling to refashion these to produce greater results.

All of this suggests that what has come to be called the "science of science" [16] —the use of scientific methods of systematic observation and quantitative analysis to study science itself—should be extended to the study of science and technology in the less-developed countries on a far broader scale. Even though in many cases the present level of scientific and technological development is small (China and India are two glaring exceptions in absolute, if not per capita, terms), the questions raised by the different economic, social and political characteristics of these societies may lead to different answers. And these answers may challenge some of the theoretical formulations about the inter relationships of science and technology and their interaction with society which have emerged from the study of more advanced countries, leading to reformulations at a more rigorous and more universal level of applicability.

In the final analysis, we need to remember that the techniques and approaches of the "science of science" in developing countries, though necessary, are insufficient. "If we are to understand the role of scientists and scientific institutions in the modern political world," Don K. Price (1966), whose pioneering contributions to the study of government and science in the United States are well recognized, has wisely observed, "we cannot be content to use only the methods of the newer and more rigorous social sciences. We must keep our minds open to the issues suggested by history and philosophy and jurisprudence and perhaps even—perhaps especially—theology."

DISCUSSION OF THE PAPER BY WARD MOREHOUSE

Mr. Sufrin: Twice you speak of foreign versus indigenous technology and later you speak of technology selfsufficiency. Do you mean technology as an idea of how to do things or as specific capital goods?

Mr. Morehouse: Primarily the former, rather than the latter, although I am not certain that, in fact, these are separable.

Mr. David: One of the important factors in development is the growth of regional politics in a national framework. Do you think that these new stresses have a favorable or unfavorable influence on industrialization in the developing countries?

Mr. Morehouse: I think the answer to your question is "both." It would certainly be possible to illustrate instances where regional politics have had an unfavorable impact. There are many difficult problems in measuring some of these variables but it might be possible to argue that in other circumstances they have had a favorable impact.

Mr. Ide: What do you see as the serious political impacts of population-control programs from the point of view of the impact of political forces on population-control programs and from the point of view of Galbraith's thesis of the Industrial State? Galbraith took issue with Devlin, who deplored the fact that it was the finance capitalists that controlled the economy, and argued that it should be the engineers who control.

Mr. Morehouse: I think the question of the political impact of population-control programs needs to be confronted from several different vantage points, from that of a developing society and from that of a more developed society such as our own. We all, obviously, have a stake in what is done about this problem. It is my impression that there has been—and again I turn to India as my source of illustration—within the past half decade of so, increasing recognition by political leadership in the central government of obvious necessities of getting some real muscle behind India's population or family-planning program. It is difficult to determine how effective this has become, but there does seem to be a quickened sense of direction and effort. Perhaps this is a recognition of political leadership that, to ignore this problem, will have some very negative political consequences.

Concerning Galbraith and some of his theses, at least as far as the United States is concerned, notwithstanding the massive growth of defense research and space research, the politicians are still in charge. But, again, we are confronted with what seems to me to be an interaction; the kinds of alternatives and policy options that are presented to the politicians obviously depend on the advances in the fields of research and development. You cannot neatly separate the two.

Mr. Farer: When you say political factors are decisive, do you mean that, through the political system or political process, we can affect a development process? Is it not an equally plausible possibility that the political factors are ready epiphenomenal, the problems basically cultural and sociological, and our ability to manipulate through political channels really very limited?

Mr. Morehouse: This, of course, is the heart of the matter. I do not think our present understanding of the interactions that are involved is sufficient to give a categorical answer to your question. It may, indeed, turn out to be, as our knowledge of these processes advances, that the political processes are epiphenomenal. On the other hand, I do not know of any overwhelming evidence suggesting that they are. It seems to me it is just as plausible to argue that we are dealing with an interlocking set of phenomena in which cultural and social factors and changes in technology and science are interacting with and affected by the political system.

TRADE UNIONS AND GOVERNMENT POLICY IN DEVELOPING COUNTRIES

Commentary by Sidney C. Sufrin

ALTHOUGH IN MANY, and perhaps most, instances in developed countries trade unions are in an arm of government from the legalistic viewpoint, from the realistic or operational viewpoint, the trade union movement has more than a moderate amount of independence. Union movements in developing countries often tend to be smaller in proportion to the total population than in the West, but they are one of the few organized urban groups and are important in key economic and social places such as government and expert industries (Knowles.)

Millen (1963) provides a classification for the government of an underdeveloped world which is useful and suggestive and has a special virtue in that it attaches to itself a conception of trade union activity which is analytically operational. He divides governments into "brittle" and "uneasily fragile."

Those that I term brittle are not without power—almost all of the African and South Asian governments can mount a great deal of power to achieve a given objective—but they have few agreed upon techniques for replacing an administration short of *coup d' état* or assassinations. Any sudden shock of a nature to be felt throughout the system presents a challenge and thus must be contained quickly. Union protests can easily become such a shock even when the objectives of the strikes are related to economic issues. . . . (On the other hand, uneasily fragile governments are) composed of a party grouping which lacks any common core (and) it is dependent on a restless coalition of heterogeneous elements.

Brittle governments essentially tend to govern single-party states, while uneasily fragile governments are found in multiparty states. It should be borne in mind that both brittle and fragile are, in a sense, synonomous in that both words imply the inability of the subject to withstand a sharp impact or shock. Thus, according to Millen, underdeveloped countries generally are governed by administrations which, because of the social structure, ideology, or other attributes of the society, have neither stability nor viability. The impact of the sudden political or social attack or a sudden realignment of the power elites may topple the government without reference to legal or legislative procedure. For one reason or another change has not been routinized and, with respect of government, slowed down, so that adjustments in government structure and composition can take place without resorting to extra legal, often violent means. The difference between the brittle and the fragile states is that the former tend to be monolithic or at least rely upon a single power group. On the other hand, the latter are made up of a coalition of power groups, none of which is sufficiently strong to assume command and authority of the whole government machinery.

Ceylon, India, and Nigeria are examples of fragile governments; Kenya, Ghana, and Tanzania are examples of brittle governments. In general, Latin American countries, with some exceptions, tend to be fragile or fluid. African countries tend to be brittle and, in the Asian world, there tends to be something of a mixture. For example, Burma, Pakistan, South Korea, and Thailand may be viewed as brittle; Ceylon, India, Indonesia, Malaysia, and Philippines may be viewed as fluid or fragile. (These views are limited to the period prior to 1964.)

Brittle governments tend to permit only a single political party—the party of the administration. The state, in truth, is politically monolithic, with party and government being so closely related as to be parts of the same institution. A Tanzanian official once pointed out that the adage of his country, "Under a tree all agree," means in the political circumstance that the political party argues matters out in its own caucus, with the caucus being divided into fractions or wings. Once an agreement is reached, however, the government is, in a sense, instructed to carry out the decisions of the party. This he viewed as a kind of elemental democracy which did not depend upon parties, but rather upon pressures within a single, legal party.

Unions in both brittle and fragile countries seek approximately the same ends, yet one would expect that union effectiveness would be different in the two classes of countries because of the differences in the power that unions can exercise in the governmental administrative structure.

Labor, government, or labor-management relations are, in the first instance, a transfer—an exchange—of information and attitudes and, in the second instance, a transfer of understanding and possible programs. That interinstitutional adjustment and transfers take place is not an especially novel idea, although it is significant for an understanding of social change and development. The specifics, that is to say the mechanisms or procedures of such transfers, are operationally important in understanding the process of change between government and unions in developing societies. The elaborate and sensitive mechanisms which the Western world has set up, mechanisms such as responsible and responsive governments based on periodic elections, fairly rigid codes of appropriate behavior, including the ideas of the Bill of Rights, and other (nongovernment) legitimated social and private restraints, are not powerful in the third world. The ideological and legitimating structures of the several Western states are more in common with each other than with the ideological structure and political and private restraints of the emerging world (Horowitz, 1966).

It is obvious that the third world does not consist of states whose composition, ideology, and history are in any sense homogeneous. The definitional category of "underdeveloped" for the third world is only a loose semantic device without any carefully defined content (Higgens, 1968.) However, there is a rough agreement that the emerging states stress growth and development as national policy. The indices of their situation are high unemployment or underemployment, per capita incomes only a fraction of the income of the more developed Western world, a weak technology, low educational levels, and, above all, the desire, stated as a matter of policy, to do something about these indices.

Although resources, social structure, politics, technology, relative dependence upon agriculture, and educational levels of these countries vary greatly, some-

148

thing would be gained by devising a criterion or criteria of differentiation. It would be difficult to the point of impossibility, however, to analyze the problems

TABLE 1

COUNTRY	POLITICAL SYSTEM b — Brittle f — Fluid	UNIONIZATION* H — High L — Low	URBANIZATION* H — High L — Low
Ghana	b	H 71.4	L 15.6
Kenya	b	H 36.5	L 6.1
Malawi	b	L 5.4	L 4.0
Mauritius	f	H 50.5	H 17.1
Nigeria	f	H 80.1	L 10.9
Sudan	b	H 41.8	L 5.7
Tanzania	b	H 71.2	L 4.4
Uganda	f	H 54.7	L 1.9
Zambia	f	H 36.8	L 7.1
Morocco	b	H 64.2	H 28.3
Turkey	b	L 11.3	H 16.5
U.A.R.	b	L 10.6	H 28.1
Burma	b	L 1.1	L 8.4
Ceylon	f	H 37.2	L 15.0
India	f	L 26.3	L 7.9
Indonesia	f	H 59.9	L 8.6
Malaysia	f	L 30.5	L 9.2
Pakistan	b	L 9.5	L 7.3
Philippines	f	L 24.0	L 11.0
S. Korea	b	L 11.4	H 26.2
Taiwan	b	L 32.0	H 29.5
Thailand	b	L 2.3	L 11.3
Argentina	f	H 48.1	H 61.4
Chile	f	L 33.6	H 41.5
El Salvador	b	L 4.9	H 27.8
Honduras	f	L 7.5	H 16.0 (median)
Mexico	b	L 32.5	H 50.6
Peru	f	H 40.3	H 26.8
Venezuela	b	H 69.3	H 34.7
Barbados	f	L 28.0	H 38.4
Br. Guiana	f	H 72.0	H 26.7
Jamaica	f	H 64.4	H 23.3
Trinidad-Tobago	f	H 35.6 (median)	H 17.3

*Median used as criterion of "High" and "Low"
Measure of Urbanization—Urban Population/Total Population
Measure of Unionization—Union Members/Wage and Salary Earners

and structure of each undeveloped country without drawing on some generalizations and asserting some common elements other than low income classification.

Even the use of "ideal types" is fruitful, though lacking exactitude for any country (Kerr et al., 1960).

Since we are concerned with the relations of unions to governments in this essay, a classification of the components of the third world into some major categories would be useful in supporting an analysis. In Table 1, the countries considered are listed and classified by our (not Millen's) conception of brittle or fluid, degree of unionization, and degree of urbanization. These three variables, in our opinion, are significant in analyzing income-union-government interactions.

One can divide the economic goals of unions into two categories, (1) direct labor compensation (DLC) and (2) indirect labor compensation (ILC). The former is essentially wages, normally expressed as real wages. The latter consists of the public income (via the public budget) devoted to health, education, and social services. ILC and DLC may be considered as dependent variables were one to construct a mathematical or model explanation. On the independent side of the equation would be such factors as the degree of urbanization, the growth rate of per capita income, gross domestic income, the growth rate of industrial production, and the ratio of capital formations to gross domestic production. Noneconomic considerations are difficult to quantify, eg the degree of unionization, index of labor protest, and the type of political system which links trade unions and governments in developing countries.

The general idea we have investigated may be stated as follows: trade unions and government are institutions whose decisions have important economic implications, even though these decisions are motivated by political and ideological considerations. For example, the number of industrial disputes, the percentage of government expenditures devoted to social services, and the enactment of a minimum-wage law obviously all have effects on resource allocation, income distribution, and the rate of capital accumulation. In carrying out their decisions, it is reasonable to assume that the leaders of one institution take into account the past and expected behavior of the other. Thus, industrial disputes may involve labor and industrial organizations, ideology, technology, and methods and techniques of bringing pressure upon government (or employers) in order to achieve the aims of the dispute. Similarly, the fraction of the budget devoted to social service expenditures or the enactment of a minimum-wage law are related to various considerations that reflect union behavior and union goals.

Decisions made by governments and trade unions involve, in a sense, a political *quid pro quo*. For example, in order to accomodate certain union demands and goals, a larger fraction of the budget may be devoted to housing and workers, a higher minimum-wage law may be enacted, or a post in the cabinet may be awarded to a union official. If unions do not find such "political" and "economic" offerings acceptable, they may react by carrying out strikes, work stoppages, and other forms of labor unrest. The government, in turn, may respond to such trade-union decisions by some of the means mentioned above or by outlaw-

150

ing trade unions, actions which in their turn, may elicit a further reaction from the union movement.

The variables considered are:

Y_1 = DLC = average % Δ Industrial Wage Rate
Y_2 = ILC = average % ΔD Public Budget devoted to Health, Education, and Social Expenditures
X_1 = average % Δ per capita real GDP
X_2 = average % Δ industrial production
X_3 = average I/GDP
X_4 = degree of urbanization
X_5 = degree of unionization
X_6 = index of labor protest
X_7 = type of political system

Attempts to compare the experiences of fluid and brittle countries with respect to the relations between DLC and ILC and government overtime proved unavailing. The lack of success probably is due to the assumed homogeneity of

TABLE 2.—"Brittle" states.

Estimation of Equation (Stepwise):

$Y_1^b = K_1^b + A_1^b X_1 + A_2^b X_2 + A_3^b X_3 + A_4^b X_4 + A_5^b X_5 + A_6^b X_6$

K_1^b	A_1^b	A_2^b	A_3^b	A_4^b	A_5^b	A_6^b	R^2	Df
11.962	.681 (.301) 5%	−.456 (.194) 5%	−.127 (.180)	−.044 (.086)			.5041	10
9.732	.624 (.320) 10%	−.395 (.214)	.078 (.195)	−.063 (.092)	.037 (.047)		.5388	9
11.485	.610 (.389) 20%	−.621 (.229) 5%	−.107 (.189)	−.100 (.093)	.099 (.067) 20%	−48.30 (19.32) 5%	.6257	8

Estimation of Equation (Stepwise):

$Y_2^b = k_2^b + B_1^b X_1 + B_2^b X_2 + B_3^b X_3 + B_4^b X_4 + B_5^b X_5 + B_6^b X_6$

k_1^b	B_1^b	B_2^b	B_3^b	B_4^b	B_5^b	B_6^b	R^2	Df
2.033	.829 (.356) 5%	.470 (.301) 20%	.083 (.381)	.050 (.184)			.1063	10
11.303	.908 (.293) 2%	.400 (.267) 20%	−.129. (.367)	.129 (.173)	−.153 (.090) 20%		.3422	9
12.161	.766 (.273) 5%	.410 (.247) 20%	−.135 (.392)	.113 (.192)	−.122 (.031) 20%	−46.57 (23.55) 10%	3600	8

Notes: R^2—adjusted coefficient of multiple determination
Df—degrees of freedom
Standard errors of regression coefficient indicated in ( )
Level of significance using t-test indicated below standard errors.

the countries within each classification; in fact, they are not similar with respect to important variables.

The next step in analysis proved more fruitful. The fluid and brittle data were pooled and treated in a cross-sectional fashion. The data, consisting of the individual countries' means of the data, were pooled and averages for each country were taken as the relevant measures, rather than specific data for each year.

General form of estimating equations:

$$Y_1 = f_1\ (X_1,\ X_2,\ X_3,\ X_4,\ X_5,\ X_6,\ X_7) \tag{1}$$

$$Y_2 = f_2\ (X_1,\ X_2,\ X_3,\ X_4,\ X_5,\ X_6,\ X_7) \tag{2}$$

The cross-section analysis was more successful in "explaining" inter-country type variations in ILC and DLC. In the cross-section regression equations, "degree of unionization," "degree of urbanization," and "type of political system" were explicitly introduced as independent variables. The treatment of these considerations as independent variables no doubt contributed to overcoming the problem in the time-series analysis of lumping heterogeneous coun-

TABLE 3.—"Fluid" states.

Estimation of Equation (Stepwise):

$Y_1^f = K_1^f + A_1^f X_1 + A_2^f X_2 + A_3^f X_3 + A_4^f X_4 + A_5^f X_5 + A_6^f X_6$

K_1^f	A_1^f	A_2^f	A_3^f	A_4^f	A_5^f	A_6^f	R^2	Df
−.997	−.511 (.580)	.523 (.243) 10%	.133 (.301)	−.012 (.199)			.1232	11
−3.332	−.218 (.526)	.311 (.148) 10%	.043 (.267)	−.022 (.106)	.135 (.063) 10%		.3819	10
−1.855	−.082 (.560)	.460 (.179) 5%	.066 (.283)	−.049 (.109)	.168 (.070) 5%	−64.36 (32.44) 10%	.4436	9

Estimation of Equation (Stepwise):

$Y_2^f = k_2^f + B_1^f X_1 + B_2^f X_2 + B_3^f X_3 + B_4^f X_4 + B_5^f X_5 + B_6^f X_6$

k_2^f	B_1^f	B_2^f	B_3^f	B_4^f	B_5^f	B_6^f	R^2	Df
−10.070	1.448 (.699) 5%	1.820 (.575) 1%	.514 (.344) 20%	.120 (.137)			.5535	11
−8.656	1.626 (.693) 5%	1.948 (.590) 1%	.567 (.325) 20%	.140 (.139)	−.082 (.0083) 1%		.5898	10
−7.065	1.452 (.734) 10%	1.823 (.617) 2%	.578 (.317) 10%	.111 (.146)	−.048 (.0094) 1%	−33.45 (11.21) 2%	.6320	9

Notes: R^2—adusted coefficient of multiple determination
Df—degrees of freedom
Standard errors of regression coefficient indicated in ( )
Level of significance using t-test indicated below standard errors.

tries into categories. To an extent, these variables serve to capture differences among the countries of the sample.

The second difference relates to the measures of the variables. In the cross-section analysis, the measures of the dependent and the independent variables (save the three mentioned above) were means over a period of time. The use of averages contributed to reducing somewhat the effect of structural and historical changes that interfered in the time-series analysis. (See Tables 2 and 3.)

In sum, the cross-section analysis suggests that "index of labor protest" and "type of political system" are important considerations in explaining variations among countries in the two types of labor compensations. As has been suggested, these two considerations are indicators of the "type" and "effectiveness of operation" of political bargaining mechanisms linking labor organizations and government. It can be broadly stated that in fluid political systems, labor protest has a greater impact on DLC than on ILC, whereas in brittle systems the relationship is stronger between labor protest and ILC than between labor protest and DLC. Although the models which have been suggested are crude, the fragmentary empirical results do suggest that different patterns of trade union-government relations can be fruitfully investigated through empirical analysis.

The implications are two-fold. First, variations in DLC and ILC are accounted for not only by the obvious economic differences such as growth rates in per real capital GDP and industrial production, but also by differences in the types and efficiency of operation of the political bargaining mechanisms which link labor organizations and government. The variables, "type of political system" and "index of labor protest," reflect the features of the political bargaining mechanisms.

Second, differences in political bargaining mechanisms are more significant in "explaining" variations among countries in DLC than in ILC. In other words, the addition of the "noneconomic" variables raises the explanatory level of the regression equation more where DLC is the dependent variable than it does when ILC is the dependent variable.

REPORT OF WORKSHOP 6

James Way, Rapporteur

NATION-BUILDERS face a basic difficulty of identifying development goals. The goals of the various interest groups within a developing society may conflict with national interests. Social, political, economic, as well as technical, criteria should be considered in the choice of technologies for industrialization and other aspects of the modernization process. Industrialization and development are not synonymous; there are other dimensions to the modernization process (such as agriculture, trade, social and political institutions, and cultural values) which must be taken into account.

Because technology is rooted in the social order, social, economic, and political structures and processes shape technological change. Political influence, therefore, vitally affects the application of engineering technology in the industrialization of developing countries. The impact of the political environment can inhibit, support, or create dilemmas for technological development.

Scientifically and technologically oriented political leaders who are well educated, who have a favorable ideological outlook, and who are committed to public versus private good exert supportive influence. Support also can be expected from scientifically or engineering-oriented government agencies which can lobby effectively for projects designed to advance national social, economic, and political objectives, as opposed to regional or parochial interests. Governments committed to the training and utilization of engineers and scientists for support also can be counted on. On the other hand, political leaders who are more concerned with personal or parochial interests than with national progress may inhibit the application of new technologies. Political action may be necessary to overcome resistance to technological change by existing institutional structures and interest groups. Satisfactory means for arriving at cost-benefit ratios which take into account not only technical and economic factors, but also social and political consequences of technological choices are sorely lacking to guide political leaders of developing societies in making these choices.

The engineering and scientific community within a developing society constitutes an important professional elite with considerable potential as an interest group for influencing the political leadership. The mere existence of such a professional group creates policy options for political leadership which would not otherwise be feasible.

The way in which a political system interacts with the scientific engineering community is not significantly different from the manner in which that system interacts with other interest groups within developing countries, with one important qualification: the scientific and engineering community has access to specialized knowledge of value to political leadership in developing societies. This, in turn, has policy implications for the kinds of structures created to advise the political leadership on scientific and technological issues.

The training of engineers and scientists for developing countries should:

1. help them to understand the country's political system and the way in which it interacts with technological development and the social order;

2. prepare them for situations in which they must assume roles beyond the technical for which they are primarily trained and assist them in understanding when they assume these additional roles;

3. be a continuing process, including mid-career training in development policy problems for engineering leaders who are most likely to be called upon to assume political and social leadership tasks; and

4. if designed for foreign students in United States universities, not be confined to technological training but include elements to assure that the student may better understand processes of change in his own society and culture.

NOTES

1. The critical importance of interrelationships among economical, social, and political factors in developing societies has been underscored by Gunnar Myrdal in his recently published study, *Asian Drama: An Inquiry into the Poverty of Nations,* New York: Pantheon, 1968: see, for example, vol. 1, pp. 28, 42.

2. The quantitative dimensions of the research communities in India on the one hand and in countries such as France and West Germany on the other are somewhat similar. I do not mean to imply a general comparability in scientific and technological capabilities between these countries, although sheer size results in a certain measure of institutional complexity. Beyond that, differences are very great, even quantitatively, if one looks at such indices as the expenditure per research worker or the relationship of research and development costs to gross national product.

3. As quoted in the Nehru Commemoration Number, *Science Reporter,* July-August, 1964, p.i. In this and many other statements, Nehru refers only to science, although the qualities and consequences he attributed to science imply at least as much concern, if not more, with technology. His failure to distinguish the two may well be, as is suggested subsequently in this paper, one of the factors which has created such difficulties in the relationship of the research community to the political system four years after he has passed from the scene.

4. Interview by the author with M. S. Swaminathan, Director, Indian Agricultural Research Institute, New Delhi, January, 1968.

5. For a policy statement favoring indigenous technology, for example, the fifth clause of the Scientific Policy Resolution, op. cit. The process through which the companies involved in Jack Baran-

154

son's case study went through to secure government approval of their collaborative arrangements, while not necessarily typical, is nonetheless revealing in its complexity and is described on pp. 49–53 of Baranson, *Manufacturing Problems in India: The Cummins Diesel Experience,* Syracuse: Syracuse University Press, 1967. See also, the *Annual Report* of the Director General of Technical Development, Government of India; Manager of Publications. Myron Weiner, in his study of interest groups in the Indian political system, observes that such groups "largely influence the administration rather than the formulation of policy" (*The Politics of Scarcity: Public Pressure and Political Response in India,* Chicago: University of Chicago Press, 1962, p. 217).

6. Interview by the author with A. C. Guha, Former Chairman of the Estimates Committee and Member of Parliament, New Delhi, March, 1967. See also V. B. Chipalkatti, "Technological swaraj—has research a role to play?," *Chemical Industry News,* February, 1966.

7. Private communication to the author, September, 1968.

8. For an analysis of the "politicized" nature of planning in India, see William J. Siffin, "Politics and planning: Perspective on a paradox," (Paper Prepared for the Conference of the Comparative Administration Group, University of Maryland, April, 1966), Bloomington: Indiana University, October, 1966.

9. See Surajit Sinha, ed., *Science and Technology in Relation to Cultural Values in Institutions of South and Southeast Asia: India and Ceylon,* Calcutta (unpublished study), 1966, for an interesting and useful series of both historical and contemporary case studies of the interaction of science, technology, and society in Bengal and Ceylon.

10. The presumption that Indian farmers were too "tradition-bound" to adopt modern agricultural technology has persisted until very recently among both foreign advisors and senior civil servants within the Government of India; see for example, National Council of Applied Economic Research, *Factors Affecting Fertilizer Consumption: Problems and Policies,* New Delhi: The Council, 1964.

11. Interview by the author with a senior agricultural official, New Delhi, January, 1968.

12. See, for example, the 1967 general election manifestoes of the Communist Party of India, CPI-Marxist or "Left" Communists Somyukta Socialist Party (SSP), Indian National Congress, and Jana Songl, as published in R. Chandidas, Leon Clark, Richard Fontera, and Ward Morehouse, *India Votes: A Source Book on Indian Elections,* Bombay and New York: Popular Prakashan and Humanities Press, 1968, pp. 7, 26, 28, 34, 46, 77.

13. For some thoughtful comments on the "state of the art" in the study of science, technology, and public policy, see Eugene B. Skolnikoff, "The difficult political choices of science, " *World Politics,* April, 1968, pp. 535–558.

14. For dicussion of needed research on science, technology, and society in South Asia, see Ward Morehouse, ed., *Understanding Science and Technology in India and Pakistan: Problems of Research in the Social Sciences and Humanities,* New York: Foreign Area Materials Center, State Education Department, University of the State of New York (Occasional Publication No. 8), 1967, especially "Science Policy and Administration Studies in India—Some Needed Research."

15. A good summary of these points appeared in *Nature:* "Problems of choice and priorities in science and technology," March 13, 1965, pp. 1039–1041.

16. A good recent account of general developments in the "science of science" is Alan MacKay, "Studying science itself" (Paper prepared for British Association for the Advancement of Science, Leeds, September 4, 1967). For these developments are related to the Indian scene, see Agveil Ahmed, *Progress in the Science of Science with Special Reference in India,* New Delhi: Research, Survey, and Planning Organization, Council of Scientific and Industrial Research, mimeo., n.d. (?–1968).

REFERENCES CITED

Ahmed, Aqueil. *Progress in the Science of Science with Special Reference to India.* New Delhi: Research, Survey and Planning Organization, Council of Scientific and Industrial Research, mimeo., n.d. (?–1968).

Baranson, Jack. *Manufacturing Problems in India: The Cummins Diesel Experience,* Syracuse: Syracuse University Press, 1967.

Basalla, George, "The spread of western science," *Science,* May 5, 1967.

Blackett, P. M. S. *Science and Technology in an Unequal World* (Jawaharlal Nehru Memorial Lecture Delivered in Delhi, November 13, 1967). New Delhi: Jawaharlal Nehru Memorial Fund, 1968.

_____, "New science or old technology" in Ruth Gruber, ed., *Science and the New Nations.* (Proceedings of the International Conference on Science and the Advancement of New States of Rehovoth, Israel, August, 1960). New York: Basic Books, 1961.

Caldwell, Lynton K., and William B. DeVille. *A Syllabus for the Study of Science, and Technology and Public Policy: Their Interactions and Their Impact upon Society and Government in the Modern World.* Bloomington: Department of Government, Indiana University, 1968.

Chandidas, R. Leon Clark, Richard Fontera, and Ward Morehouse. *India Votes: A Source Book on Indian Elections.* Bombay and New York: Popular Prakashan and Humanities Press, 1968.

Chipalkatti, V. B., "Technological swaraj—has research a role to play?," *Chemical Industry News,* February, 1966.

Government of India, Parliament. *Scientific Policy Resolution No. 131 C. F. 57.* New Delhi, March 4, 1958.

Haskins, Caryl P. *The Scientific Revolution and World Politics.* New York: Harper and Row 1964.

Higgins, B. *Economic Development* (Rev. Ed.). Norton, N.Y., 1968.

Horowitz, I. *The Three Worlds of Development Theory and A Practice of International Stratification,* New York: Oxford, 1966.

Kerr, Clark, John T. Dunlop, Fred Harbison, and Charles Myers, *Industrialism and Industrial Man.* Cambridge: Harvard University Press, 1960.

Knowles, W. H., "Industrial conflict and the unions" in W. E. Moore and A. Feldman, *Labor Commitment and Social Change in Developing Areas.*

MacKay, Alan, "Studying science itself" (Paper prepared for British Association for the Advancement of Science, Leeds: September 4, 1967).

Maddox, John, "Choice and the scientific community," *Minerva,* Winter, 1964.

Marglin, Stephen, "Problems of irrigation planning and research in India and West Pakistan." in Ward Morehouse, ed., *Science and the Human Condition in India and Pakistan.* New York: Rockefeller University Press, 1968.

Millen, Bruce H. *The Political Role of Labor in Developing Countries.* Washington, D.C.: The Brookings Institution, 1963.

Morehouse, Ward, ed. "Science policy and administration studies in India—some needed research," *Understanding Science and Technology in India and Pakistan: Problems of Research in the Social Sciences and Humanities.* New York: Foreign Area Materials Center, State Education Department, University of the State of New York (Occasional Publication No. 8), 1967.

Myrdal, Gunnar. *Asian Drama: An Inquiry into the Poverty of Nations.* New York: Pantheon, 1968.

National Council of Applied Economic Research. *Factors Affecting Fertilizer Comsumption: Problems and Policies.* New Delhi: The Council, 1964.

Nature, "Problems of choice and priorities in science and technology," March 13, 1965.

Piel, Gerard, "Role of science in India's self-discovery," *Nature,* June 20, 1964.

Pirie, N. W. , "The maldistribution of research effort," in Maurice Goldsmith and Alan MacKay, eds., *Society and Science.* New York: Simon and Schuster, 1964.

Price, Derek J. deSolla, "Is technology historically independent of science? A study in statistical historiography," *Technology and Culture,* Fall, 1965.

_____, "Is there a science-based technology? Theoretical issues and prospects for investigation" (Paper Prepared for Conference on Theoretical Issues in the Study of Science, Scientists, and Science Policy, Institute for the Study of Science and Human Affairs, Columbia University and Social Science Research Council, New York, February 29–March 1, 1968).

156

Price, Don K, "Science and government: Some fundamental issues" (Paper Prepared for Science Study Unit Seminar, University of Edinburgh, November 3–5, 1968).

Science Reporter, Nehru Commemoration Number, July–August, 1964.

Siffin, W. J., "Politics and planning: Perspective on a paradox," (Paper Prepared for the Conference of the Comparative Administration Group, University of Maryland, April, 1966). Bloomington: Indiana University, October, 1966.

Sinha, Surajit. *Science and technology in Relation to Cultural Value in Institutions of South and Southeast Asia: India and Ceylon.* Calcutta: (unpublished study), 1966.

Skolnikoff, E. B., "The difficult political choices of science," *World Politics,* April, 1968.

Snow, C. P. *The Two Cultures: And a Second Look.* New York: New American Library, 1963.

Toulmin, Stephen, "The complexity of scientific choice: A stocktaking," *Minerva,* Spring, 1964.

————, "The complexity of scientific choice—II: Culture, overheads, or tertiary industry?" *Minerva,* Winter, 1966.

Ward, Barbara, *The Lopsided World.* New York: Norton, 1968.

Weinberg, A. M., "Criteria of scientific choice—I," *Minerva,* Autumn, 1963.

————"Criteria of scientific choice: The two cultures—II," *Minerva,* Autumn, 1964.

Weiner, Myron, "India: Two political cultures" in Lucien W. Pye and Sydney Verba, eds., *Political Culture and Political Development.* Princeton: Princeton University Press, 1965.

————. *The Politics of Scarcity: Public Pressure and Political Response in India.* Chicago: University of Chicago Press, 1962.

Williams, B. R., "Research and economic growth," *Minerva,* Autumn, 1964.

9

INFLUENCE OF THE AVAILABILITY OF TECHNICAL ASSISTANCE

Principal Paper—P. C. Asiodu

Commentary—Mordechai Lador

Commentary—George McRobie

Report of Workshop 7—Stephen Blank, Rapporteur

The Western world has been engaged in programs of assistance to the emerging nations for the last quarter-century. In many cases, these programs have been but marginally successful. This chapter presents an analysis of technical assistance to the emerging nations of the world.

The Editors

INFLUENCE OF THE AVAILABILITY
OF TECHNICAL ASSISTANCE

Principal Paper by P. C. Asiodu

TECHNICAL ASSISTANCE is a broad subject and one that has great importance for the entire world now and in the future. The U.N. Development Decade, proclaiming with such expectations in 1961 a minimum average growth
target of 5 per cent for the underdeveloped world, has been one of unfulfilled
hopes. We do not see many signs today of rapid growth in the amount of
resources devoted to aid and assistance programs and, indeed, the assistance is
diminishing from some sources, making this Conference all the more important
in terms of maximization of effectiveness. An OECD appraisal of recent financial flows from the major donor countries (Table 1) reveals a generally downward trend. Expressed as a proportion of GNP, total aid has declined from 1.04
per cent in 1962 to 0.88 per cent in 1966. This aspect is, perhaps, particularly
important to the smaller emerging countries not yet in the mainstream of aid
flows. We must not overlook the fact, however, that the transfer of technology,
and thus the ability to develop, is really a problem of people—their leadership,
motivation, and abilities—and that, therefore, the improvement, expansion, and
acceleration of this process need not necessarily involve massive new capital
expenditures. There is no model country (with the possible exception of Nationalist China which was a very unique situation) where one might see clearly a
development of technology and genuine economic growth that had arisen as a
direct result of organized economic assistance programs. Thinking along these
lines, however, one is inclined to pause for a careful look at Japan's 19th century
modernization. We can point almost to the precise date in fairly recent history
when Japan's leaders determinedly embarked on the avowed path to total modernization of their country, starting from a very low base. In fields of technology
they very realistically examined their shortcomings, imported the first generation expertise, and established educational programs to form successive generations of experts from within. Theirs was a "bootstrap" endeavor, almost entirely
selfadministered. The results have been startlingly successful; yet, there was no
aid program as such from the outside world.

THE FAILURE OF PRESENT AID PROGRAMS

Why is it that we cannot isolate a clear example of this type of success generated
by modern day aid programs? The answer might be found in the fact that
Japan's determined adoption of a clear goal of rapid growth and its ruthless
pursuit of the necessary policies have not yet been repeated by national leaders of
recipient countries today. Nor has any donor country ever seriously accepted the
full implications of using aid to transfer technology on a sufficient scale or to
create a situation in a developing country where local initiative and talents
become the prime movers for further development. The reasons for this failure
may be partly political and partly traditional. In this context it has not made
much difference whether the aid is bilateral or multilateral.

TABLE 1.—The flow of financial resources from Development Assistance Committee (DAC) countries as a percentage of national income, 1962–1966. (Figures in per cent.)

Country	Total Official Flow					Total Private Flow					Total Official & Private Flow				
	1962	1963	1964	1965	1966	1962	1963	1964	1965	1966	1962	1963	1964	1965	1966
Australia	(0.59)[1]	(0.60)	0.61	0.64	0.67	—	—	0.11	0.12	0.04	(0.59)[2]	(0.60)[2]	(0.72)	0.76	0.71
Austria	0.25	0.04	0.22	0.49	0.49	0.31	0.06	0.10	0.19	0.17	0.56	0.10	0.33	0.68	0.66
Belgium	0.77	0.81	0.67	0.90	0.64	0.47	0.86	0.76	0.91	0.67	1.24	1.67	1.43	1.81	1.31
Canada	0.19	0.32	0.39	0.34	0.52	0.19	0.11	0.09	0.09	0.14	0.38	0.43	0.48	0.43	0.66
Denmark	0.12	0.15	0.15	0.17	0.30	0.12	0.01	0.30	0.03	0.02	0.25	(0.17)	0.45	0.22	0.32
France	1.76	1.39	1.25	1.08	0.95	0.71	0.68	0.83	0.80	0.75	2.53	2.07	2.08	1.88	1.70
Germany	0.66	0.59	0.53	0.50	0.54	0.27	0.23	0.34	0.33	0.27	0.93	0.82	0.87	0.83	0.81
Italy	0.35	0.31	0.14	0.22	0.24	0.96	0.65	0.48	0.43	1.04	1.32	0.96	0.62	0.65	1.28
Japan	0.19	0.26	0.19	0.37	0.37	0.44	0.26	0.31	0.37	0.32	0.63	0.52	0.50	0.74	0.69
Netherlands	0.83	0.32	0.35	0.41	0.55	0.48	0.92	0.58	1.12	0.93	1.30	1.24	0.93	1.53	1.49
Norway	0.17	0.48	0.35	0.22	0.23	0.10	0.19	0.20	0.49	0.07	0.27	0.66	0.55	0.71	0.29
Portugal	1.69	1.98	2.29	0.75	0.70	—	—	—	0.33	0.44	1.69[2]	1.98[2]	2.29[2]	1.08	1.14
Sweden	0.16	0.18	0.24	0.25	0.34	0.16	0.24	0.25	0.20	0.31	0.32	0.42	0.48	0.45	0.65
United Kingdom	0.64	0.60	0.67	0.61	0.60	0.47	0.40	0.56	0.56	(0.56)	1.11	1.00	1.22	1.17	(1.16)
United States	0.80	0.78	0.67	0.67	0.60	0.18	0.18	0.25	0.31	(0.16)	0.97	0.96	0.92	0.98	(0.76)
Total DAC Countries	0.74	0.70	0.62	0.61	0.57	0.30	0.27	0.34	0.38	0.31	1.04	0.97	0.96	0.99	0.88

1. Figures in parentheses are estimates.
2. Official flows only.

This serious failure also may be partly explained by the small size, in most cases, of the countries involved. The effective application of modern technology requires a large-scale operation which is simply impossible in many countries individually. The new regional approach, however, may provide a more hopeful base for the process of modernization. The regional approach has its corrollaries in the politics to be pursued by the bigger and richer countries towards the developing countries, and in the models of social and political structures suggested for the developing countries. We cannot on the one hand provide aid towards modernization, which requires integration of several countries into single economic units and, on the other, encourage, for any isolated reasons, internal divisions within any of those countries.

THE IMPACT OF TECHNICAL ASSISTANCE AND AID

Quite a lot has been done about aid from the richer to the less rich countries over the last twenty years. Much also has been written appraising the achievements and criticizing the inadequacies of aid. Certainly the availability of technical assistance and bilateral and multilateral aid has made an impact. In the first place, technical assistance has been used to identify projects, plan development programs, and thus to attract economic assistance more effectively leading to construction of new projects and the provision, where necessary, of labor to run them. In this sphere of assistance, large infrastructure projects—dams, highways, railways, harbor—have been preferred. Much less attention has been paid to agricultural or industrial projects or educational extension projects which, in many ways, could have made a greater impact on the lives of the people and on the problems of development. Developing countries have had the products of technology but little of the technology itself is now available in the countries of the developing world with a few exceptions such as India, which is not really an exception since it has followed a rather lengthy and classic process of development over the last forty years.

The projects have not been planned in such a way as to maximize the use of local resources. In the few industrial projects where a greater range of selection among acceptable technological answers was possible, it does not appear that engineers and other technicians responded sufficiently. In effect, the "solutions" of Europe and America have been reproduced wholesale in Africa and Asia. So, although through aid and their own quantitatively much larger investments, the developing countries are accumulating factories and plants, there is the danger that, if they continue with the present approach, it will take decades or centuries to achieve an industrial revolution. Since there is no time for this, the problem before this Conference is how to remedy the failure of aid to initiate the revolution which the developing countries consider imperative.

BUILDING A TECHNOLOGICAL BASE

In dealing with the question of building a technological base and the transfer of technology, some definitions are necessary. I think of technology as a broad concept involving all fields of technical knowledge—all the technical specialties and supporting functions bearing on the development and operation of economic infrastructure, public services, agriculture, industry, and commerce. The technological base has already been defined by this Conference as "the existence of technical knowhow and skills plus a suitable environment and an atmosphere conducive to development."

The teaching process obviously plays an important role in creating a suitable base. At the level of trades and crafts, many types of training and testing facilities have been established and operated in developing countries with varying degrees of success. Public trades training institutes are commonly established at early stages in national development programs, sometimes independently but more often as elements of bilateral or United Nations aid programs. There are also many examples of commercially sponsored testing and training facilities. Some of the major expatriate industrial and trading companies in Nigeria have had notable success in this field and I am sure there are many similar endeavors elsewhere. Perhaps commercial training facilities have an advantage over public institutions in terms of motivating the trainee because they can point to immediate job opportunities for successful graduates and also can demonstrate more rapid advancement for the more skilled operator. Such commercial programs generally also may have more specific objectives and therefore make better use of their resources. I believe this field of trades and crafts training can be vastly improved by organized study of the many case histories available to isolate the variables and identify areas for improvement. Professional training also presents many interesting areas for study. It is obviously desirable that all young men entering university should be buoyed up by an attitude of anticipation at the opportunity for challenging new experiences in learning and that they should show keen interest in new developments and advancements of sophistication in their chosen profession. It is natural that the young graduates will want to find employment where they can use and extend this knowledge. However, in the developing countries, it is more often than not true that technological problems require tailored or "custom-made" solutions which draw heavily on basic fundamentals of technical fields, meaning that the new technologist or technician will, to an extent, be divorcing himself from the more glamorous aspects of his field.

Another related point concerns work habits and attitudes of young technicians. It seems to me that one good direct means for acquiring knowledge of these fundamentals I have been referring to is through actual working experience, often of the type which dirties the hands and clothing and chips the fingernails. Yet, how often do we find young professional graduates ready to move in this direction in developing countries? Not often enough, I submit, and I wonder whether this might suggest a need for revisions in the undergraduate environment. (I do not of course ignore the need for better public education and leadership in changing the traditional concepts regarding positions of prestige in developing countries.)

Internships and understudy assignments are areas that can be more fully exploited in postgraduate training. There have been many attempts in this field, but none widely successful to my knowledge. Barriers we often hear mentioned are the high cost of such programs to host enterprises, and the unwieldy circumstances that arise when attempting to employ understudies where there may be contact with work of a confidential nature.

In my view, one of the vital fundamentals frequently overlooked is the cost-consciousness of engineers, architects, and others who design projects for developing countries. This arises from the fact that the local supervisor of the project does not apply the same basic rules in selecting a solution as his counterpart in the developed country and all too often accepts as the best solution, one arrived at in a rich-country situation, as satisfying all the relevant engineering criteria. This can lead to disastrous results or indefinite postponement of development projects.

As an illustration, I once was requested to review plans for a proposed new 500-bed teaching hospital in Nigeria which called for a gloriously sophisticated, air-conditioned skyscraper complex that surely would have gladdened the hearts of doctors, staff, and patients in *any* of the world's most advanced countries— where the electrical supply hardly ever fails! Had the plans gone to contract in that form, however, the people of Nigeria would have paid nearly $40 million for a gleaming monument entirely unsuited to the medical teaching needs of the time and place. At the same time, the plans ignored suitable and already existing facilities which could have been improved and made adequate for about $3 million.

In more of an engineering vein, I know of a high-cost electric generating station built at great expense to serve critical needs where the engineers selected gas turbine power units of a very advanced design that had not yet been proven out. The result has been rather tragic—frequent power failures, high operating costs, and a large number of technicians tied down to keep the operation going.

I believe that selective study planning can focus on such problems and lead to very beneficial expansion of the internship and understudy method of training. The object must be to force the student to find original answers to problems as cheaply as possible and without being a mere copycat.

Once the right training principles are established, surely commercial and industrial leaders in the advanced countries will find that very noticeable benefits will arise from their participation. Trainees returing to their home places of employment not only will reduce the continuous demand for expensive and often overcommitted foreign experts but also will be very effective good-will ambassadors.

I am convinced that similar techniques could be used to great advantage for the civil service which has a very important development role to play in the less-developed countries. We often see young men at middle-management levels in government service, ripe for promotion to posts of higher responsibility but not sufficiently imbued with the right attitudes towards responsibility and decision making. In such a situation, a few months of intensive exposure and experience in the corresponding department of a cooperating-country government could do a lot to improve the competence and confidence of the trainee and raise his awareness of wider horizons of excellence.

Finally, in postgraduate training, it is my opinion that professional circles in many parts of the developing world suffer from what might be termed a "formal degree complex" which causes them to overemphasize the importance of the certificate at the expense of respect for knowledge itself. Responsibility for this condition must not be assigned only to the student, for it is his home professional environment that has evolved systems of advancement which are intimately keyed to possession of academic degrees. This is true in many commercial enterprises but even more noticeable in civil service establishments throughout the world. If this attitude can be changed I believe the result would be much greater relevance in academic postgraduate training.

THE TRANSFER OF TECHNOLOGY

We have looked at the subject of the technological base in the developing world and related influences of the education process. Now we should look at the technological structure itself—the organized means for applying technical knowledge in the developing country. The first thought that comes to my mind in this connection is about the use of local engineering services and consultants on development projects in bilateral aid programs. Far too often the engineering team coming into the developing country to plan and build a bridge, dam, or port facility comes in and does its job very quickly and efficiently, then leaves the country with a shining new asset but little or no knowledge about the planning or construction work transferred to local organizations. If they had made a point of integrating counterpart staffs into their team directing planning and execution, they would have left behind valuable knowledge as well as the facility. Far too many examples of this in Nigeria lead to a permanent demand for the same type of assistance for subsequent similar projects.

A new approach need not be confined to bilateral programs; it can also be extended regionally in developing areas. There should be a continuous seeking out of means to formulate such projects to maximize utilization of local technical services and consultant groups with the aim of expanding their fields of competence and encouraging more formation. It also may be argued that such a move will tend to reduce the "brain drain" from developing areas as it creates more areas of professional challenge at home. If one of the objections is cost and delays in completing a job and moving on to another in this highly competitive world, we should try and find an answer. In Table 2, I have tabulated some data illustrating the magnitude of technology-intensive projects funded by the World Bank in some large and small developing countries over the past five years. Such projects surely offer many opportunities for improvements in the transfer of technology.

Looking perhaps a bit further ahead and on a higher plane of sophistication, I

164

can also perceive the developing countries improving their industrial sectors through more efforts to establish quality-control facilities. In the industrialized

TABLE 2.—Technology-intensive projects funded by the World Bank in selected countries in fiscal years ending June 30, 1964–1968 (in millions of US dollars).

	1964	1965	1966	1967	1968	Total
India						
Railways		62.00	68.00			130.00
Electric power		84.00	23.00			107.00
Telecommunications		33.00				33.00
Iron and steel industry				30.00		30.00
						300.00
Brazil						
Electric power		79.50	49.00	100.60		229.10
Transport survey				1.73		1.73
Livestock production					40.00	40.00
Aluminum production					22.00	22.00
						292.83
Nigeria						
Electric power	30.00	82.00				112.00
Roads		15.50	32.00			47.50
Transport survey					0.30	0.30
						159.80
Kenya						
Tea production		2.80			2.10	4.90
Roads		7.50		5.30	10.70	23.50
Railways[1]			38.00			38.00
Telecommunications[1]				13.00		13.00
Transport survey[1]				0.68		0.68
						80.08
Malaysia (including Singapore)						
Electric power	51.90			47.00	15.00	113.90
Water supply		6.80			8.00	14.80
Irrigation			45.00	10.00		55.00
Transport survey				1.30		1.30
Telecommunications					3.00	3.00
Port development					15.00	15.00
						203.00
Tunisia						
Port development	7.00					7.00
Transport master plan				0.49		0.49
						7.49

[1]Regional projects together with Tanzania and Uganda.

countries, quality-control technicians often are the developers of new or improved products, a condition arising from the natural tendency to apply their creative instinct in association with intimate product knowledge derived from their day-to-day work. Quality control is certainly an input vital to the success of any manufacturing industry, but all too often it is loosely organized or not organized at all. This is especially true in the case of smaller establishments. Expanded development of specialized units serving groups of small industries might be quite fruitful.

Technology certainly is dynamic, in the sense that the technology of any given field is living, growing, and constantly evolving. In the natural process of competitive selection, its products and the means for making them are constantly changing and improving, one hopes for the benefit of man and the improvement of his environment. Also, the technical director always is faced with areas of choice which can be of great importance to progress in developing lands. There are alternative standards for products themselves, for their components, and among various patented or licensed processes for production. There is the ever-present choice between labor- and capital-intensive methods, and all that this implies. In many industries there is a choice to be made in terms of integrating forward or backward, or of planning ahead for future integration. Often there are opportunities for developing countries to acquire secondhand plants from their industrialized neighbors. This alone is a subject where there are many diverse views, but I personally believe that used equipment or complete second-hand production complexes may frequently offer very real benefits to developing countries. There have been many dismal examples of failure in this connection, but I am convinced that the problems can be overcome if an appropriate organized international survey can be introduced to assure the developing countries of full value for money.

What do all these characteristics of change and choice mean to implementing the transfer of technology to the developing countries? Certainly technical assistance programs must always take cognizance of the special character of the planning and selection process applicable for sound programmed development suited to the environment thay are serving. Typically today, technicians in industrialized countries often work individually in narrow spheres at high levels on the technological spectrum, a natural result of the high degree of sophistication and specialization in their environments. Yet the most successful technician in economic development often will be the one who is more of a generalist, offering a good mixture of engineering and project economics and, above all, an awareness of the differences between national and commercial benefits and their meanings in terms of economic development.

Universities in both the industrialized and the developed countries can undoubtedly do much to foster the right kind of thinking among technicians serving the process of economic development today as well as in the future.

Before leaving the subject of transfer of technology I should like to make a few remarks about standardization and sophistication. There are many aid-giving countries today, representing quite a variety of standards. As a result we are beginning to find a growing diversity of standards in individual developing countries which, if left unchecked, will tie down undesirably large amounts of machinery and manpower for maintenance and operation. I do not profess to have any clear-cut solution to this problem, but I am sure that it needs attention. I have also seen many examples pointing out the danger of oversophistication in facilities provided under aid programs. Highly sophisticated installations carry with them the need for lengthy and sometimes indefinite services of foreign technicians, costly to the developing countries in foreign exchange. Often it is also necessary to rely permanently on the costly importation of servicing components from the originating country. Excessive numbers of local technicians must be employed to learn and execute operation of these sophisticated plants, usually at the expense of retarded progress on other development projects requiring these scarce local manpower resources. I recognize that there is a genuine dilemma here because the developing world is not closed unto itself but is open to competing products from outside. It also needs to sell manufactured items to the developed world which, in effect, means keeping abreast with standards and peculiarities set by the latter. The point really is that attention must be paid constantly to this problem and an appropriate choice made in each instance on its merits, taking all the factors into account.

SUGGESTIONS FOR THE FUTURE

I do not belong to the camp of the pessimists who are very skeptical over the whole proposition of the "have" nations helping the "have nots." The methods and purpose of aid in the Western world have developed in a haphazard fashion and the need now is to redefine our approach in the interest of genuine development, divorced as much as possible from social theories not really related to development. We need, perhaps, to concentrate more on imparting basic knowledge and attitudes which create local technological ability. This would inevitably mean a new type of technical assistance activity, the development of planning and executive resources for every major development project, however financed. Where private enterprise in involved, public aid bodies and the recipient governments must bear the cost and ensure this essential aspect of development.

There are also solutions to be found to the dilemma of adapting technology to suit the varying needs and resources of the developing world while ensuring that the latter are abreast of the latest developments in the modernizing process where it is essential.

Finally, regarding the most important problem—suggestions on how poorer nations should make development their most important and urgent goal and on how the developed nations should realize that their policies and activities, political, commercial, and economic, must be coordinated and coherent to justify their oft-repeated interest in seeing the poorer nations develop to the stage of self-sustaining growth—I should like to list a few ideas which we should explore further:

1. Economic development should be accepted as a priority goal for the under-

developed countries. The goal of rapid economic growth may be incompatible in the short run with certain models of liberal social organizations in affluent societies.

2. Decisions on the flow of aid to such countries should be less subject to capricious reductions on political grounds because the alleviation of poverty will be a prior condition for stable liberal regimes.

3. Given this approach, projections of the resources to be devoted to aid will be more certain and we can plan better for the use of such resources to:

a. Create local training institutions for trades, crafts, and technology emphasizing the need for original answers to existing situations in developing countries, answers which are, to the fullest extent possible, determined by, and make full use of, available local resources;

b. Insist on associating indigenous nationals or people from the "region" in the planning and execution of projects financed under AID programs in order to accelerate the transfer of technology; and

c. Provide additional funds to cover the cost of crash training programs within publicly and privately owned factories, plantations, and other enterprises to ensure the earliest possible take-over of management by local people.

4. Long-term trade policies should be urged which will enhance more rationalization and product specialization on a world basis allowing for exports of manufactures and semimanufactures by developing countries, thus guaranteeing larger market bases for viable industries and the concomitant transfer of technology.

In all this, of course, the choice, the determination of the underdeveloped world to develop must be the prime mover in any change for the better.*

---

*For a discussion of the paper by P. C. Asiodu, see p. 184.

TECHNICAL ASSISTANCE TO ISRAEL

Commentary by Mordechai Lador

ISRAEL REALIZES that, before engineering technology can be applied to the industrialization of developing countries, the role and place of industry have to be examined in the light of demographic, social, economic, and resource conditions of the developing world.

Already in 1963, the Israeli public was made aware of the difference between the developed and the developing world at a confrontation of politicans, scientists, and other professional men in Rehovot at the Second International Conference on the Role of Agriculture in Developing Countries. This Conference was attended by those from both the developed and the developing world; the vast difference between problems of industrialization in the two worlds was emphasized.

Israel tends to accept the basic premise of Gunnar Myrdal, that industry in the developing countries is not in a position to absorb the ever-growing labor force arising from a basically rural society. There are two reasons for this; first, much of the available manpower from rural areas is incapable and untrained to accept employment in industry, especially heavy and precision industries. In many countries, the rural population has been under a yoke of archaic institutional structures that have blunted initiative over centuries and impeded the desire of people to work more to specialize in one clearly delineated activity. Without a basic institutional change, either by agrarian reform or transformation, the mobility of labor into industry can hardly be expected or achieved. Second, industry with its rate of automatization cannot absorb even the increment labor force, assuming the absolute number of peasants in a given society remains static and even this situation is most undesirable. Furthermore industry requires investments in plant locations that are often far higher than investments in agriculture to attain family income targets.

This is a vicious circle. The approach we have adopted, both in Israel and in collaboration with developing countries, is to concentrate on the agricultural base to modernize farming, to phase its development, and introduce modern technology to the rural population. We see this as a pre-industrial development stage that can prepare society for an eventual leap into industrialization. In this stage we believe it is already possible and feasible to link farm production to the first phase of industrialization by processing higher protected food stuffs and fibres.

We feel that it is of utmost importance to locate these processing industries in rural areas so that new work places can be established for the coming generation in the region of their origin. Thus the crisis of urbanization can be reduced and the smaller town will develop into a dynamic urban nucleus. Agricultural products usually involve bulk transport, an added reason to locate industries near the source of supply. Around these processing industries, secondary and tertiary industries will develop, initiative will be mobilized for neutral industries, and the town will grow and assume its own laws of urban development.

Kiryat Gat, an urban center in a new agricultural region in Israel, is illustrative. The town started with people serving in a regional administration to develop 250 000 acres comprising 52 villages and administered farms. The region produces cotton, sugar beet, ground nuts, and vegetables. The town began its industries based on the processing needs of these crops. As a result, cotton gins, mills, weaving plants, a sugarbeet factory, a peanut-grading plant, refrigeration, and storage facilities were created.

From this base, secondary and tertiary services developed and, after seven years, the first signs of larger neutral industries not related to agriculture developed. The interesting aspect is that the percentage of people engaged in agricultural industries and services and processing is on the increase, parallel to a phenomenal diversification of agriculture in new spheres such as grain storage, citrus packing, vegetable export grading, and agricultural credit services. Today Kiryat Gat has a population of 20 000 people, of which 37 per cent of the labor force is employed in industry. This is higher than the average for the country as a whole. One of the underlying reasons is that different types of in-service training were programmed to convert unskilled people into people with the required skills.

In our bilateral and multilateral programs of technical cooperation with developing countries, we tend jointly to develop functional rural regions that synchronize rural and urban development and locate the first industries linked to farm production which our experts promote.

Israel also has a technological base for industrialization which can be attained only by widespread vocational and management training. We have used two training methods. First, we use in-service training when, for instance, we are asked to give assistance in running power plants where the personnel lack the technical ability to run such a plant. We link the assistance to training programs for running the plant and for an incubator for manpower in other factories. For instance, an expert we were asked to send to run the power plant in one of the Carribean countries found that the power house was over-employed. Instead of sacking manpower, he embarked on a vigorous training program to prepare the personnel for other outlets of employment, using the equipment of that power house in training for the different disciplines needed elsewhere. In Israel, hundreds of engineers and technicians were employed to plan and implement our national water conduct. After the work was completed, the companies trained their people to diversify disciplines to serve in other fields such as our infant oil, electronics, and computer industries.

Our second training technique is to send high-powered, technically trained people from our productivity institute to conduct management courses for the young industrial sector in other countries. The main activity of these people is to teach the value and use of motivating local managers to adopt a human approach in their dealings with industry's manpower and shop managers. This aspect is no less important than the acquistition of technological skills; the two must go together. Finally, a prerequisite for industrialization is the creation of a technological base. Unfortunately, in less-developed countries, this technological base must start with the development of infrastructure and power. The marginal return on such investments in the initial stage of development is often low yet, without it, there can be no development. The intangible benefits for developing infrastructure power are often most significant in the development of manpower suited for first phase industrialization.

In analyzing the influence of the availability of technical assistance in terms of both economic assistance and the transfer of technology, the following points would seem most relevant to me:

1. Assistance should be directed into those industrial activities that can gainfully employ a maximum number of workers at compatible technological levels with the abilities of the potential labor force. This will restrict to some extent the degree of technological sophistication of the industries chosen.

2. Industries should be located within the original environment and location of the potential labor force. This, *a priori*, implies the location of industries, where possible, in towns within rural areas.

3. Modernization of agriculture implies the development of services for peasant communities. Within those services special attention should be focused on the development of vocational training facilities which prepare the youth for eventual absorption in the industrialization process.

4. Redundant factories (in many cases, outdated agricultural industries) should be converted into vocational education centers, instead of being abandoned completely.

5. Interdisciplinary teams should be created for rural development as well as for the development of multipurpose urban concentrations where the main economic pillar of activity is the planning and promotion of new industries.

6. Feasibility studies for the possible establishment of industries should be undertaken jointly by the donor and the receiving countries. This is the only way by which industrial planning skills can be developed from within the countries.

AN INTERDISCIPLINARY STUDY OF THE APPLICATION OF ENGINEERING TECHNOLOGY TO THE INDUSTRIALIZATION OF DEVELOPING COUNTRIES

Commentary by George McRobie

THE BULK of aid and technical assistance over the past twenty years has attempted to transplant Western technology—often the most advanced available—into developing countries. But instead of the selfgenerating economic growth for which it was hoped Western aid would be the pump primer, the gap between the rich and the poor countries is growing wider. Within the less-developed countries themselves, the general picture is of mass migration to a few metropolitan centers, mass unemployment in the rural areas, and the specter of famine. For many countries, political independence has not brought economic liberty; we are now told that "The external public debt of developing countries has increased fourfold in the last 10 years to about $30 billion. If recent trends of borrowing and repayment continue, net lending would become negative by 1970" (Survey of International Development, July 15, 1968).

That the developing countries stand in need of more aid is beyond question. But must it be "the mixture as before"? Except in a few cases where meticulous attention has been given to preserving some kind of structure of rural/urban balance, the greater part of aid has gone into relatively few slum-ridden, rapidly growing, and ever more costly cities, rather than into the rural areas; relatively few large capital-intensive, rather than many small labor-intensive, projects; and has favored a relatively small number of rich people rather than many poor ones.

It would seem that a new approach to aid is called for. This new approach might start with the recognition that world poverty is chiefly a rural phenomemon. Of the world's poor, roughly 85 per cent live in the rural areas and the rest (mostly of recent rural origin) inhabit the slums of a few big cities. Even in the rich industrialized countries, the economic, social, and political cost of explosive city growth is daunting enough. For the developing countries, the costs of metropolitan growth are a present nightmare and, for this reason alone, it seems highly improbable that widespread development can be primarily or even largely city-based. Nor is there any past or present experience to suggest that industrialization ever springs from a base of rural stagnation, unemployment, and misery. What manifestly does spring up is the "dual society," a phenomenon largely attributable to the impact of Western technologies exported to the developing countries on the assumption that "what's good for us must be good for them."

The technology of the industrialized countries, of course, reflects the factor endowments of the West: an abundance of capital and a high rate of capital accumulation; a relative scarcity of labor; mass markets; highly sophisticated equipment with matching institutions in the fields of education, finance, training; and populations which have generations of organization, urbanized life, and industrial disciplines behind them. The developing countries present quite a different set of factor endowments: a relative scarcity of capital and an abundance of labor; predominantly rural populations, markets which are small, scattered, seasonal, or fragmented; and a variety of forms of social organizations and tradition, all nonindustrial.

The economies of scale which Western technology is continuously exploiting are not just the product of technical coefficients. If the cooperating economic and social factors are not favorable, the high productivity and profitability of advanced technology cannot be realized. The assumption that capital breeds like mice, as if it had a life of its own, often is made when the merits of advanced technology are being canvassed.

Looked at in another way, mass production at the level of high capital intensity can benefit the masses by providing cheap consumer goods, but only if the masses have the income, the work, which enables them to buy anything at all. It is a universal experience that, even where mass production methods do find a market for instance in the cities, there is no "percolation" effect, only a "dual society" effect. Mass production, based on capital-intensive, labor-saving technologies, stands opposed to production by the masses.

Western technology is expensive, often because of costly labor-saving devices; this inhibits its widespread adoption. For instance, if the cost per new workplace is $6000 or more, relatively few new workplaces can be afforded by most developing countries and, if the import content of the equipment is high, overseas debts mount and balance of payments come under strain. Where advanced technology competes with widespread traditional activities it can, in fact, add to the unemployment problem. All in all, no less an authority than Gunnar Myrdal has concluded that Western technology is a negative form in the developing world.

But is the export of expensive hardware the only way that the West can contribute its scientific and engineering achievements to the developing countries? A different approach is necessary and possible. If it is accepted that the problem of poverty is essentially a problem of rural areas, it is in the rural areas and small towns of developing countries that an appropriate technological base must be established. This means devising and transmitting technologies which are cheap and simple enough to be afforded by large numbers of poor and unskilled people. It also means that we must start by recognizing that technology is a variable, flexible instrument in aid for development, not a given factor to which all others—economic, social, educational, psychological—must adapt themselves.

If we want to give effective aid, we must give knowledge and equipment appropriate to the needs of the recipients. So far we have given it mostly in a form which solves our problems in the West; now we must help the developing countries solve their problems which are quite different from ours. The rich man's problem is how to get the best value for money with the aid of management techniques, accountancy, and the like. The poor man's problem is how to get something without money out of resources that are lying idle. The unemployed man's problem is how to turn his unused labor power into something useful, into the creation of capital or consumption goods.

To illustrate the kind of technology with which we must become more concerned, envisage a poor region, semi-arid, with intermittent rainfall. The people raise cattle. Their first problem is efficient water storage, but this must be done in such a way that it involves little, if any, outside expenditure. They need a system of controlled grazing and stall feeding. This calls for an adequate means of fencing. Next, there cannot be any development without building. They need low-cost building methods, low-cost again being defined as "low outside expenditure." They need efficient storage methods for their products and efficient, low-cost transport; small-scale plants for processing crops or products and for utilizing byproducts; some provision for health within their reach; and the possibility of turning their permanent or intermittent unemployment into productive activities. This list of needs clearly could be multiplied. The point is that each of these needs presents concrete practical scientific problems to which aid effort should be applied. If one took a market town, the focal point of a number of such regions, a new set of needs would present itself but the answer would remain: to apply the resources of the West in science and technology to solving the problems of the poor and the un- and under-employed by furnishing them with technologies for selfhelp.

Many of the traditional ways of doing things in developing countries have reached the limits of their productivity. The essence of the task is to provide the rural areas with technologies which are more productive, more useful for controlling the environment, but not too expensive and sophisticated to be out of reach of the great majority of the population. One of the essential characteristics of such technologies would be that they are widely reproducible from indigenous resources, both of existing skills and of indigenous raw materials.

It is often said that the developing countries themselves insist upon the capital-intensive, prestige technology. If they do, whose fault is that? What choice are they now offered by the West? It is easiest and most convenient to channel aid on a government-to-government basis and to offer the developing countries what it suits the West to produce and sell. To some extent this may be a necessary condition of creating a technological base if a proper distinction is made between those capital-intensive technologies which are really useful for developing countries and those which are not; but it is not by itself a sufficient condition. There is a large gap in the present aid effort, which must be filled. To fill this gap we must assemble new kinds of technological information and present it in ways that reach far "beyond the metropolis" in developing countries.

To a group of us in the United Kingdom this need called for a new method of approach. To pursue the conventional aid effort, conventional administrative channels and routines have been established, but the work required to assemble appropriate information on low-cost technologies and disseminate it to "action points" in developing countries appears to us to call for a new combination of expertise. Since its formation two years ago, our Intermediate Technology Development Group has been attempting to build up, in various ways, a clearinghouse for information on low-cost tools, equipment, and methods by involving the administrators concerned with aid, the industrial and business community, and the communicators—universities, professional associations, the intellectual fraternity.

Early this year the ITDG published a 200-page illustrated directory, "Tools for Progress," the first directory ever published in the West devoted solely to low-cost tools and equipment. The first edition was restricted to items manufactured in the United Kingdom; discussions now are proceeding about the possibility of a European edition. Recently a series of specialist panels was set up on subjects of general interest to developing countries—low-cost building, water and power, rural health, food technology, cooperatives, and agriculture. The aim of each panel is to assemble data on efficient, low-cost ways of meeting these needs and to discover effective ways of communicating this information to developing countries. Some of the panels already are associating themselves with projects overseas. The ITDG is also encouraging the formation of groups similar to itself in developing countries; already groups are active in India, Ghana, Kenya, and the Carribean, and one is likely to be formed soon in Pakistan. These groups we hope may develop into documentation centers on low-cost technologies in the respective countries. We are currently working on setting up an information clearing system in the United Kingdom and on building up a consultancy service on low-cost technologies. The ITDG, which has the legal status of a charitable trust and nonprofit limited company, depends upon private sources of finance: membership subscriptions and donations. It is through this type of flexible organization, which is free to involve itself with public and private research and educational bodies, individuals, voluntary aid organizations, governments, and international agencies, that we are starting to marshal information on the range of low-cost technologies available and to discover effective ways of communicating such information to people in developing countries.

REPORT OF WORKSHOP 7

Stephen Blank, Rapporteur

IN DISCUSSING our subject we had to take into account certain limitations imposed by the situation we were examining. First of all, we constantly had to face the problem of the great variety in the conditions of developing countries, which made any generalization difficult. We also had to take into cognizance the variety of resources and endowments of the developing countries. Too great an emphasis on agriculture, for instance, would not be meaningful to countries in certain zones of the world which, in fact, have many other types of resources which could justify development.

We constantly recognized in whatever we discussed that we really could not find any new strategy for development as such, and that we had to work within the specific ambitions, resources, and policy situations in individual countries. We also had to recognize that technical assistance and aid activities were not too generous and that national government projects or projects financed by private investors were a satisfactory basis for the transfer of technology and increase in the technological base.

Finally, we had to bear in mind that some of our limitations in discussing the subject, especially when we talked about appropriate technology, were sometimes dictated by the limitations of the market and the inadequacy of the present organization of international trade. Perhaps a strategy for enhancing the transfer of technology would call for greater emphasis on reorganizing the patterns of international trade so as to increase the scope in the developing countries singly or regionally as the basis for these transfers.

TECHNICAL ASSISTANCE

We evaluated the existing programs of technical assistance, and concluded that, in terms of returns for money spent, much of it has been quite useful. It has helped in developing planning techniques, in transferring knowledge, and in building teaching institutions.

Our feeling was that technical assistance, although useful in a wider variety of tasks, was inadequate and restricted by too limited an operating definition. Technical assistance in the past has not taken the form of programs such as agricultural and industrial projects or educational extension programs which have a major direct impact on the lives of people or on the most important and difficult problems of development.

Technical assistance, of course, may take cognizance of the need to gear assistance to specific projects in the aided countries whenever possible, and to create a closer relationship between training and the provision of specific jobs. Again, we hoped that assistance can often be directed into these industrial activities that can gainfully employ a maximum of workers at compatible technological levels with the abilities of the potential labor force.

What is of primary importance is that the aims of technical assistance be much wider, concerned centrally with the creation of indigneous technology which rests upon a maximum of local resources. Technical assistance must not be limited to merely reproducing technology which is related to other problems and other solutions than those of the developing world, but must be concerned with creating a vital new technology wherever necessary.

BILATERAL AND MULTILATERAL AID

We did not pay much attention to the question as to which was better, bilateral or multilateral aid, in the context of the transfer of technology, because we had a wide agreement, if not expressly stated, that it did not make much difference and was not a burning issue since many of the aid-giving countries still prefer to operate in the bilateral context. Even where we had so-called multilateral aid, it very soon degenerated into a tender procedure in which, in fact, if one country on a panel of nine won a contract, if often assumed control within this so-called multilateral framework.

TRANSFER OF TECHNOLOGY

The next set of questions we examined pertained to the transfer of technology. We discussed the forms of technology—industrial, agricultural, and "intermediate"—and the need to create a wider choice for the developing countries of the type of technology which is available to them. We were agreed that technology should be "appropriate" both in the specific project itself and to the environment in which it is to be utilized. We were also aware, however, that the criteria of "appropriateness" lies not only in the project and in the environment, but also is a factor of the over-all strategy of development determined by the developing nation. We did not feel that there was one single appropriate technology relevant to all cases, just as there is no single growth strategy for all cases.

We received many comments on technology in the agricultural sector and agreed that there was an obvious gap in this area. There were certain simple techniques that we could introduce to help increase productivity in the agricultural sector and we agreed that attention should be paid to this.

But we did not accept the idea that this could constitute a new or an alternative strategy for development which would be of universal impact. In fact, we had to recognize that even where a country had potentiality for greater agricultural development, over-all development might not necessarily be increased by increasing agricultural productivity. The danger of creating unusable agricultural surplus had to be recognized. In the absence of suitable international trade arrangements, the expansion of the production, even of agricultural projects for which there was a global scarcity, was not necessarily helpful. Nevertheless, we did feel that there was much to be said for introducing more relevant, more appropriate technology into the rural sectors of the developing countries.

We spent much time, too, discussing appropriate technology in the context of aid to transfer technology. But again we had to register the fact that room for maneuvering was limited. We recognized that we were talking about creating a technology which would require enormous research and development resources from the developed countries and the creation of new media through which this type of information and knowledge could be spread. Given the insufficient motivation in terms of incentives, in terms of how many units might be sold if resources were diverted to this, this might be very difficult. There were many appropriate and helpful suggestions that could be profitably manufactured in the developing countries themselves, utilizing local raw materials.

We had to recognize that, for certain industries in the developing countries, the appropriate technology was the latest technology. In the oil countries, for example, where petrochemical industries are a possibility, the most advanced technology is the most appropriate. A nation cannot buy any but the latest because of the rapid rate of obsolescence. Here again we were forced to come back to the importance of the reorganization of international trade to expand the base for technological transfer in the developing world.

We went on to examine how, given the limitations of the moment and the fact that any form of radically new development technology would be created in the very near future, we might accelerate the process of technological transfer. Management, we felt, could prove to be a new element, and we devoted considerable attention to ways in which, both in joint ventures and in private industries, we might force the pace of management development. There was some disagreement as to whether, in fact, this is not what the international corporations always like to do. But we concluded from looking at the results that this is a gap which technical assistance or bilateral or multilateral aid could help to fill.

The need to insure that training was an integral part of all forms of aid, and particularly that funds for the development of skills be included with all grants for projects, was strongly felt. We favored an international approach to the development of skills, which would create a framework for training and the development of training programs on an international level. The use of development funds to create institutions would make technology selfperpetuating and involve universities in the developing nations much more intimately in this whole process, particularly by improving their consultive abilities.

Throughout our discussions we always had to confine ourselves to the limitations imposed by the facts of the moment and the facts of the foreseeable future. We came out with no magnificent innovations, but we thought that a greater qualitative emphasis on developing the habits of technology in institutions for training people and on enlarging the role of aid-giving agencies in the development of management skills could contribute to a more satisfactory pace of transfer. Finally, we did recognize that there was a gap in the old field of agricultural development which, while there was no alternative to what exists now, could at least be intensified.

REFERENCE CITED

Society for International Development. *Survey of International Development,* Vol. 5, No. 7, July 15, 1968.

10

THE INFLUENCE OF INDIGENOUS RESEARCH AND DEVELOPMENT EFFORTS ON THE INDUSTRIALIZATION OF DEVELOPING COUNTRIES

Principal Paper—Jorge A. Sabato

Discussion of the Papers by P. C. Asiodu and by Jorge A. Sabato

Commentary—C. H. G. Oldham

Report of Workshop 8—Maurice A. Shapiro, Rapporteur

The emerging nations have, in most cases, devoted themselves to their development problems to the limit of their capacities. These efforts have enjoyed varied degrees of success. Chapter 10 presents an analysis of indigenous research and development efforts aimed toward industrialization within the developing countries.

The Editors

THE INFLUENCE OF INDIGENOUS RESEARCH AND DEVELOPMENT EFFORTS ON THE INDUSTRIALIZATION OF DEVELOPING COUNTRIES

Principal Paper by Jorge A. Sabato

THIS PAPER is a study of indigenous research and development in relation to engineering application; however, the author considers that the most important reason for a developing country to carry out research and development is cultural or, as C. H. G. Oldham (1966) has put it:

An ability to contribute to the world store house of knowledge is a sign of self respect and a goal of many nations. This is partially a question of prestige and the search for national identity but it goes much deeper than just this. It is also recognition of a basic human right that a person with a first class mind should have the opportunity to contribute to the advancement of knowledge.

Modern economic theory has definitely recognized that in the production function, technological innovation is a factor as important as the "classical" factors: capital, labor, raw materials (Block-Laine and Perroux, 1966). Technological innovations are produced by the incorporation of knowledge with production, with the objective of modifying an existing process of production or creating a new one. Innovation may be produced to satisfy existing demands or to generate new ones. Knowledge incorporated by innovation can be the direct or indirect results of research but it can also be the result of chance observation, unexpected discovery, intuition, or a fortuitious connection of facts (Sabato and Botana, 1968). Some of the motivating forces for innovation are the requirements of the market, import substitution, scarcity of raw materials, availability and quality of labor, expected profits, availability of capital, and last but not least, war (either cold or hot). Obstacles to innovation are socio-cultural (a backward set of values of society, lack of managerial skill and entrepreneurial drive, fear of trade union action); economic (monopolistic or highly protected markets, rigid marketing mechanisms, artificial cost and price structures); financial (scarcity of capital, resilience to new financing schemes, reluctance to invest in new processes); political (tax system, patent legislation, industrial promotion legislation); and scientific (basically related to a weak or nonexistent scientific-technological infrastructure).

Since World War II, innovation has become more and more a concerted effort, an explicit target, a coordinated action of three fundamental elements of society: government, the scientific-technological infrastructure, and the productive structure of the economy. Among these three elements we can conceive a system of relationships represented by a triangle in which each vertex corresponds to one of the elements and each side to the corresponding interactions (Woytinsky, 1967; Galbraith, 1967).

The government vertex consists of all the institutional roles responsible for the formulation of policies and the corresponding mobilization of resources with respect to both the productive structure and the scientific-technological infrastructure. The productive-structure vertex is the set of all the productive sectors that provide goods and services demanded by a particular society.

The scientific-technological infrastructure includes:

1. the educational system that produces, with the necessary quality and quantity, the individuals who direct and/or perform research: scientists, technologists, assistants, technicians, administrators, librarians;

2. the laboratories, institutes, centers, and pilot plans—composed of men, buildings, and equipment—where research is carried on;

3. the institutional system of planning, promotion, coordination, and stimulation of research (national research council, national academy of science, science foundations);

4. the legal-administrative mechanisms that regulate the operation of the institutions and activities described in 1, 2, and 3; and

5. the economic and financial resources utilized in the above.

Each vertex represents a point of convergence of multiple institutions, decision-making agencies, production units, and various other activities. In the triangle relations are established within each vertex, which shall be called intra-relations, and relations between vertices, called inter-relations. There are also relationships established between a functioning triangle or between each of the vertices with the external environment (ie external to the triangle) called extra-relations.

If a society accepts that innovation is a main component of development and that it must be considered as a conscious socio-political process, it follows that the most efficient way to generate and propagate innovation is to establish "triangles" corresponding to different sectors of the economy, the different branches of one sector, to two or more sectors having a common target, and so on. Also, it may happen that all triangles—or the majority of them —"integrate" into a "big triangle" corresponding to the society as a whole when a common objective has been defined, such as in war. From this point of view the degree of development of society, or of a part of it, could be expressed in terms of the "perfection" of its corresponding triangle and comparisons made between different countries and between different sectors of the same country.

In this context, a "well-developed country" is one where the existence of many well-established triangles can be recognized, including one corresponding to all the country. However, inside this country "less developed" sectors can exist side by side with "very well developed" ones. In the United States, the steel industry, with a very "poor" triangle, exists with the electronic industry, with a "good" one. Analyzing vertices and sides, a "ranking" can be established among "well-developed" countries, differences analyzed, and "technological gaps" measured. For instance, the United Kingdom's triangle has one stronger vertex—the scientific-technological—than the Japanese "triangle," but its sides are less "perfect."

In developing countries different situations can be present:

1. *Vertices acceptable, but sides very poor.* This is exemplified by Argentine industry where the productive structure-vertex is reasonably good, the scientific-technological vertex is acceptable, but the government-vertex is weak (there is no scientific, technological, and industrial policy), and the intra- and inter-relationships are practically nonexistent. Consequently, innovation in this sector is far below socio-economic possibilities and comes mainly through extra-relations of the productive structure vertex with foreign industry. The situation is different for Argentine agriculture, where inter- and intra-relationships are sufficiently well developed to counteract the weakness of the government vertex.

2. *Vertices and sides very poor or nonexistent.* This is the case in underdeveloped countries such as Paraguay, Bolivia, Peru, and Ecuador.

3. *Vertices taking shape but sides as yet nonexistent.* Such is the case in Venezuela, Chile, and Colombia.

4. *Vertices and sides in steady development.* This is at present true of Brazil, where budgets for research and development have increased greatly, scientific policy is being established, and intra- and inter-relationships are being improved.

THE ROLE OF INDIGENOUS RESEARCH
AND DEVELOPMENT

In the context of the frame of reference just described, indigenous research and development is of paramount importance, not in an isolated condition, but as the main component of the scientific-technological infrastructure that makes possible the existence of a vertex essential to establish "triangles." In the proper "triangles," research and development and its intra-relationships with the other components of its vertex produces various effects. Mainly through inter-relationships with the other two vertices, it produces the capability to make decisions about problems such as exploitation of natural resources: introduction of new technologies (nuclear energy, petrochemistry, microelectronics); investment priorities—foreign and/or native—among several sectors of the economy; technologies to be imported and how; and technologies to be developed locally and how and where.

Mainly through extra-relations with foreign scientific-technological infrastructures research and development provides the capability to forecast technological changes, thus making it possible to design better development strategies, taking into account the forcasted changes. At different stages of the industrialization process, research and development improves the capability to adapt, of particular importance at the stage of "substitution of imported goods"; permits capability for sustained creation, of particular importance at the stage when "substitution of imported goods" is over; strengthens the capability to find specific answers to its own specific problems; improves the capability to get and to absorb external aid; improves the technological balance of payment; generates confidence in its own forces and a climate favorable to absorb and produce change; increases the probabilities—mainly through a "demonstration effect"—that executives, administrators, and managers will employ analytical techniques and objective criteria for decisions; improves the quantity and quality of human resources; and is a powerful deterrent to the "brain drain," not only because it provides more opportunities to work, but also because—through the "triangle"—it gives scientists a sense of belonging to a socio-economic structure.

RESEARCH AND DEVELOPMENT INTERACTIONS

In our context, a research and development system interacting with other elements of society is what really matters. A strong but isolated research and development system would certainly produce good science but its impact on the process of industrialization would be rather weak. Moreover, isolation produces alienation and, as a consequence, emigration. This is one of the factors behind Argentina's "brain drain," one of the highest of the world; its research and development does not belong to any triangle.

Among some of the main effects produced by an interrelated research and development system are:

—*Capability to Make Decisions.* In matters related to industrialization, a developing country must make scores of decisions involving scientific and technological variables; some of these decisions may even commit the future of the country for many years ahead. It is therefore important for a country in such position to be able to analyze, judge, and decide according to the present and future best interests of the country. There is, of course, plenty of foreign advice available (consultants, international and regional agencies) to be hired, to be bought, and even free. But in any case, the final decision is in the hands of the "natives." At that moment of truth they must take into account parameters that are better evaluated by "indigenous" advice. This is what the "developed countries" always do and, thus, what the "developing countries" like to do, if only for reasons of self-respect.

The scientific-technological infrastructure—to which the research and development system belongs—would fully participate in decision making only if it has a fluent inter-relation with the decision-vertex. Problems such as the installation of the first nuclear power station, the establishment of a fully integrated steel industry, the uses of new sources of energy (solar, tides, wind), the most efficient development of mineral ores, require the existence of as perfect a "triangle" as possible. Only if the research and development system is mobilized and employed at its full capacity, will the decision be truly controlled by the country.

—*Capability to Forecast.* Technology changes at an increasing rate and the danger of obsolescence is a serious one in every sector of the economy. Mistakes in forecasting can be very expensive and much more so for the developing countries which, by definition, are not in a condition to afford them. But where is "the crystal ball"? Research and development is the main sources of technological change—"the crystal ball"; to "read it" requires a key that only research and development can provide. Through its extra-relations and its own developments, a very active and academically very solid research and development system is the best answer to technological forecast, provided, again, that a flow of "answers" and "questions" go and come between research and development and the other two vertices. In many developing countries it is quite common for a government agency or a private company to decide to introduce a technology, while a scientist "round the corner" has all the elements to know that it is already superseded by recent discoveries.

—*Capability to Adapt.* Imported technologies must be frequently adapted to local circumstances (raw materials, labor, management, "scale" of the economy). Indigenous research and development provide ways and means for more efficient adaptation simply because, through its actions, those "local conditions" have been known and can be mastered. A note of caution here: research and development must be used at this stage in the process of industrialization, but it must not be designed *only* for adaptation.

—*Capability to Create.* Once the "substitution of imported goods" is over, the process of industrialization is more and more obliged to be creative: new processes and products must be developed, and innovations must be produced, not only to satisfy existing demands, but also to generate new ones. This is when it is necessary to have a creative research and development system; an adaptative one would fail. Developed countries show that research and development is the most powerful tool for this operation.

What is the most convenient kind of research for developing countries? "Any type, provided it is creative," as the author stated in a recent paper (Sabato, 1968):

It is becoming more and more fashionable—particularly among economists—to try to decide the most convenient kind of research for B-type countries [developing countries] and much time and effort are spent assessing the relative advantages of pure research versus applied research, basic applied versus applied basic, basic inspired versus applied inspired, and other equivalent and convenient combination of similar words. For some of these happy fellows the problem is just to hang a label to any of the research activities, to transform it into an economic entity, to insert it into a neat input-output scheme, to do some odd calculations and then to assign it a priority. This is a nice exercise, but unfortunately not a very useful one yet; there are not only the epistemological difficulties of a meaningful distinction between one kind of research and another or the problem of the many surprises in history where scores of abstract pure research have produced tremendous technical and economical transformations, but also something else, more concrete in nature, more immediate in effects. B countries, where the scientific and technical infra-structure is weak, just do not have the minimum potential for research—what we can call a threshold research potential—that would permit [them] to channel, to focus, to direct research to a priority target. In B countries, quantity of research is too little and its quality too heterogeneous; moreover, the lack of a high standard scientific tradition makes [it] difficult—and many times impossible—to recognize if a piece of research is original and rigorous enough as to permit its qualification as excellent. In any of the B countries, then, it is less important to discuss if either pure or applied research—or any other similar combinations—is the most convenient one, than getting society to incorporate to its set of values two very basic but fundamental concepts: that the only way to build up a research infrastructure is doing research and that there are only two kinds of research worthy of discussion—good ones and bad ones. A primary conclusion would then be immediate: for the country, the most convenient and urgent thing to do in science and technology would be to produce as much good research as possible, with independence of the specific field from which it originates (were that field topology or topography, for example), or of the question it likes to answer—the path of a particle in the Minkowsky universe or the viscosity characteristics of an oil film—or of the problems it tries to solve—the nature of space time or the creep of high alloyed steels. Priorities could then be assigned with some sense at all when the threshold research potential has been reached and overcome. Otherwise it would simply be to put the cart before the horse.

TECHNOLOGICAL BALANCE OF PAYMENTS

For developing countries, the technological balance of payments is negative and its importance as an "invisible import" is growing. Research and development is the only hope for a more equilibrated balance, particularly if it is creative enough to establish a permanent flow of "invisible exports" in the form of licences, patents, engineering, and processes.

Again, only an inter-related Research and Development system, particularly with the productive structure, would be able to transform its academic results into "marketable goods."

DISCUSSION OF THE PAPERS BY
P. C. ASIODU AND JORGE A. SABATO

SHORT-TERM TECHNICAL ASSISTANCE VERSUS THE TURNKEY ARRANGEMENT

WHEN ASKED to comment about the problems of the hit-or-miss approach that most bilateral or multilateral agencies seem to use (for example, having technicians stay a year and then leave) versus turnkey arrangement in which responsibility is taken for the total project, including training personnel properly, as a method of maintaining the kind of continuum needed in a technical assistance activity, Mr. Asiodu replied that it depends upon the nature of the turnkey contract. Many of the traditional technical assistance projects, if well managed, can produce results. For instance, Nigeria's Federal Ministry of Industries has a team of industrial experts, economists, engineers, and others provided by contract from the United States who are helping to plan and to develop projects with Nigerian counterparts. A lot depends on the competence of the country obtaining aid.

Mr. Teare added that, in making a choice between sending technicians or using the turnkey operation, there is another important factor—the necessity of permitting the engineers or the people who are to become engineers in the developing countries help with the design. The training that goes with the turnkey operation is for production, for maintenance, but, most importantly, for helping the country train people at the engineering or innovative level.

Mr. Lador of Israel commented that he felt a country must decide whether it wants the finished goods or the training of personnel and that he thinks a synthesis exists between the two. Through Israel's limited involvement in developing countries for the last ten years it has created a system of joint economic ventures. There have been rather positive results by creating an impetus within the developing countries; by assisting them to invest large amounts of money in construction, building, agriculture, water, or hydrology; and by investing a certain amount in the creating of a company. Furthermore, the investing partner from outside trains personnel so that, at the end of the contract, local personnel are really able to take over operation of the joint venture. This is one way of creating a stimulus within the developing world and using knowledge available from outside to do so.

RETURN DESIRED FROM TECHNICAL ASSISTANCE

Mr. Vernon described a project where the contractor was to produce a completed project and also give great emphasis to personnel training. Some 500 indigenous personnel were trained. The result was a pile of books, but no project. Does the recipient nation want the project results or to develop technical personnel for the country and, perhaps, stop there?

Mr. Asiodu replied that these factors are all, of course, inter-related. He suggested that, if the training was of the right kind, namely, training to assume responsibility, then the 500 people could be very productive for their country. Many developing countries lack people who really are trained outside the narrow confines of specialization and who are willing to take the kind of plunge which people from the United States took a hundred years ago. Such people create the jobs and then start training other people.

PURPOSES OF TRAINING ACCORDING TO THE DEVELOPING COUNTRIES

When asked what instructions they gave young men who come to the developed countries for engineering or social science education, representatives from Africa, South America, and the Middle East replied.

Nigerians feel it is necessary to be more specific about the purpose of training. Students come to the United States because of the scholarships it provides. They are too young to decide what kind of curriculum they must pursue. They get what is available and half the time they return and want to imitate what they are used to. Because of the questioning now going on, because of the frustrations arising from 20 years of running and getting nowhere, Nigeria is beginning to articulate some of these questions and, hopefully, to give its students a clearer message. On the other hand, to become more scientific, Nigeria is restructuring its scholarship policies and the kind of people it sends for postgraduate training in order to give better direction to the people who are trained abroad.

Along the same lines, Argentina has been trying to give a clearer message to its people who come to the United States or to other countries. Argentina is in crisis, has been in crisis for 20 years, will be for another 25 years. It will not have political stability and many other things before it "takes off." The duty of our students going abroad is to return and contribute. Therefore they are required to spend two years in Argentina before going anywhere.

If a student comes to the United States, he must learn well the specific subject for which he has been sent here. He must try to be first. This is an obligation. Secondly, he must try to understand the United States, which is developed. He must try to understand the history, sociology, and economic and current life in the United States, and, above all, why it is "developed."

A representative from the Middle East said that, from the Arab world alone, at least 15 000 students are in the United States. They are told to try not be seekers of new degrees, but messengers between two civilizations.

THE WILL TO DEVELOP AND THE WILL TO HELP

One discussant agreed with Mr. Asiodu that the will to develop is very important. Unless the country has the will to develop, any help will be wasted. But there is a counterpart to that: the will to help. It is legitimate to expect this counterpart here in the developed world. The world is confronted today with a historic contradiction—the stronger the will to develop, the weaker the will to help. How we shall overcome this historic contradiction is the challenge to this Conference.

One of the major causes for this lessening of the will to help is "frustrated aid." Aid has thus far had bad propaganda in the developing world. Having had the chance to study the aid which the Arab world received from the Western world, the discussant felt that perhaps one of the poorest Arab countries is Jordan. Just prior to the six-day war, thanks to Western assistance and to the United Nations assistance, Jordan had a rate of development of 11 per cent. This was one of the highest throughout the developing world. The discussant has come to the conclusion that the best and most successful form of aid has been technical aid, technical assistance, and, particularly, multilateral technical assistance, perhaps because engineers are involved with this form of assistance more than any other form. There should be more technical assistance and, if possible, more technical assistance through international channels.

Mr. Saab of Lebanon stated that there is no doubt that, at present, there is a slowdown of assistance from developed to developing nations. This Conference should emphasize the need for greater effort and greater assistance from the developed countries to the developing countries—greater emphasis on the pioneering role of government in the promotion of science technology, scientific research, planning, and programming in all those areas with which the West, particularly the United States, is so familiar. The West is familiar with large companies and great entrepreneurs working as innovators in this field, but in the developing part of the world, unless the government itself assumes the cost of innovating, the private sector does not do it. Therefore, emphasis on the pioneering role of the government in this area may be very meaningful. As a case in point, it took many years to convince the government of Lebanon, with 80-percent literacy and six universities, to create a council for scientific research.

On the one hand, the West welcomes the improvement of the developing countries in the name of free enterprise, but on the other hand the developing countries feel that the West's capital and entrepreneurs are not ready to take the risks which are involved in such development. In the development of the United States, capital and entrepreneurship took many risks, as is quite evident from a study of the economic history of the United States in the nineteenth century. No matter what legislation it may provide, no matter what guarantees it may give to capital, a developing country has and will have, at least until the end of the century, a situation of political instability. This is a fact of life and unless Western private capital will accept this fact of life and accept the risks, the West may be directing developing nations towards government-to-government relationships rather than towards broadening or preserving the private sector. The acceptance of risk from private capital is very important to private entrepreneurs and an essential element in the preservation of democracy in the developing world.

186

THE INFLUENCE OF INDIGENOUS RESEARCH IN THE INDUSTRIALIZATION OF DEVELOPING COUNTRIES

Commentary by C. H. G. Oldham

EVERY COUNTRY has two alternative sources for the new technologies it requires for modernization: its own research and development or technologies imported from abroad. In practice no country can afford to be entirely selfsufficient in the production of new technologies, but neither can any country always continue to depend entirely on the imported technology.

The need for an indigenous research effort is most evident in such areas as agriculture and health but, as a country develops, it must also be engaged in industrial research. This is necessary to adopt foreign technologies to local conditions and to help design new technologies more appropriate for local needs. Also, as a developing country seeks to gain access to world markets with its manufactured goods, it will frequently need its own source of new ideas and techniques. Japan provides an interesting example of a country which, by a judicious combination of imported technology and domestic research, has successfully developed an advanced industry which is increasingly competitive with other nations in the world market.

One of the more important ways of transferring technologies between enterprises is by means of licensing and technology agreements. Japan has published detailed statistics on the nature of such agreements between Japanese and foreign firms. These statistics do not reveal the full picture of technology transfer—there are hidden transactions between subsidiary and parent companies which are not revealed—but they do indicate the minimum amount of technology transfer. The Japanese payments for foreign technology are summarized in Table 1, which also compares these payments with the amount spent in Japan on industrial research and development during the same period. One of the most interesting facts to be learned from this Table is that, ever since the statistics were first published in 1953, Japan has consistently spent between four and five times as much money on industrial research and development as she has on importing foreign technology. Furthermore, those industrial sectors which spent the most on technology transfer also spent the most on research and development, as shown in Table 2.

The comparison with India is instructive. No statistics on the value of the contracts for foreign technology are available for India, but the numbers of such agreements are published (Kapoor, 1966). Between 1957 and 1964 roughly the same number of agreements were negotiated between Japanese and foreign enterprises as were negotiated between Indian and foreign enterprises. The principal difference was that very few Indian enterprises carried out their own research and development. In fact, Kapoor showed that less than 10 per cent of the Indian firms which he interviewed, who had bought foreign technology, carried out any research or development activity.

A further difference between Indian and Japanese industry is that over 90 per cent of industrial research is carried out by government in India, and only 30 per cent by the government of Japan (Parthaswathi, 1968). Also, in complete

TABLE 1.—Japanese expenditure on transfer of technology
compared with expenditure on industrial R & D.

Year	Expenditure on industrial R & D (1) (Billion/Year)	Payments for transfer of technology by contracts (2) (Billion/Year)	(2) as % of (1)
1953	25.0	5.0	20
1954	29.2	5.6	18
1955	29.3	7.2	24
1956	43.2	12.0	27
1957	62.4	15.3	25
1958	69.7	17.2	24
1959	96.6	22.3	23
1960	124.4	34.2	27
1961	163.8	41.7	25
1962	179.4	41.4	24
1963	204.3	52.5	25

Source: Science and Technology Agency, Tokyo. Cited by C. H. G. Oldham, C. Freeman, E. Turkcan, UNCTAD paper TD/28/Supplement 1, *Transfer of Technology to Developing Countries*. November 10, 1967.

TABLE 2.—Expenditure on R&D in
Japanese industry compared with contracts
for imported technology

Industrial Section	Percentage of total expenditure on industrial R&D 1959–63	Percentage of total approved contracts 1950–52 for imported technology
Electrical Machinery	23.6	12.7
Chemicals	23.5	21.6
Transport Machinery	10.5	9.5
Iron & Steel	6.3	10.5
Other Machinery	5.5	8.6
Textiles	3.5	3.3
Non-Ferrous Metals	2.7	4.4
Ceramics, Glass, Cement	2.3	4.4
Rubber Products	1.8	2.0
Precision Machinery	1.6	1.3
Petroleum & Coal	1.3	2.1

Source: Science and Technology Agency, Tokyo. Cited by C. H. G. Oldham, C. Freeman, E. Turkcan, UNCTAD TD/28/Supplement 1, 1967.

TABLE 3.—Indian investments in industrial R&D
and in foreign technology.

Industrial Section	Sectoral R&D outlay of central government as percentage of total outlay 1960–61	Sectoral imports of technology, number of collaborations as percentage of total 1957–1965
Chemicals	23.1	10.0
Steel & Metal Products	14.1	2.3
Textiles (all kinds)	6.6	1.7
Machinery (Other Than Electrical & Transport)	5.8	28.7
Transport Machinery	5.2	3.6
Electrical Machinery	4.1	11.2

Source: A. Parthaswathi, Appearance and reality in two decades of science policy.

contrast to the Japanese case, there is no correlation between sectoral investments in industrial research and development and sectoral purchases of foreign technology, as demonstrated in Table 3. Lack of industrial research and development is not the only reason that India has not been as successful as Japan in industrialization, but evidence suggests that it may be one of the more important reasons.

Although the observations on the correlation between research and development investments and success in industrialization are instructive, there are other compelling reasons why developing countries will need to increase their industrial research. Firms in the industrialized countries are increasingly reluctant to provide their technologies to enterprises in developing countries on a royalty basis (National Bureau of Standards, 1967). Such firms are more willing to part with their technology if the other enterprise has a different technology to offer in return. Enterprises in developing countries are thus at a double disadvantage: not only are they short of foreign exchange to buy licenses, but they rarely have their own technology to offer in exchange. The implications for developing an indigenous scientific and technological capability are clear. The alternative is direct foreign participation in a domestic company, and this is sometimes not acceptable to the developing country on political and economic grounds.

Thus, if the developing countries are to industrialize and compete with the more advanced countries in world markets with the products of their industrialization, the conclusion that they must expand their industrial research and development activities seems to be inescapable.

REPORT OF WORKSHOP 8

Maurice A. Shapiro, Rapporteur

ENHANCEMENT and improvement of the industrialization process of developing countries requires—in addition to the "classical" triad of capital, labor, and raw materials—technological innovation produced at the local level and not merely obtained by importation. These innovations are the product or end result of utilization of new knowledge from an existing production process or from wholly new ones. In recent times, innovation has increasingly become the object of concerted and deliberate effort, a coordinated action of three basic elements which make up the "triangle" of society: government, the scientific technological infrastructure, and the production structure of society.

Within developing countries, it was agreed that indigenous research and development plays a crucial role in their future industrialization. Such research and development can be expected to help provide:

1. Improved decision-making capabilities in exploitation and use of natural resources; introduction of new technologies (nuclear energy, petrochemistry, microelectronics); investment priorities —foreign and/or indigenous—among the several sectors of the economy; technologies to be imported; and technologies to be developed locally.

2. Improved capabilities for forecasting technological changes, thus allowing improved development strategies.

3. Improved evaluation capabilities.

4. Improved capability to differentiate roles at varying stages of the industrialization process. This is composed of capability to adapt, of particular importance in the stage of "substitution of imported goods;" capability of "sustained creation," also important during the stage of "substitution of imported goods" with emphasis on the subsequent stage of industrialization; specific problem-solution capabilities; the capability to obtain and properly absorb external aid; improved technological balance of payments; improved level of confidence in indigenous forces of development, and favorable climate for absorption and production of change; and employment of analytical techniques and objectives criteria in the decision-making process.

5. A continuous improvement in the quantity and quality of human resources.

6. Development of conditions within the socio-economic structure of the developing country which provides scientists and technologists with a sense of opportunity and belonging, thus acting as a deterrent to the "brain drain."

The workshop then agreed that the following areas of suggested research are of importance to the elucidation of the proper role of indigenous research and development in both time and place.

1. Research and development to be undertaken by foreign companies operating in developing countries. There is a difference of opinion as to the amount; however, the workshop consensus was that it should be more than it is. Research is needed to provide an answer to the questions: "How much research and development?" "At what time?"

2. Research as the best means of improving the relationships between the three vertices of the "triangle," so that the concept can be applied on a regional, multicountry basis.

3. Studies in different countries and in different industries to show the relative importance of the factors identified in the "triangle." Such research can be expected to identify the key factors which promote innovation and those which hinder innovation.

REFERENCES CITED

Bloch-Laine, F. and F. Perroux. *L'entreprise et l'économie du XXe siècle*. Presse Universitaire de France, 1966.

Galbraith, J. D. *New Industrial State*, 1967.

Kapoor, A., "Foreign collaboration in India: Problems and prospects," *Idea*, Vol. 10, No. 2, 1966.

190

National Bureau of Standards. *Technology and World Trade, Proceedings of a Symposium,* November 16–17, 1966. Miscellaneous Publication 284, Washington, D.C., 1967.

Oldham, C. H. G., *Science, Technology and Development.* The Institute of Development Studies, University of Sussex, University of Sussex, November 1966.

Parthaswathi, A., *"Appearance and Reality in Two Decades of Science Policy."* Address to the Association of Scientific Workers of India, April, 1968.

Sabato, J. A., *Some Comments on the Problem of the Best Utilization of Scientific and Technical Resources.* Panel on Science and Technology, Committee on Science and Astronautics, U.S. House of Representatives, January, 1968.

Sabato, J. A. and N. Botana. *Science and Technology in the Future Development of Latin America.* Paper presented to the World Order Models Conference, Italy, September, 1968.

Woytinsky, E. S. *Profile of the U.S. Economy, 1967.*

11

THE INFLUENCE OF PUBLIC HEALTH

Principal Paper—Alfred K. Neumann

Commentary—John C. Cutler

Report of Workshop 9—A. E. Axelrod, Rapporteur

Health problems have sapped the strength and the energies of many peoples throughout the world and often have presented significant barriers to national and aided development efforts. This chapter addresses itself to the influence of public health factors on the efforts of nations in moving towards industrialization.

The Editors

THE INFLUENCE OF PUBLIC HEALTH

Principal Paper by Alfred K. Neumann

WITH RESPECT to the provocative theme of the Conference, it is desirable to conceptualize goals, criteria, and the role of the health sector.

—The *goal* is viewed simply as the transformation of underdeveloped economies to the developed state.

—The *criterion* is an increase in per capita income to a stated level.

—The *central hypothesis* of this paper is that health programs can materially aid in achieving this goal.

A corollary hypothesis contends that an increase in the capital value of human resources is essential for the economic growth of underdeveloped areas and that the cost of such improvements are, in the intermediate and long run, greatly offset by the benefits accruing. Increased investment in human resources increases the size and productivity of the labor force (Mushkin and Weisbrod, 1964), leading, other things being equal, to an increase in the per capita income. Given these assumptions, it then follows that efforts to enhance and protect the capital value of man are essential. Such efforts include properly planned and executed health programs.

HEALTH PLANNING, A CONCEPTUAL FRAMEWORK

In planning a health program, I would list four essential elements: curative, public health, family planning, and research programs. Curative programs focus mainly on existing disease in individuals. Public health programs focus on the community or nation as a whole. Both should contain illness and disability prevention components. Prevention is, in a sense, a fifth, all-pervasive element. Both would tend to enhance the productivity and size of the work force. An effective planning program is an essential component of a health program if the full benefits accruing from increased productivity are to be realized. Research programs would help determine that resources are spent in an effective and rational manner. Research units also would focus on the potential spillover effects of unlimited and unplanned population growth on the economy.

PURPOSE OF THIS PAPER

The purpose of this paper is to stress the usefullness of the health sector in industrial development and to stimulate workers outside the health field to consider how health programs can be used to best advantage in the industrial development process. The many-faceted nature of health problems will be emphasized and the programs designed to deal with the problems described. It is hoped that the nonmedical reader, especially the engineer, will be stimulated to become concerned with the industrialization of developing areas, to learn more about health problems and their solutions. To do this, attention will be focused upon a number of apparently widely separated areas—including family planning, urbanization, industrial development schemes, occupational medicine, and on thorny questions arising out of consideration of the economic value of health programs. These will be presented as a series of vignettes. Throughout these pages a broad perspective has been deliberately taken.

FAMILY PLANNING

The most urgent consideration in health programming today, I believe, is the family-planning component. It is useful to consider the need for family-planning programs from an economic and historical perspective.

The paramount question, which constantly arises, is to what extent scarce development capital should be invested in the health sector in the early stages of economic development. Also, how should the allocated health funds be spent? The questions have never been satisfactorily answered. Calculations of the economic value of major health programs, such as malaria control, did not take into account significant increases in population, and many planners in the years immediately following the second World War overestimated the rate of economic growth of developing areas. This led to a lower rate of increase in per capita income than anticipated. Consequently, there are today many who believe that the major effect of health programs in the past in underdeveloped areas has been to slow the rate of economic growth by causing an increase in the population. This was accomplished by reducing the death rate and increasing the life span, without effectively reducing the birth rate at the same time.

The few, in the immediate post-World War II era, who thought about problems of family planning, tacitly assumed that as industrialization progressed, educational facilities were developed, and purchasing power increased, the masses would soon feel a need for family planning and would find a way of so doing without help from the public sector. Others, represented by a considerable number of writers about Africa, were and, to a great extent, still are, of the opinion that Africa needs to populate its sparsely settled regions and develop its natural resources (Smith and Blacker, 1963; East Africa Royal Commission 1953–1955 Report, 1955; Economic Commission for Africa, 1962; Hance, 1968). In order to accomplish this, a relatively rapid growth of population was thought desirable.

In order to explain further why family planning programs were not made a part of health programs twenty years ago, let us, for the moment, go back to the immediate post-World War II era. The inhabitants of many countries were suffering from the immediate destructive effects of war and from secondary effects due to shortage of proper nutrients, medications, and the effects of disease afflicting a weakened population. In addition, the mass programs, as we know them today, for malaria control, yaws control, and smallpox eradication were yet to be developed. There was a great and highly commendable desire on the part of the nations, relatively untouched by the ravages of war, to help those who were less fortunate and to bring the latest advances of medical technology to those who had not yet benefitted from them. There was, unfortunately, little concern for potential problems of population increase.

The results of international health programs carried out on an unprecedented scale were not fully appreciated or their implications clearly understood—particularly with regard to lowering mortality rates and to prolonging human life—until the late 1950s or early 1960s. This was partially due to the lack of good vital statistics. In much of the world, government planners simply did not know with any degree of accuracy how many people there were in their countries or what the rate of increase of the population was. A most notable example of this is India, where it was not realized until the end of the second five-year plan that the rate of population increase was about double that which had been projected (Government of India Planning Commission, 1961–1966; Myrdal 1968). Pakistan had also underestimated the rate of population increase. The result was that many nations, though working at a rapid pace to develop, were like the traditional squirrel in the treadmill.

Beginning in the late 1950s and continuing through to the present time in virtually all areas of the world, attention has been dramatically focused on the "population explosion." It was also realized that populations were not initiating family planning pari passu with the development of steel mills, oil refineries, chemical plants, and the building of additional schools. Thus, rather belatedly, a great deal of attention, time, effort, and money is being brought to bear on the problems attendant to population growth beyond the capacity of the economy to absorb the increments of population and to increase the standard of living at the same time.

Health programs need not be regarded as luxuries resulting in population increases which counteract the effect of economic development. The economics and technology of family planning are such that an area can develop economically and enjoy basic health services, *provided* it concomitantly develops an effective family planning program. Fortunately, today, more than ever before, national planners are assigning a high priority to family planning programs in terms of time and money, as well as verbal support.

INDUSTRIALIZATION AND URBANIZATION

Another area of vital concern to engineers and health workers alike relates to the role of health and social welfare programs in urbanization. Urbanization is defined as "the process whereby an increasing proportion of the country's population lives in urban areas." Every country of the world is experiencing rapid urban growth. Industry, one of the factors bringing urbanization about, can help mitigate its worst aspects. The degree of recognition of the resultant problems and actions which are taken to deal with them, however, vary considerably. Many problems, because of years, frequently decades, of underattention, have assumed such huge proportions that only a massive effort will succeed in remedying them. An example of such a situation is the greater Calcutta area, whose population within another generation will reach 25 to 50 million people (Senn and Ferguson, 1967).

As industries are established and grow, potential workers are attracted (Senn and Ferguson, 1967). Because societies in underdeveloped countries are largely rural and agrarian, most of those who come to the cities are from villages and have had no prior experience with urban life. Moreover, a large percentage of those who leave the village represent the lower socio-economic group. In the city, they live under crowded circumstances. Water supplies are frequently inadequate in quantity and often of dubious quality. Sanitation measures are absent, rudimentary, or irregular. Patterns of nutrition are apt to change. "Status" foods, such as white bread, refined sugar, and Coca Cola may replace more nutritious, traditional, but unspectacular fare. The typical result is an increase in morbidity and mortality caused by epidemics such as cholera, plague, and smallpox, as well as upper-respiratory and other gastro-intestinal and nutritional disorders. What psychiatric problems come about as a result of radical changes in patterns of living are not known with precision, except that they are considerable (World Federation for Mental Health, 1965). Traditional extended family structure is disrupted and, with this, certain checks and supports. Venereal disease rates, for example, go up. When families shift, they are frequently young nuclear units in their most fruitful reproductive years. Often great hardships are experienced. This group has high rates of maternal and infant mortality. According to a recent report from India (Senn and Ferguson, 1967), 79 per cent of Calcutta families live in a single room or less, 30 to 50 persons in certain districts of Calcutta share a latrine.

As industry grows, it is not unknown to cause pollution of the immediate countryside, including nearby rivers. Again, I particularly have in mind the example of Calcutta and the Hooghly River pollution. One of the immediate effects of this, quite apart from the esthetic, is a radical drop in the fish population of the river and the area of the ocean into which the river discharges. The practical result is that the supply of fish, an important source of protein of the population of the Calcutta area, declines and the price of fish goes up, resulting in further nutritional disorders (Personal Communication).

Why, apart from humanitarian reasons, should the engineer, primarily concerned with promoting industrialization, be concerned with health problems concomitant to urbanization—especially in an underdeveloped area?

One can reply along at least two lines. First, it would seem to be of interest to the engineer to have a healthy, stable, maximally productive labor force. Secondly, it is hoped that the efforts of the engineers, builders, and industrialists will be successful, in the long run. If so, requirements for labor will increase, and job roles will become more sophisticated. More skills will be needed by workers. Growing numbers of supervisors, managers, and top executives will be needed. The unskilled, but gifted, country boy of today may grow up, if he survives the process, to be a part of management in the future. It, thus, is prudent policy to protect the health of the employed and to ensure a healthy labor force in the future by providing good health service for all.

Similarly, now is the time to initiate programs to prevent the chronic diseases associated with the economically advanced countries. Diseases which can be prevented include, for example, lung cancer and other pulmonary disorders linked to cigarette smoking and air pollution, coronary artery disease, problems associated with obesity, accident control, and mental problems associated with an industrialized, urban culture—especially one in rapid transition.

Health problems in the most rapidly growing urban areas of developing countries, many which are in the tropics, are among the most complex in the world. Quite apart from the considerable sanitary engineering problems are the differences in personal health profiles of various segments of the population. A small upper class has health problems similar to those found in the West. The recent arrivals from rural areas have morbidity patterns in which gastro-intestinal, pulmonary, nutritional, and other disorders, including a host of parasitic and communicable diseases, figure prominently. In between is an emerging middle class with health characteristics of the other two classes. These characteristic patterns, as analyzed by Arnoldo Gabaldon[1] and others, can serve as a vital aid to health programming. Ideally, the health problems should be anticipated while new industrial projects are in the design stage, and administrative and budgetary provisions for dealing with them made before the pressure of a crisis situation necessitates a fire-fighting type of action.

THE VOLTA RIVER PROJECT

The Volta Dam Project of Ghana is an example of an extensive industrial development project which did include a great deal of anticipatory planning to keep health problems within reasonable bounds. It is instructive to consider measures taken and some of the far-reaching health implications of the overall project.

The Volta River Project (*The Volta River Project II*, 1966; *Report of the Commission of Enquiry into the Health Needs of the Gold Coasts*, 1955; Sai, 1967) encompasses the building of a dam, construction of hydroelectric power facilities, an aluminum smelter, an oil refinery, a soap factory, a coca processing factory, steel works, a textile mill, and the construction *de nova* of the harbor and city of Tema. Although time and funds were limited, measures were taken to avert some of the most serious of the anticipated health problems. First of all, the main problem in the new Accra/Tema metropolitan area was the demand for large quantities of water to provide for both the rapidly growing population and the new industries. The second problem had to do with an efficient system of sewage and solid waste disposal (Wright, 1967).

A practical problem occurring in almost every developing city in the underdeveloped, and in many of the so-called developed, areas of the world is the rapid growth of slums, often in the form of shanty towns ringing the cities. As fast as new housing is put up and people move from the shanty towns into the new housing, replacements seem to come from the rural areas. The serious health problems of the shanty-town dwellers are of concern to industry. Ill workers are not as productive as healthy ones and are a focus of infection for the relatively skilled workers in the plants.

One part of the solution is to deal directly with the slum problems. Perhaps a more important parameter of the solution is to improve conditions in the rural areas, both health and employment, thereby slowing the rate of urban shift. Towards this end, Ghana for many years has been developing rural health services and, in recent years, especially in conjunction with the Volta River Project, has developed agriculture and some limited industry in the heartland of the country.

The creation of conditions which, as a result of an industrial development, are conducive to the development of disease vectors constitutes another very serious problem which development experts sometimes overlook. For example, two major health problems in Ghana are malaria and bilharzia. Extensive new expanses of water, which in the case of the Volta Dam project will be more than 3000 square miles, will promote the breeding of mosquitos and also of the bilharzia-carrying snails. Unless the situation is quickly put and kept under constant surveillance and control, the new health problems will vitiate a good part of the economic advances hoped for as a result of the new development schemes planned.

Similarly, the government is hoping to settle people along fertile river basins now largely uninhabited or only sparsely settled because of the high incidence of onchocerciasis, or river blindness. The vector of this disease is the fly *simulium damnosum*, which breeds only in fast-flowing waters with flow velocities of 2–3 ft/sec. One way to combat this problem and also to promote the irrigation schemes is to build further subsidiary dams to reduce the flow rate of the rivers.

Unless the health portions of these projects are carefully coordinated with the development of the major construction components, serious consequences will result which will have significant economic repercussions.

OCCUPATIONAL MEDICINE

From the broad perspective of a regional, comprehensive development program, attention will now be shifted to the role of occupational medicine. It is ironic that industrial management very easily becomes excited over the prospects of a new machine which will decrease costs of production and will very carefully evaluate the machine before purchasing it and thoughtfully consider how it can best be utilized. An engineer can convince management that machines should be periodically shut down, carefully examined, and regularly oiled, and should have worn parts replaced or renewed in the interests of more efficient production and greater returns on capital. However, when it comes to the man running the machine, it is much more difficult to convince management, especially in a developing area where a large unemployed or underemployed labor force exists, that it is a good idea to select workers carefully for a given job. Similarly, it is difficult to convince management to see to it that workers obtain careful medical examinations and also to take whatever measures are necessary to correct serious problems which are uncovered, thereby ensuring labor's optimal performance on the job.

Unfortunately, there are all too many industrialists in developing areas who persistently disclaim the need for special health programs for labor at the early stages of a nation's development. They regard such programs as luxuries which can be afforded only when a considerable degree of affluence has been attained. In justification, they point to the example of the early Industrial Revolution in England and America, where captains of industry were not exactly known for their social conscience and humanitarian activities, including the establishment of employee health programs. They further point out that during the English and American Industrial Revolutions, industry reinvested capital to a maximal extent in order to accelerate and maximize the process of industrial capital formation. Labor was then, and in many areas is today, regarded as an easily replaceable commodity.

Quite apart from the moral and ethical questions involved, one fact which has been overlooked is that a higher degree of labor skill is required today than at the time of the early Industrial Revolution in Western Europe and America when it was relatively easier to replace a factory worker with an unskilled man (Schultz, 1962). As the value of the worker rises, it becomes increasingly worthwhile to invest in worker health programs.

In the United States, a survey of hundreds of organizations shows "evidence of consistent profits of $3.50 to $5 per $1 spent on medical departments." This includes preventive, as well as curative, services. American oil companies working abroad have found it profitable to institute employee health services, including nutritional programs and, under health services, have even instituted area-wide malarial control programs (Proudfit, 1957, McDonald, 1957; Page, 1957; Gabaldon, 1960; Frederiksen, 1960).[2] In contrast, there is a paucity of evidence indicating that industrial concerns in developing countries have focused on the role of health programs in minimizing absenteeism and maximizing worker efficiency.

It is of value to note the experience of a major Indian industry which did introduce and develop an extensive and widely acclaimed occupational medicine program—that of the house of Tata, which encompasses textile mills, oil mills, a chemical factory, hydroelectric companies, and a steel industry, and employs more than 20 000 workers. The program began in 1964 with one part-time doctor in a Tata textile mill. The beginning was slow and the problems many, as related by one of the central figures in the program, Dr. H. P. Dastur (1960), who is also one of the prime movers of contemporary occupational medicine in India. By degrees, however, the program expanded, so that today, there is the equivalent of one full-time physician for about every 1000 workers, a corps of safety engineers, training officers, and subsidiary technicians. The program also includes a family-planning department. Workers who are willing to undergo vasectomy after the third child are offered incentive of Rs 250/- and a few days leave with pay (Chandrasekhar, 1968). Dastur's plea that "An industrial health service has to be a joint effort of medical, engineering, and social sciences" seems particularly noteworthy.

UNFORESEEN HEALTH PROBLEMS

In order to emphasize further the point that industrial and technical projects for the developing areas should have the benefit of health consultation early in the planning process, I would like to cite a number of examples of programs where this was either absent or inadequate.

One example concerns the establishment of sugar and cotton industries in the sparsely settled malarious lowlands of Ethiopia. In order to operate the plants, it was necessary to import workers from the malaria-free highlands. These workers had little natural resistance to malaria. Before control measures were instituted, malaria had taken a considerable toll of the workers and slowed up the establishment of the enterprises.

Another example pertains to a pure water supply scheme to parts of the Sudan in an effort to reduce gastro-intestinal disease. An evaluation of the program after the piped water system had been installed revealed that there was no significant decrease in gastro-intestinal disease. Investigation revealed the water was pure at the taps. However, in the homes, water kept in the traditional earthenware jars was contaminated. Omitted from the otherwise well-conceived program was a health education component necessary to convince the people not to use their apparently contaminated hands in the traditional manner to dip drinking water out of the water storage jars.

A fine example (Personal Communication) is the current problem of an increase in malaria incidence in parts of Indonesia which is adversely affecting nickel production. Since it is much cheaper to prevent malaria than to treat malaria cases (Tropical Health, 1962), savings realized by relaxing control measures probably will be more than wiped out by treatment costs and intensified control efforts now seem essential to industrial development.

THE ECONOMIC VALUE OF HEALTH PROGRAMS

I would now like to repeat some thorny questions which oftern arise when economic justification of health programs is discussed, in the hope that they will further illustrate the complexities of health program planning, underscore the need for much more research, and suggest some avenues for research.

Do mass disease control or eradication campaigns result in long-run effect of lower per capita income? Particular reference might be made to the pioneering effort of Professor Barlow (1967) of the University of Michigan to analyze the economic effects of malaria eradication in Ceylon. He has designed a model to estimate the effects of the successful 1947 malaria eradication program on Ceylonese per capita income over the ensuing 30-year period. He indicates that in the short run, until about the early 1950s, malaria eradication in Ceylon contributed to an increase in per capita income. This immediate effect is thought to be the result of an increase in worker output due to increases in the quantity and quality of labor inputs because of reductions in morbidity, debility, and mortality (Mushkin, 1962).

Within five of six years, the infants who would have died but for the eradication campaign began to reach school age and to impose burdens on the educational system and other aspects of the economy. By the time they were seventeen, a "second-generation" effect began to be felt, and was compounded by higher fertility rates coming in the wake of the eradication program. Thus, by 1955, it is estimated by Barlow, per capita income began to fall below the point where it would have been without eradication.

Barlow (1967) himself indicates the resolution of this kind of dilemma. He points to an increase in the population of children resulting from marked changes in birth rates and infant mortality rates as being the main economic disadvantage of eradication. He then suggests that a "twin program of eradication and birth control" would have made a dramatic contribution to the growth of per capita income.

If family planning is so important, should countries concentrate on controlling the rate of population growth and reduce expenditures on traditional preventive and curative health programs to the politically acceptable minimum? Analysis of trends in allocation of resources to the health and family planning sector by finance ministries in some developing countries suggests that this is just what is taking place. The utility of this approach is open to serious question. In most underdeveloped countries, children and the extended family are the source of support in old age, illness, and disability. A high infant mortality exists. Sons are particularly important. One wonders how likely people are to undergo sterilization or even to practice reversible forms of family planning, unless they are reasonably assured that the children they have will reach old age.

One also wonders about the future of an agency or government which is identified as being more interested in preventing life than it is in improving the quality of existing life. Where overzealous agencies have promoted family planning among populous lower socio-economic groups to the apparent exclusion of curative programs and without adequate educational programs, dark accusations of "racial genocide policy" have been leveled.

Are health expenditures to be classified as consumption or investment? The answer depends upon the general level of health and especially on the concrete situation (Klarman, 1968). The setting of a silversmith's broken hand or the successful treatment of malaria in a skilled machinist can be classified primarily as an investment. A rest cure at the seaside would probably be classified as consumption expenditure if the person is a laborer. It may have a large investment component in the case of a factory vice president if he returns to the job better able to function. It is widely agreed that better health contributes to an increased output for the economy (Klarman, 1968; Mushkin, 1958; Weisbrod, 1961; Fein, 1958, 1964).

Analysis of the investment value of health services is greatly complicated by the fact that health services are both consumer goods and producer goods. In addition, as the health level of a country goes up, it seems likely that a growing proportion of health expenditure will lead to consumer satisfaction rather than economic growth.

Should a factory owner in an underdeveloped area with a labor surplus having high morbidity, debility, and mortality rates invest in programs to "increase the value of human capital," if he apparently stands little chance of recouping his expenditures? (For argument's sake it is assumed that the factory is large and only marginal health services exist in the community.) This question illustrates the "cycle of poverty and disease" dilemma. Because workers are ill and debilitated, their productivity is low. Because their productivity is low, there is little money available to improve their health. On the assumption that an increase in the capital value of human resources is essential for the long-run economic growth of underdeveloped areas (Mushkin and Weisbrod, 1964; Schultz, 1961, 1962), the problem becomes one of identifying ways of breaking the cycle and determining the role of the individual factory in what must be a massive effort on a broad front.

If the increase in productivity resulting from a health program more than offsets the costs of a health program, that program is, of course, justified on economic grounds. The problem is to develop the means of making such a determination. We also need to determine the most efficient way of providing health services for workers. If, because of small size, it is beyond the means of a factory to establish an occupational medicine program, the desirability of government subsidy for such programs should be considered.

A corollary question is if the principle of an occupational medicine program for factories beyond a certain size is accepted, what guidelines are there for determining the percentage of operating budget which the factory or industry should devote to the program? Much as one might wish for such guidelines, the sad fact is that little exists in the literature directly applicable to developing areas. Concrete figures and statistics are not readily available. The case study of Stanvac (Standard-Vacuum Oil Co.) in Indonesia quotes a figure of 10 per cent of total wages and salaries being budgeted annually for the health program (National Planning Association, 1957). It is said that this investment in health paid off in an extremely low "non-effective sickness rate."

The writings of men such as Dr. H. P. Dastur (1960) and Dr. Siro Vazquez (1961), to name but two, reflect years of occupational medicine experience in developing areas. From such work, one can gain an idea of the annual man and material requirements of a health program. The cost of establishing a similar program elsewhere can then be calculated. There is, in addition, considerable literature pertaining to the "direct" (claims by workers) and "indirect" (property damage and production interference) costs of industrial accidents and the economics of preventing them as part of a health and safety program (Simonds and Grimaldi, 1963; Heinrich, 1959). The lack of readily available good data to answer this question, or of guidelines indicating how to go about obtaining the needed information, points to a need for a wider sharing of existing information plus additional research.

This list of "thorny" questions could, of course, be greatly extended. It is hoped, however, that by now an appreciation of the contribution health can make to industrial programs has been conveyed (Proudfit, 1957; Fuchs, 1966) —as well as the need for developing careful evaluation techniques (Klarman, 1967). In order to accomplish this, problems will have to be clearly formulated, required data identified, and steps taken to identify data where they do not now exist. The efforts of workers from a variety of disciplines will have to be enlisted. And, finally, we must continue "to strive for good judgment in making decisions when major elements of the cost benefit calculations are missing, as they frequently are" (Klarman, 1957).

SUGGESTIONS FOR THE FUTURE

I would like to close with four suggestions for the future.

1. I think health representation must be included among those responsible for planning, implementing, and evaluating industrial programs in developing areas.

2. Many more contemporary studies pertaining to the economic returns to be realized from health programs are needed in developing areas and must be conducted by both industry and government.

3. So that the citizenry of the various developing areas may benefit to the greatest degree possible from development efforts, population growth must proceed at a controlled rate. In order to ensure this, large-scale family planning programs implemented in conjunction with health programs must be an important, soundly financed part of overall national development efforts. Every new industrial project, if necessary, must devote a portion of its budget to the area of health and family planning.

4. Better guidelines for the allocation of development resources to the health sector are urgently needed. Once an allocation is made, we need to know more about how to utilize the funds in order to gain the greatest benefits in terms of decline in morbidity, debility, and mortality, and to maximize the increase in human happiness.

NOTES

1. In a paper presented at the Fourth Conference of the Industrial Council for Tropical Health, Harvard School of Public Health, July 20, 1960, Arnoldo Gabaldon, M.D., Minister of Health and Social Welfare in Venezuela, has developed indices for categorizing countries on the basis of mortality patterns and life expectancy at birth.

2. A relatively low-cost yaws control program in Haiti has produced an immediate increase in productivity. (Source: World Health Organization Bulletins and private correspondence with personnel involved in the program.)

THE INFLUENCE OF PUBLIC HEALTH

Commentary by John C. Cutler

IN APPROACHING the subject it seems appropriate to refer to the statement made in 1967 at the Second PAHO/WHO lecture on the Biomedical Sciences, given by Dr. Abel Wolman, Professor Emeritus of Sanitary Engineering and Water Resources of the Johns Hopkins University:

> I have taken the position that the promised land of modern science and technology has been over-promised to the common man. His lot still remains abject, sad, and almost hopeless in too great a part of our globe. Recognizing that scientific and technologic progress will inevitably afford a better world to all, it is too far distant to satisfy the urban and rural dweller in developing, and in pockets of most developed, countries.
>
> The scientific and technologic resources are already available in rich amounts to convert the environment from a hostile one to a beneficient ally. The conversion has been dismally slow. We should not accept the present rate of change with fatalistic patience. Nor need we wait upon the emergence of all theoretical answers before militant, and perhaps fumbling, steps of improvement are insisted upon. Orthodoxy of approach must give way to innovation, not the least of which must be in the postures of professional leaders themselves. Fortunately, increasing evidence is emerging in many countries that change, per se, is not suspect. One can point to fundamental and successful re-directions of policy, method, and institution.

If properly and effectively utilized and put to the most constructive use through effective national planning and implementations, engineering technology can be made the full contributor to national social and economic development that it is theoretically expected to be. However, the contribution of this engineering technology to social and economic development—and to health, which is considered as both one of the elements and an end product of social development—can be slowed, or even reversed, if the health of the individual and community is not taken into consideration when planning for the introduction of new technology.

An easily demonstrated example of the interdependence of technological progress and human health is found historically in the construction of the Panama Canal. The technological knowledge was at the disposal of the French who had built the Suez Canal by 1869. When attention was turned to Panama, the venture was a failure primarily because of the inability to control yellow fever. The losses from death and illness and the inability to attract and hold workers because of the fears of death or disease resulted in a failure to utilize technological tools and knowledge. When the United States undertook the project, Major Gorgas was given the responsibility for managing the health hazards, and the project was successfully completed.

It is of interest to go back even further in this analysis of the relationship between health and utilization of technologic advances in facilitating socio-economic development. With the coming of the steamship in 1810 and of the railroad in 1830, quarantine systems which had been established on the basis of knowledge existing at that stage of public health and medical development had to be modified, but with continued concern for the public welfare, so as to remove barriers to trade and commerce as well as to the application of the new technology. In fact, the growth and increasing fruitfulness of international cooperation to prevent the spread of disease and to promote improvement of health can be said to have been one of the social consequences of the application of engineering technology at this time.

This interrelationship has, from the point of view of most citizens of the more developed countries, been forgotten in recent decades. Perhaps the reason is the very fact that successful utilization of technological advances in the promotion and protection of the health of the public has become so much a part of the activity of government that we have forgotten that untimely death and unnecessary disease and disability are constant dangers held in check, in part, by public health action. This is perhaps best illustrated by the fact that, even when today's jet travel brings people who are in the incubation period of a disease such as smallpox into North America or Western Europe—areas that have not known large smallpox epidemics for decades, and in which levels of immunity are low—the national and international machinery for preventing epidemic spread are so well prepared and efficient that, to date, and in spite of potential risk and occasional cases, no major epidemics have occurred.

The developing nations present quite another picture. The quality of manpower and the health of the community and of the individual are essential elements to be considered if modern technology is to be able to make the fullest contribution. In terms of simple energy output for such a basic engineering enterprise as the construction of the Pan American Highway, the work output, as measured by the index of volume of earth moved per man per time unit, increased substantially as steps were taken to improve nutrition by increasing the caloric intake of the laborer.

On a more sophisticated level the application of modern technology to agriculture as measured by the effective use of new seeds, fertilizers, and mechanical equipment requires education. In studies of the relationship between increased agricultural output and education, Brown (1965) has found that:

One factor facilitating a yield-per-acre takeoff is a reasonably high level of literacy. A trend of rapidly rising yields implies the continuous movement of new ideas and techniques from the research plot to the farmer, and this is much easier in a largely literate society.

Rates of yield increase vary widely among countries with widely varying literacy levels. Major grain producing countries with literacy levels below 50 percent raised yields at 0.2 percent per year between 1935–39 and 1960–62. Those with literacy levels between 50 and 80 percent achieved a 1.1 percent annual rate of gain; those above 80 percent averaged 1.4 percent.

We are now, however, becoming aware of the fact that malnutrition, protein deficiency in particular, during the latter part of pregnancy or in the early months of life results in actual diminution in the number of cells in the brain and causes inferior intellectual potential. This malnourishment results in mental deficiencies which show in both intelligence and certain types of neuromuscular abilities (Scrimshaw, 1968). Here, again, the relationship between the basic quality of the human intellect and the muscle required to participate in and contribute to a modern technology-based society and the underlying health factors is evident. The knowledge of this significance must be reflected in national planning for social and economic development.

Even when basically good nutritional status exists when measured by availability of animal protein, a highly sensitive index, the neglect of other parameters of public health can seriously impede the application of modern technology. For instance, because of administrative failures in the Paraguayan malaria eradication program, there recently has been an increase in malaria following earlier successful efforts to eradicate the disease. This epidemic is concentrated in areas of the country where programs are under way to open new agricultural lands, accompanied by large-scale road building and hydroelectric construction projects. In the past year the epidemic reached about 50 000 cases, seriously interfering with programs for colonization, as well as for construction.

It should be remembered that the pattern of attack for a disease such as malaria is unpredictable except in very general terms if no medical programs exist, so that the labor force available to work on any one day during the malarial season is a function of the epidemiologic pattern of the disease rather than of the planning of engineers or availability of technically sophisticated equipment.

Technological developments in engineering have had an incalculable impact already upon health and wellbeing and hold promise for increasingly greater contributions in the developing areas. So small a contribution as the perfecting of a simple hand-operated spray pump which can be carried on the back of the spray man has been a major element in the success of the worldwide campaign to eradicate malaria.

In a more complex way technological advances in processing cotton seed to remove toxic material has made possible the use of cotton seed meal in association with other grains to produce "synthetic" foods equivalent to meat in protein value, yet made from local products and at a price within the reach of the worker or peasant. The time and effort required to translate technological potential into food in the mouths of the mother and child is a factor that must be constantly appreciated. The physiologic and technologic breakthrough in this was made by the Institute for Nutrition of Central America and Panama, a regional intergovernmental enterprise, in association with and financial aid from Pan American Health Organization and World Health Organization. The product developed, generically called INCAPARINA, has a variety of formulations and is now widely copied all over the world. But it took almost sixteen years from the establishment of the Institute, through Kellogg Foundation financing in 1948, to carry out the basic research, the developmental phase, market testing, and finally the introduction of INCAPARINA into the commercial food industry. This involved not only basic biological and chemical studies, but also extensive social studies on the acceptability to various social groups with widely differing patterns of food preparation and use and the problems of large-scale processing, distribution, and marketing.

Note also should be taken of the health problems accompanying the application of modern technology. These can range from water and air pollution, if proper precautions are not taken, through injuries to workmen, to the opening of entire areas of a country to the introduction of diseases or vectors of disease which have heretofore been confined to limited geographic sites primarily because of the lack of roads or railroads and the limited movement of people and animals.

What emerges when the health sector is considered in the context of application of engineering technology is that planning for social and economic development must, as has been repeatedly stated, consider the health sector and various related social and educational parameters and that health inputs must be assured in order to achieve the maximum output from the introduction of new technology. In this way the health of the nation itself can benefit very substantially as one of the nonspecific outputs of technology (Pan American Health Organization, 1965).

In conclusion, note must be taken of the factor of population size, one of the principal determinants of whether it is possible for a nation to make the investment of capital required in order for the benefits of modern engineering technology to be made available to all (Brown, 1967). This has been succinctly summarized in a quote from Goran Ohlin (1967) of the Organization for Economic Cooperation and Development:

> There is no way of telling how many billions may in the future be sustained by this earth. The rate of population growth is of more immediate concern. Given time, there is no doubt that the world economy could accommodate populations several times larger than the present ones. In time, the capital may be formed; in time, the necessary social reforms will be undertaken. But as things stand, the developing world faces a transitional period of uncertain length in which time will be exceedingly short. Mortality will continue to decline, and populations will increase at rates which will absorb the bulk of the resources that could otherwise be deployed to meet the irrepressible demand for modernization and development. Millions will be born out of phase with history.
>
> It seems clear now that something can be done, and even that in time something will be done to reduce the gravity of this problem. No country that accepts the powers of modern society to combat death will in the end be unable to control birth. The only question is how soon. The modest contributions that rich countries might make to facilitate this crucial part of the modernization process could well count for more than all they are prepared to do in the realm of conventional aids.

207

REPORT OF WORKSHOP 9
A. E. Axelrod, Rapporteur

WORKSHOP 9 was attended largely by physicians who had many years of experience in overseas settings, much of it in association with industry. The remarks summarized reflect this background and are directed mainly toward industry-associated health programs.

Three points emerged from the discussion:

1. *Health is an important aspect of the valued, multifaceted role industry is playing in the comprehensive development of many areas of the world.* Industry building is thus viewed as much more than the building of factories, employing of men, and production of goods. It is viewed as being intertwined in the fundamental process of social change. Moreover, the successful application of technology is viewed as depending, to a considerable extent, on human factors.

2. *Health experts must be represented in the preplanning group contemplating a new industrial project, especially one in an underdeveloped area.* Each new project must have a health program tailored to its special needs and circumstances. There is no such thing as a standard, comprehensive health program for an industrial project in a developing area because of the great variation in the health problems, in the resources available to deal with the problems, and in the anticipated health problems arising as a result of the industrial project. For the same reasons it is impossible to predict, without a careful study, the cost of a new health program. Certain health problems may have to be solved even before plant construction can be initiated. This may be so costly that the entire industrial operation may be uneconomical. It is obviously desirable to determine this before capital, time, and effort are committed.

3. *The greatest value of industry-associated health programs lies in the contribution they make to enhancing what is called the "human equation."* This is difficult to quantify, but all, including many experienced industry executives, agree it is extremely important. The contribution to the human equation is comprised of many factors. The obvious aspects are those inherent in creating the preconditions for a program, without which little could be done, such as the control of malaria, yellow fever, and onchocerciasis. There are other effects of health programs, however, which are extremely important. There is, for example, a general morale-building effect. Part of this is the creation of an informal channel of communication via the health staff, and often the nurse or technician, form the workers to management. Suggestions passed on to an alert management have often resulted in desirable changes which have increased worker morale and production. It is reported that physical and socio-psychological adjustment problems have come to the attention of health workers and managers earlier when there is a health program available.

The difficulties of putting a monetary price tag on the value of a health program are best illustrated by a case report that involves the early diagnosis and prompt removal of rectal polyps in two company officials. In each case the polyps had malignacies *in situ,* and follow-up visits over a period of years elicited no sign or symptoms of malignancy. The costing problem is obvious. The simplest aspect is to estimate the cost of what inevitably would have been drawn-out and painful terminal illnesses, but it is not so easy to estimate the value of the two men to the company over the rest of their working years. It is even more difficult to evaluate the impact on the men of the realization that, were it not for the company-sponsored health program, they, in all likelihood, would have died.

Another aspect of the "human equation" difficult to evaluate is the effects of the image of a factory, in an underdeveloped area, which is concerned with enhancing and protecting human resources, as well as developing natural resources.

Other important questions and issues which arose and were discussed are essentially corollaries and elaborations of the above:

1. *Ideally, what should be the competencies of the people responsible for the health program preplanning phase of an industrial development project?* They should have a broad orientation to public health, including an understanding of the principles of environmental medicine. They must

have an understanding of medical care economics. They also must have an orientation to clinical medicine and a considerable occupational medicine background.

2. *What are the components of the health preplanning survey?* A rough idea of the demographic profile of the area in which the industry is to be established and information about the numbers of workers available in the region must be obtained. The possibilities of attracting workers from more distant areas have to be estimated. The age breakdown of the population and the natural rate of increase are also necessary for making projections of the availability of manpower over time. In addition, it is essential to obtain fairly detailed information about the incidence and prevalence of disease in the area and about the nutritional status of the people. The physical ability of the workers to carry out the tasks which will be expected of them if a particular industry is established will have to be ascertained.

Adequacy of water supplies for the industry and the people who will inevitably be attracted by the industry will have to be determined. Plans for waste disposal, both solid and liquid, will have to be made and problems of housing and food supply considered. A very difficult problem is to estimate the secondary effects on health of the contemplated industry. Will there be pollution of water and air, for example? If workers must be brought in from a distance, will new diseases be introduced into the local population? It is also very important to consider the general customs and mores of the society. Related to this are the laws which will affect the new industrial enterprise with respect to the health, housing, and the general care of the worker population.

Finally, it is essential to assess the general level of current medical activity in the area. Included are curative services, public health services, and occupational medicine services. If they are thought to be inadequate to deal with the influx of workers which will be attracted by the industry, estimates will have to be made of the capacity of the existing system to deal with the new problems and alternative solutions considered.

In order to do a complete evaluation, valuable information can be obtained from publications of the country concerned. It is essential, however, to send a group to the contemplated plant site to talk with local officials and health workers and to make first-hand personal estimates of some of the health problems which will be faced if the contemplated enterprise is, indeed, launched.

3. *Should an attempt not be made to cost out the health program, with various alternatives, once it is drawn up?* It may well be that the cost of even a minimal health program, but one deemed essential to the success of the enterprise, will be so high as to cancel the benefits which it is estimated will be obtained from the operation. In that case, the entire matter may be dropped. On the other hand, it may well be that management will decide to proceed with the project, subsequently raising the question of how to provide the services. Should the company attempt to organize them and adjust its pricing structure accordingly, or should the company adjust the royalty payment to the host country and expect them to organize the program? Often each carries a share. In many cases, both industry and host country have found it advantageous to have the new industry, because of its operating flexibility and experience with similar programs elsewhere, establish the needed health program.

4. *Should not the precise composition and organization of the program reflect individual circumstances?* In general, it can be said that there must be a curative aspect, a public health component, and an occupational medicine component. All must have a strong prevention component. The importance of health education in all areas of the health program must also be stressed. An industrial medicine program can serve as an important training ground for health personnel of the country—especially in occupational medicine, an area of specialization which is new to some developing countries. It is also thought to be very important to establish, organize, and operate health programs in such a way that they may be integrated with the health structure of the host country and eventually become a permanent part of the health system of that country.

5. *Can an expatriate industry make a real contribution to the family planning program of its host country?* The important issue agreed upon by the workshop is that industry must follow the policy guidelines established by the host country. In some situations industry-associated family planning guidance has been restricted to special cases, such as mothers who have tuberculosis or diabetes, and

to those who have come and asked for help. In other situations industry has been able to help develop effective family planning programs within the area served by its health service.

CONCLUSION

Industry can, and in many instances does, play a very statesmanlike role in helping a country to develop economically and attain important social goals. One of these goals is the establishment of health services. It was observed that more and more industry health programs have evolved from a primary concern with the "man-on-the-job" to the broader role of the "industry-in-the-community."

REFERENCES CITED

Barlow, Robin, "The economic effects of malaria eradication," *American Economic Review*, May, 1967.

Brown, H. *Population, Food, and the Energy Transition in Fertility and Family Planning, a World Review*. Ann Arbor: University of Michigan, 1967.

Brown, L. *Increasing World Food Output*, Foreign Agricultural Economic Report No. 25. Washington, D.C.: U.S. Department of Agriculture, 1965.

Chandrasekhar, S., "How India is tackling her population problem," *Foreign Affairs*, October, 1968.

Dastur, H. P. *A Doctor's Approach to Industrial Medicine*. Bombay: Tata Institute of Social Sciences, 1960.

East Africa Royal Commission 1953–1955 Report. London: Her Majesty's Stationery Office, Cmd. 9475, 1955.

Economic Commission for Africa, *Seminar on Population Problems in Africa*. E/CN, 14/ASPP/LF.2, October 29–November 10, 1962.

Fein, Rashi. *Economics of Mental Illness*. New York: Basic Books, Inc., 1958.

Fein, Rashi, *Health Programs in Economic Development*. Ann Arbor: The University of Michigan Press, 1964.

Frederiksen, Harold, "Malaria control and population pressure in Ceylon," *Public Health Reports*, Vol. 75, No. 10, October, 1960.

Fuchs, Victor R., "The contribution of health services to the American economy," *The Milbank Memorial Fund Quarterly*, Vol. 44, No. 4, October, 1966, Part 2.

Gabaldon, Arnoldo, "Aging problems of preventive medicine in the tropics." *Industry and Tropical Health*, IV, Harvard School of Public Health, 1960.

Hance, William A., "The race between population and resources: A challenge to the prevailing view that Africa need not worry about population pressure," *Africa Report*, January, 1968.

Heinrich, H. W. *Industrial Accident Prevention*. New York: McGraw-Hill, 1959.

India, Government of, *Planning Commission, The Third Five Year Plan*. New Delhi, 1961–1966.

Klarman, Herbert E., "The contribution of health services to economic growth and well-being," *Federal Program for the Development of Human Resources*, Vol. 2, Part IV, Washington, D.C.: Government Printing Office, 1968.

————, "Present status of cost benefit analysis in the health field," *American Journal of Public Health*, Vol. 57, November, 1967.

Mushkin, Selma J., "Health as an investment," *Journal of Political Economy*, October, 1962.

————, "Toward a definition of health economics," *Public Health Reports*, Vol. 73, No. 9, September, 1958.

Mushkin, S. J., and B. A. Weisbrod, "Investment in health—Lifetime health expenditures on the 1960 work force," *The Economics of Health and Medical Care*, Ann Arbor: The University of Michigan, 1964.

Myrdal, Gunnar, *Asian Drama, An Inquiry into the Poverty of Nations*. Vol. 2, 1968.

210

National Academy of Sciences, *Tropical Health.* Publication 996, National Research Council, Washington, 1962.

National Planning Association. *United States Business Performance Abroad: The Case Study of Stanvac in Indonesia.* Washington, D.C., 1957.

Ohlin, Goran, *Population Control and Economic Development,* Paris: OECD, 1967.

Page, Robert C., "Practical aspects of employee nutrition," *Industry and Tropical Health, III.* Boston: Harvard School of Public Health, 1957.

Pan American Health Organization. Health Planning, *Problems of Concept and Method.* Scientific Publication No. 111, Washington, D.C., 1965.

Proudfit, Arthur T., "Health is good business," *Industry and Tropical Health, III.* Boston: Harvard School of Public Health, 1957.

Report of the Commission of Enquiry into the Health Needs of the Gold Coast. Accra: The Government Printer, 1955.

Sai, F. T., *Health and Nutrition Status of the Ghanaian People.* Accra: 1967.

Schultz, Theodore W., "Investment in human capital." *American Economic Review,* Vol. 51, March, 1961.

————, "Investment in human capital in poor countries," in Paul D. Zook, ed., *Foreign Trade and Human Capital,* Dallas: Southern Methodist University Press, 1962.

Scrimshaw, N. "Malnutrition, learning, and behaviour," *Boletin Oficina Sanitaria Panamericana,* Vol. 47, September, 1968.

Senn, C. L. and T. Ferguson. *The Challenge to Public Health of Urbanization,* W.H.O. Background Document, A20/Technical Discussions/1, 1967.

Simonds, R. H., and J. U. Grimaldi. *Safety Management, Accident Control.* Homewood, Illinois: Richard Irwin, 1963.

Smith, T. E., and J. G. C. Blacker. *Population Characteristics of the Commonwealth Countries of Tropical Africa.* London: University London, Institute of Commonwealth Studies, 1963.

Vazquez, S., "Management responsibilities for health services in developing areas," *Industry and Tropical Health, IV.* Boston: Harvard School of Public Health, 1961.

The Volta River Project II, Appendices to the Report of the Preparatory Commission. London, published for the Governments of the United Kingdom and of the Gold Coast by Her Majesty's Stationery Office, 1956.

Weisbrod, Burton A., "Anticipating the health needs of Americans: Some economic projections," *Annals of the American Academy of Political and Social Services,* Vol. 337, September, 1961.

Wolman, A. *The Unreasonable Man.* Scientific Publication No. 152. Washington, D.C.: Pan American Health Organization, 1967.

World Federation for Mental Health, "Industrialization and mental health," Geneva, 1965.

Wright, A. M. *An Inventory of Environmental Health Needs of Ghana.* WHO Expert Committee on Educational Programs in Environmental Health (SSH/INF/67.3), Geneva, July 1967.

12

ORGANIZING THE TRANSFER OF TECHNOLOGY TO DEVELOPING COUNTRIES

Principal Paper—Arthur Paul

In a dinner address, Arthur Paul discussed technology transfer, a relatively new concept and one for which organizations and organizational structures are only partially prepared, and emphasized the need for more attention to this problem.

The Editors

ORGANIZING THE TRANSFER OF
TECHNOLOGY TO DEVELOPING COUNTRIES

Principal Paper by Arthur Paul

DURING MOST of the last ten years, I have been living in Asia where I have worked in close association with a number of the leading Asians who are struggling with the desperately difficult problems of economic development in that continent. Throughout this period, the organization of the transfer of technology has emerged as a matter of prime importance.

Along with many others who are working in this field, I believe that one of the most important factors in the developmental process is the way in which technological improvements are applied in a growing economy. To try to discover how to accelerate the transfer of existing technology and how to carry out this transfer more skillfully, thus avoiding "backlashes," seems to me to be something which deserves the highest priority in our efforts to help developing countries.

We should not, however, confine our efforts to the transfer of existing technology. It is equally important to help create new technology specifically designed to meet the key problems of developing countries in fields to which modern science has not yet been applied. In order to do this we must find out how to divert a larger share of the immense research budgets of the United States and of Europe, both governmental and private, to the key problems of development, especially in areas where there has been insufficient effort.

Many people who are actively engaged in developmental work share this view. At the Conference on World Trade and Development held in New Delhi in March 1968, Dr. Raul Prebisch, the Secretary General of UNCTAD, made the following significant statement:

Why is it that most of the developing countries are still adrift, and have not reached the growth objective which has been set for them? The more I think about this, the more I am convinced that the world is confronted with a new problem; new in kind, in characteristics, and in dimensions. It is the problem of taking technology which has evolved gradually in the developed countries—and which has already reached fantastic heights there—and transferring it to an environment which is not yet quite ready to absorb it. Although scientific and technological advances represent the developing world's best hope for a rise in its level of living and for eradication of poverty and its inherent evils, they also bring with them severely adverse consequences for the developing world, and confront it with vast contradictions. Unless we go thoroughly into this problem, unless we analyse these adverse consequences and these contradictions, we shall not succeed in formulating an enlightened policy.

Philippe de Seynes, the Under-Secretary of the United Nations for Economic and Social Affairs, used the same theme in his address at the New Delhi Conference. He said:

There is no factor whose potential effect on the development of international relations is more promising and at the same time more explosive; no factor which highlights more dramatically the vast inequalities that shape those relations as well as the possibilities to eliminate these inequalities, given the necessary will.

It was a disappointment to me, and I am sure to many others who were present in New Delhi, that this theme was not picked up more readily by the delegates at that important Conference. The subject of *Transfer of Technology* was assigned to one of the committees of the Conference, but the same committee was given the task of considering the *World Food Problem,* which absorbed almost all of its time, so that there was practically no discussion of the other assignment. It is very important that there should be a greater concentration of effort on the question of how to apply new technology and modern science more skillfully to the problems of the developing countries.

Some dramatic examples of what well-managed and strategically directed applications of modern technology can achieve have recently been seen in Asia. The adaptation to the Asian climate and environment of some special varieties of wheat developed in Mexico and the creation of new strains of high-yielding rice by the International Rice Research Institute in the Philippines have been so successful that, in a comparatively short period of time, the results of these two achievements alone have changed the outlook for food production in Asia. A few years ago the rate of increase in population was exceeding that of food production to an extent that caused many observers to feel that serious shortages, if not widespread famine, were inevitable by the mid-1970s in many parts of Asia. Today the prospect is different. Many factors have contributed to this change, but among the most important are the aforementioned acclimatization of Mexican wheat to Asia and the creation of IRRI's rice strains. They are striking examples of shortcuts to development achieved by a skillfully directed application of modern technology and scientific knowledge.

Although the food situation has improved, there are other problems of development emerging in Asia that may be even more difficult to solve. Chief among them is the inability of the economies of many countries to absorb the increasingly large numbers of young people who are seeking useful occupations. Generally speaking, youth in Asia today is better fed, has more energy, and is better educated than ever before. But the rate of economic growth is not sufficient to create employment opportunities for more than a small percentage of those who seek occupations in urban environments. Farm labor is overabundant, and the new agricultural techniques require fewer, not more, people on the land. A superficial glance at the demographic figures of most countries of Asia shows that the annual increment to the number of young people seeking occupations is mounting rapidly and soon will reach alarmingly large figures, whereas economic growth rates in many of these countries remain disappointingly slow. The various methods of population control which are beginning to take hold in a number of countries will eventually alter the ratios of the rate of economic growth to the rate of population growth, but the youths in question already have been born. There are twenty waves of young people now living, each wave larger than the preceding one, all of which must be provided for in the coming decades. This poses problems that appear to be almost insoluble.

Five years ago there seemed to be no chance of avoiding a food crisis in Asia;

catastrophe seemed inevitable. But a growing awareness of the problem, brought about by gathering the facts and by bringing them to the attention of people who could do something about the situation, led to a concentration on this matter on the part of many of the best minds and allocations of large amounts of research funds were made to projects for increasing agricultural productivity in Asia. A similar airing of the youth problem of Asia may bring about a concentration of effort in that field. The need to start soon is pressing. An awareness of the seriousness of the problem will not solve it but it may cause many people to try harder to find shortcuts that will increase economic growth rates more rapidly and thus relieve some of the pressure.

We are all well aware of the urgency of applying technology to the problems of developing countries. In spite of our domestic difficulties and a widespread feeling that we must put our house in order, we know that thinking people throughout the United States are fully conscious of the impossibility of our escaping the results of foreign catastrophes.

An immense amount of effort already is directed toward the transfer of technology to the developing countries. Many organizations are actively engaged in this work. Two of the United Nation bodies, UNIDO and FAO, are directly concerned with industrial and agricultural technology, respectively. USAID and other bilateral donor groups have sponsored technical assistance projects that have resulted in the use of modern technology in many fields. I have already mentioned the successful projects of some of the large foundations in the United States. The great international corporations and many smaller companies have made foreign investments and already taken abroad much of their technology and scientific knowledge.

Even though these organizations have accomplished much and there have been some dramatic successes, present efforts appear to be scattered and fragmented. The absence of over-all direction and the "hit-or-miss" approach now used seems to justify the reservations and fears of adverse consequences that Dr. Prebisch voiced in his wise and important statement to the UNCTAD Conference.

The chief shortcoming seems to be a lack of concentration on the key problems that retard development and the absence of a mechanism for selecting projects that contribute most to the acceleration of economic growth rates. Much of the present effort is carried on by people who have specialized knowledge and are looking for ways and means of applying it to new fields or by corporations seeking out markets for their existing products. There is no guiding agency that can indentify the most important problems and the most urgent needs of the various areas and use this information to initiate or direct efforts and financing to solving those particular problems and filling those special needs. Therefore, I feel there should be a new organizational approach to technological transfer, one that might help to concentrate efforts on what I have referred to as the "key problems" of developing countries and one which might induce the diversion of a larger slice of the research budget of the United States government and of the resources of large foundations and of private corporations to the financing of these efforts.

I have discussed these organizational matters with many people in recent months. I talked to Washington officials at many administrative levels in most of the departments or agencies concerned with the subject. I also have had discussions with United Nations officials, with corporate executives, and with a number of persons in academic institutions and in foundations engaged in related work. I found some degree of consensus on two points: first, that there is an organizational gap with respect to the functions that I had in mind and, secondly, that the nature of the organizational work needed was such that it should be undertaken outside of government.

Regarding the functions to be performed by the proposed new organization, I suggest that the primary task is to identify the "key problems," the situations in which a concentration of scientific effort could make the greatest impact on development. Some of these are almost selfevident. It requires little knowledge of Asia to be aware of the importance of creating new strains of seeds that could increase the yield of land used for the growing of wheat and rice. There are other similar circumstances, not quite so evident perhaps, but potentially of great significance; for example, the need to find better methods of converting marginal rubber plantations to new uses, a development which is vital to the economies of Malaysia, Ceylon, Vietnam, and Thailand. Another important task is to overcome the obstacles to the production of high protein human and animal food from unused, or improperly used, indigenous resources.

Two markets which show every indication of immense expansion in Asia in the coming decades are those for paper and for meat. Conversely, the markets for many existing products on which vast numbers of people are dependent for their livelihood, such as jute and other hard fibers and rubber, are shrinking rapidly, largely due to the competition of substitute materials synthetically produced in the West. Cotton and wool also will suffer eventually. The application of modern technology to ease the impact of the economic dislocations created by these shifts which were caused by technological progress is a great challenge.

The whole field of processing locally available raw materials offers opportunities for technological progress, but the identification of priorities for the use of available resources must not be a scattered effort. There must be a central point for the collection of information and the appraisal of possibilities. These tasks should be carried on by persons or groups with developmental experience in Asia, working closely with Asians who have had similar experience.

The second function of a new organization would be to provide facilities for determining quickly and authoritatively, from a scientific point of view, the feasibility of applying modern technology to these various problems. The question of whether a specific proposal for solving a key problem would have a "run for its money" must be answered professionally before the next steps are taken.

This would require a kind of organizational structure that has "channels" of ready access to the scientific community. There is no thought of creating a new and separate staff capable of answering a wide range of questions.

For those projects which professional scientists have endorsed as feasible, there remains the task of executing the projects themselves. Initially this is entrepreneurial work; people and money must be found, and a new organizational unit be formed for each project.

This general decription of functions points to the kind of central organization that is needed. Gathering information and proposals, evaluating the proposals, and then arranging the organization of operational activities for a limited number of high-priority projects, are the functions. Performance of these functions would require a group which would enlist the services and cooperation of many existing organizations, but the group itself must have a small, but permanent and full-time, professional staff of its own. The central group should consist of people whose professional qualifications and standing would help create channels to the other organizations associated with the work.

Assistance in identifying "key problems" could come from relationships with established regional organizations such as the Asia Foundation which maintains offices in almost all Asian countries; from institutions such as the Asian Productivity Organization with a dozen branches in Asia; and from information made available by the commercial officers of United States embassies and the foreign staff of USAID. National development plans prepared by the planning ministries of Asian countries and the studies and reviews of these programs by international organizations such as the IBRD and IMF would be of great importance in identifying "key problems."

For its second and evaluative function, the central group would have to establish "channels" or close relationships with the scientific and academic community so that in the case of each proposal, it could arrange to have the determination of the feasibility or likelihood of finding acceptable solutions handled by the most suitable and competent professional people. In addition to getting answers to questions of feasibility, it would be necessary to obtain, through similar sources, preliminary information on the cost of organizing and operating the proposed projects.

Once this information has been gathered and an affirmative opinion reached as to the feasibility of a proposal in a field of high priority, the next step is to organize the execution of the project. This would require relationships with the sources of funds: governments, large foundations, and, in some cases, international corporations. The first steps are entrepreneurial and would require the services of some people with special talent of that kind. Once a group or unit is formed to carry out a project, there remains the general supervision of the operation and eventually the dissemination of the results.

Other questions that arise in considering these matters are: Should an initial start be global or regional in scope? Should a new organization limit itself to eight or ten projects or should sights be set higher? What group should take the initiative in organizing a group or board and finding the initial funds to support a small professional staff of people who could cultivate the relationships represented by the board and could open the channels to the other organizations whose cooperation would be required? Is it possible to start something right now?

As partial answers to these questions, I offer some of my own conclusions. I think that it is possible to start almost immediately. The receptivity of many groups and individuals who are active in development work to the approach that I have suggested has been encouraging. I think the cooperation of many of the organizations now engaged in technical assistance of one form or another would be forthcoming. A number of leaders in the field of applied research in important scientific institutions have indicated an interest in associating with such an organizational structure.

The institution which has sponsored my work in Asia, and for which I now act as an advisor, the Asia Foundation, is giving serious consideration to a plan to assemble a group which might form the board proposed in the organizational plan I have discussed. The Asia Foundation also is considering the advisability of making available a grant to fund the initial cost of recruiting a small staff and establishing such an organization.

As to the larger sums that would be required to operate any approved projects, all that can be said at present is that there are provisions in the current authorization bill for AID which would permit assistance to projects of the type envisioned in these proposals. In general, it seems to me that, in the case of carefully chosen projects of high priority, projects which are clearly related to the key problems of Asian development and endorsed as feasible by scientists of high standing, it should be possible to find the right people to carry out the necessary tasks and secure funds. It probably would be easier to start this work regionally, but it could later become global in scope if the pattern proved effective. Similar groups could be formed for other regions of the world.

I have not attempted to describe in any detail the relationship of such an undertaking to the activities of private corporations. To do so raises questions of ownership of the results of research and other matters that require careful analysis. However, it is obvious that there should be as active participation as possible by private business and that there should be representatives of leading international business organizations on the proposed board.

Finally, I do not want what I have said about present activities in this field to be taken as disparagement of any work now being carried on. The more that is done, the better. The needs are so urgent that it is unnecessary to be too concerned about some degree of overlapping efforts. What I am proposing is supplementary to the present efforts. I do, however, repeat that existing activities are scattered and sometimes so fragmented that there is no follow-through to a conclusion.

13

THE ROLE OF INTERNATIONAL ORGANIZATIONS AND THE GOVERNMENTS OF DEVELOPED COUNTRIES

Principal Paper—Jesse D. Perkinson

Report of Workshop 10—D. S. Cheever, Rapporteur

Have the international organizations of our world played a suitably effective role in international development efforts? How can they be made more effective? Such questions are the focus for Chapter 13.

The Editors

THE ROLE OF INTERNATIONAL ORGANIZATIONS AND THE GOVERNMENTS OF DEVELOPED COUNTRIES

Principal Paper by Jesse D. Perkinson

IT APPEARS THAT international organizations and the governments of developed countries may have little in common except that they are both engaged in assisting developing countries. For instance, a governmental assistance program usually is concerned with only one country whereas an international organization usually directs its efforts in a regional framework even if assistance is given to a single country. This applies not only to regional organizations such as the Organization of American States (OAS), but also to the United Nations family where many of the agencies plan their programs for a group of countries. The political aspects that influence governmental assistance efforts are obvious and important.

For these reasons, and because my experience has been primarily with the OAS, I will limit this paper primarily to the role of the OAS in increasing the effectiveness of the application of technology to industrialization of the Latin American countries. The Organization's associations with and knowledge of world organizations and other regional organizations indicate that most of our experience is valid for other areas.

PROBLEM STRUCTURE

In looking at the problems which exist in assisting the developing countries in their industrialization, the most outstanding and encompassing is the lack of ability of the developing countries to use effectively the assistance that is offered. This statement merely summarizes the multitude of interacting problems that exist.

Education and Training. In Latin America the total educational system and educational level of the population are perhaps of greatest concern. In an area where fewer university students study sciences and engineering than in almost any other part of the world, it is not hard to see that one of the major problems in the introduction of technology is the lack of the required personnel. The primary and secondary schools are rigidly controlled by the ministries of education of the national government so that reforms are difficult to achieve and require much effort and time. In a country where there are not enough trained teachers for even general courses, it is obvious that the number of teachers who can present a modern course in a scientific or technological subject is woefully inadequate. As you may know, the university system in Latin America is primarily based on the French system introduced during Napoleon's time. If the "professor" is not interested in developing his staff, it is difficult for the young, well-trained engineer or scientist to obtain research funds or to advance in his career in the university. The "catedra" or professorship controls the institute or faculty. The system also may result in a waste of time, talent, and money. For instance, a few years ago it was discovered that there were over one hundred basic biological courses taught in various institutes and faculties at one of the major universities. There was no coordination or contact between these courses; each had its own laboratories and staff. It is true that the introduction of science and engineering into the Latin American universities has frequently been a major impetus for reform—some universities now have departments of basic sciences—but the change in the system is very difficult to achieve. About three years ago the Brazilian Congress passed a law that required each university to have what are called "institutes" of biology, chemistry, physics, and mathematics. These would be equivalent of university departments in the United States. Thus. reform is taking place, but not rapidly enough.

One of the major problems in the production of the engineers and scientists required for industrialization is how to interest young people in careers in these subjects. Where the instruction is very poor and very few secondary schools have science laboratories, there is not much stimulus for the young student. Fortunately, this situation too is changing. The OAS, with the cooperation of the National Science Foundation, instituted some years ago a program of bringing science supervisors from the ministries of education and science professors from teacher training schools to participate in NSF summer institutes. The most promising of these participants were asked to conduct similar institutes on a regional basis in Latin America. As a result of this effort, almost every Latin American country now has a national program of further study for secondary-school science teachers.

Another problem which is frequently ignored, but which is of fundamental importance, is the high level of illiteracy in the total population. While there are countries such as Uruguay which have some of the highest literacy rates in the world, these countries are exceptions. It is frequently stated that about 50 per cent of the population in most Latin American countries is literate. These figures are usually based on the fact that perhaps 50 per cent of the citizens attended at least two or three years of primary school. It has been shown many times that, unless such individuals have continuing access to reading material, their rudimentary skills are soon lost. Using as a basis the numbers of copies of newspapers produced each day and assuming that an average of four people read each copy, it can be calculated that, in reality, only 20 to 30 per cent of the population in many countries is literate. It is obviously difficult to industrialize such countries rapidly.

These are but some of the problems in the educational area which create inhibitions to the introduction of technology. It is recognized by many that, at the moment, most Latin American countries may be increasing their industry and their scientific and technological base but, relative to the developed countries, they are getting farther behind each day. Those who are aware of and interested in Latin American education and particularly in science and technology know that new and more efficient techniques must be adopted if the Latin American countries are to achieve the quantum jump in development that will allow them to approach the status of the advanced countries. Many ideas for reform have been advanced but so far few, if any, of these new approaches have been put into operation.

Science Policy. Another major obstacle to the introduction of technology in the industrial development process is a lack of understanding or concern within the leadership group of the national governments. This fact and the changes that are occurring are perfectly illustrated in the experience in the OAS. Until ten years ago there was no scientific or technological program in the Organization except in the specialized agencies of the Pan American Institute of Geography and History, the Pan American Health Organization, and the Inter-American Agricultural Institute. Within this relatively short period the attitudes and knowledge of the decision makers in the member countries have changed to such an extent that when the chiefs of state met in April 1967 in Punta del Este, for the first time in the history of the OAS a major section of the Presidents' Declaration was devoted to science and technology. As a result, a much expanded regional program is being initiated. While this is encouraging, it is only a beginning. In examining the country development plans which are analyzed by the Committee for the Alliance for Progress, it is distressing to see that there is almost no recognition of the scientific and technological basis for economic and social development. Further, the technological implications of many parts of the development plans apparently are not even recognized.

This situation stems in large part from the fact that the scientific community exists outside the mainstream of the life of most countries. The isolation of the intellectual leaders in the universities from participation in industry or in the councils of government means that there is almost no input from the scientific community into governmental deliberations or decisions. The autonomy of national universities has been necessary and its achievements are recognized, but the autonomy concept has perhaps been carried to the point of alienation. Again, there are hopeful indications of reform in this area. Some of the universities are developing technical research institutes to cooperate with local industries and with government agencies.

The lack of understanding or of action in science or technology by government leaders is evidenced in the fact that only three or four Latin American countries have viable national research councils or their equivalents. In only one or two cases do these councils advise government agencies or participate in national development plans. In most countries there is no effort to arrive at a national technology structure or policy. Here again changes are occurring. At the moment, we have requests from three of the major countries for assistance in the area of science policy. One does not wish to be unduly critical of the government leaders for it is recognized that it is their difficult task to achieve the most productive balance among the many major problems of their countries. They must balance attempts for industrialization with concerns for general education, transportation, agricultural production, and export-import payments.

Technical Information and Transfer. Another major problem in the introduction of engineering technology is the paucity of information that is available and the poor channels of communication. Those Latin Americans who have attempted to introduce new technology have expressed great frustration. If we recognize the difficulties encountered in this country and in Western Europe in making appropriate individuals aware of technological advances, we realize immediately what a grave problem this is in Latin America.

Very few individual engineers or scientists can afford to subscribe to international journals. Since there is a proliferation of what passes for libraries in most universities, the resources are spread very thin and few of the universities have a technical library that is anywhere near adequate. This creates the obvious difficulty of technical personnel being quite behind in recent advances.

Because most Latin American industries have no tradition of conducting research on their own problems, such technical knowledge rarely exists in these industries. Even when an entrepreneur or manager wishes to purchase foreign technology, he meets with many problems. According to individual reports, he encounters far too many foreign representatives who are apparently interested only in selling the technology and very little, if at all, in whether what they are selling is appropriate and useful. Today, many attempts are being made to improve the availability of technical information, but so far as I am aware, no one seems to have arrived at a practical solution to the problem.

Population Increase. When we consider the problems that exist in the introduction of engineering technology to the industrialization of developing countries, there is one overriding factor which must always be taken into account but is too seldom recognized—the uncontrolled increase of population. Where the increase in population exceeds the increase in gross national product, it is axiomatic that all social and economic problems are intensified. The strains put upon already inadequate educational and health systems will become intolerable unless changes occur in this ratio. If the rate of population increase is not lowered, all of the problems that exist in regard to the introduction of technology will be intensified.

ACTIONS

Evaluation. When we look at what international organizations and the governments of developed countries may do immediately and in the near future in regard to technology-based industrialization, we recognize several efforts that could be made. We need a far better knowledge of the real situation in the developing countries. Anyone who works in this area is aware of the woefully inadequate statistics, or even the lack of methods for obtaining valid statistics. Efforts are being made in this area. The Inter-American Statistical Institute of the OAS is assisting each of the member countries in the improvement of its data reporting facilities. The Committee of the Alliance for Progress reviews of country development plans feed back to each country information on the inadequacy of important statistics. Many infrastructure studies remain to be made.

Policy. In the matter of increasing the awareness and understanding of government leaders and other decision makers, it is clear that international organizations and the governments of developing countries must work more closely with these individuals. All too frequently, foreign-assistance efforts are conducted at a peer level so that there is a professor of engineering working with other professors, and educators with educators. More efforts must be made with the mass media systems, the ministries of education, the planning office, and other such groups. Only through assistance to such agencies can changes in national policy be effected that will allow the international organizations and governments of developed countries to be more effective. Only thus can fiscal policies related to import duties, and the tax policies which might encourage investment in new technologies, be obtained.

Private Sector. Far more needs to be done in working with the private sector through the encouragement of professional associations and trade associations in the promotion among the entrepreneurs of the advantages and the necessities for technological innovation.

Institutional Mechanism. International organizations and governments should devote more of their efforts to the promotion and establishment of the necessary institutional mechanism for technological innovation in such areas as education and training, the support of technical research institutes, and the improvement of information and extension services.

An important contribution that can be made by an international organization or a foreign government is bringing about the kind of internal coordination that is frequently required. It is often easier for an outside force to achieve the cooperation of ministries of economy, education, and planning.

Summary. I have attempted to identify some of the major problems that are encountered when international organizations or governments of developed countries attempt to assist in the application of engineering technology to the industrialization of developing countries. Some of these problems are (1) insufficient education and training in the sciences and engineering and the inadequate extent of general education; (2) the lack of both governmental science policy and appreciation of the role of technology in development; (3) inadequate technical information and methods for the transfer of technology; and (4) the effect of uncontrolled population increase. It is suggested that far more basic studies need to be made to determine the priority requirements in the developing countries in the formulation and structure of science policy in private and governmental sectors.

It must always be recognized in the plans and efforts of international organizations and assisting governments that the problems are many and varied and that they interact so that solutions can hardly ever be simple. Assistance must be based upon an adequate knowledge of the true situation within the recipient country and one must be willing to work within the recognized limits at the same time that assistance is being given in the achievement of desirable reform.

REPORT OF WORKSHOP 10

D. S. Cheever, Rapporteur

A RELEVANT follow-up to Mr. Perkinson's paper would be to list the major problem areas confronting developing countries in their efforts to achieve industrial growth. Such a list would provide a first step toward a conceptual framework of potential international organization and developed country activities in promoting the basic objective of industrial growth through the application of technology. It would aid developing nations in establishing their own priorities and might also assist both developed countries and international organizations in the use of the limited resources they are willing and able to devote to assistance in this field.

The basic task and larger effort for industrialization must come from the developing country itself but, in most cases, external assistance can speed up the progress. The problem is to determine when the objective is served better by multilateral aid, bilateral aid, or a combination of both.

Most developing countries face three types of major problems in their quest for industrialization:

1. Creating a sound base for industrial development
2. Improving performance of existing industrial plants
3. Starting sound new industrial plants

CREATING A SOUND BASIS FOR INDUSTRIAL DEVELOPMENT

To create a sound basis for industrial development, developing countries typically need help in a number of problem areas. The first of these is the development of sound industrial plans and programs. With little experience to guide them, developing countries are necessarily dependent upon the experience of advanced countries. The problem they face is to find appropriate models for guidance. In the case of former colonial areas, such industrialization as may exist usually was designed originally to meet the economic objectives of the mother country. A newly independent country often is reluctant to follow a colonial development pattern that would imply continued economic subordination to the former metropole. Moreover, a model of industrial planning derived from another advanced country may be unsuitable for a pre-industrial society. In framing industrialization programs, international organizations can be helpful in drawing upon the experience of many countries and economies at various levels of development.

A second problem area is the development of appropriate industrial legislation and regulation. Legislation is needed to establish the administrative agencies which will develop industrial plans and guide public and private investment. Since a developing country usually has only recently assumed responsibility for this area of public policy, either because of its former colonial status or its traditional agrarian economy, it needs to draw selectively on the experience of industrialized countries and other developing countries.

A third problem area involves the administration of industrial legislation and the implementation of industrial plans. Again, many developing countries require external assistance. They need to establish agencies to plan, implement, and evaluate industrial development programs, and also to render direct assistance and support to industry. Because industrialization is a new goal for developing countries, they are unfamiliar with the public administration that is required. The private sector cannot undertake the task alone. Even when private enterprise makes a large contribution, public authority is necessary to insure consistency with the national goals of industrialization.

A fourth problem area is the physical and institutional infrastructure for industrial development. Examples of this infrastructure are transportation systems, irrigation systems, power and communications, and public administration in new urban areas.

IMPROVING PERFORMANCE OF EXISTING INDUSTRIAL PLANTS

Improvement in the performance of existing plants is a special question for countries where industrialization began under colonial auspices. This often involves a number of problem areas difficult for one country to solve unaided. One of these problem areas is the identification of barriers which limit present industrial output. Many factors of this nature may be involved including the supply and allocation of raw materials and other resources, distribution mechanisms, plant location, and a shift from import-substituting to export-oriented industries where foreign exchange is or will be a serious constraint.

A second problem is the improvement of equipment. Frequently, if not typically, developing countries are unable to mobilize the necessary domestic capital or foreign exchange needed to replace or modernize obsolescent equipment. Moreover, because of their limited experience with modern industry, they may not be familiar with improved manufacturing techniques. As a consequence, their industrial efficiency is low and they are unable to compete in world markets. Overprotection of existing industry also may be a serious problem.

A third problem area is the improvement of technology. Typically a developing country has not reached a "take-off" point where its own technological development is self-sustaining. Technical assistance is needed from overseas if it is to provide for the continuing improvements of its industrial technology.

A fourth problem area is the improvement of management. Where industrialization may have had a beginning under an alien (colonial) regime, new managers and executives must be trained through operational executive programs (such as the United Nations OPEX program and the United States International Executive Service Corps) and technical assistance to replace the work of expatriates returning to the mother country. In the case of countries long independent who already have some industrial development, there is often a need for external aid to introduce the management techniques required to bring modern technology to bear on manufacturing processes. Unless a country is heavily industrialized, selfimprovement in management techniques is hard to attain. New applications of science and technology require innovations in industrial management and public administration.

The fifth problem area is the improvement of manpower. Indeed, lack of capacity to improve the quality of its manpower is a hallmark of a developing country. Development or change may be needed in the private and secondary school curricula. Often problems arise out of cultural traditions, work habits, and social attitudes that impede industrial growth. The manpower problem of social adaptability.

Sixth is the need for improved industrial financing. Developing countries do not save enough from domestic production nor earn enough foreign exchange to finance such improvement. Some external aid or capital investment is necessary as was once the case with countries already industrialized.

Seventh, industrial products must be improved to earn foreign exchange and to reduce import requirements. A developing country may need advice on the marketability of its new products overseas as well as on improving their domestic sale. Products suitable for one market environment are not necessarily acceptable in another.

Closely related to the problem of product improvement is that of export production and widening of the markets. For most developing nations, a larger volume of production is necessary to support the development of modern industrial plants and the use of more advanced—and more efficient—technology.

All of these problem areas are interrelated. All require or benefit from some degree of external assistance.

STARTING SOUND NEW INDUSTRIAL PLANTS

The establishment of new industrial plants involves most of the problem areas noted in connection with the second subobjectives such as developing manpower, improving products, and increasing markets. In addition, however, developing countries often need assistance in identifying and documenting the feasibility of the new plants they desire. While it may know in general what it is equipped to produce by a comparative advantage in resources, a pre-industrial society usually is inexperienced in determining what types of industrial technology are suitable for its natural resources and factors of production.

228

A second problem is to provide financing for new industrial plants. Financing is particularly difficult in the case of new plants because of the high costs of the new technologies, including plant and product design, and the necessary management and entrepreneurial skills. While these expenses usually are greater for new plants than for existing plants needing improvement and modernization, even in this latter case the financial requirements may be very heavy.

EXTERNAL AID CAN ONLY BE SUPPLEMENTARY

However great the need for external assistance to accelerate or commence industrialization, the basic job must be done by the developing country itself. External aid, whether multilateral or bilateral, private or public, can only be supplementary for several reasons.

First, if the provision of capital and technical assistance is *primarily* from external sources, recipient countries are apt to feel that their political independence is jeopardized by economic subordination. Moreover, external capital aid and technical assistance are unlikely to be forthcoming in amounts sufficient to do the job in countries where the need is greatest.

Secondly, experience over the years indicates that both donors and recipients must agree upon certain standards of performance. External assistance must be available on political and economic terms acceptable to the recipient, but administrative, economic, and sometimes political conditions must be satisfactory to the donor. The donor is not in a position to create the conditions that stimulate industrialization. It can only advise and assist. With this overriding limitation, there are nonetheless four types of external activity which can be helpful in providing inputs needed by developing countries to help solve particular problems of industrialization.

Direct Assistance by International Organizations and Developed Nations. The first of these is by providing *direct* technical assistance. Such assistance may include training programs, financing feasibility studies, funding demonstration factories, and the provision of operational executive and management staff on a temporary basis until counterparts are trained. Direct assistance of this type may come from individual donor countries or from multilateral sources such as the United Nations Industrial Development Organization (UNIDO). This new United Nations body is financed principally by voluntary contributions, largely from the developed countries, and its services are in much demand by developing nations. UNIDO is beginning to conduct industrial training programs, provide advisors for existing factories, and fund demonstration units.

Other United Nations bodies also provide direct inputs on a modest scale. The Operational Executive Program (OPEX) is able to provide staff for industrial planning. The United Nations Development Program (UNDP) finances feasibility studies of relevance for industrialization, such as studies on resource availability. The central United Nations organization itself provides technical assistance in public administration, community development, and other key areas for a society which is transforming from an agricultural to a industrial economy. Other non-United Nations international organizations, such as the Development Center of the Organization for Economic Cooperation and Development (OECD) and the Inter-American Development Bank (IDB), are able to provide similar direct inputs on a modest scale.

The United States, France, Germany, the United Kingdom, the Soviet Union, Italy, Japan, and other industrialized countries provide bilateral assistance to countries seeking help in industrialization. The types of aid they provide vary; they may supply technical assistance on a grant or loan basis but, in general, they make funds available for the development of industrial plants and the supporting infrastructure only on a loan basis. In most cases these loans are "tied," in the sense that they require that the machinery and other major imported components be procured in the donor country. Interest and repayment terms may be on concessionary terms which offer the recipient country a lower interest rate, a longer time for repayment, or the possibility of repayment in its own currency. The Soviet Union appears to prefer a type of "turnkey" arrangement under which it makes loans providing for complete, packaged plants which are installed by Soviet technicians.

An Institutional Emphasis. A second means of solving particular problems of industrialization is to invite an external agency to assist a local organization in providing the needed inputs. For example, UNIDO might be encouraged to provide technical and OPEX assistance to industrial development organizations and institutions, such as industrial development corporations and centers, technical institutes, and industrial estates. The institutions assisted may be local or countrywide in their activities. Several United Nations Specialized Agencies, such as the International Labour Organization (ILO) and UNESCO, emphasize this institutional approach. UNIDO is prepared to be the executing agency for Special Fund Assistance to local institutions so that its program scope is not restricted exclusively by its own financial resources.

A somewhat parallel institutional approach has been utilized by some of the developed countries in their bilateral assistance programs.

Catalytic Activity. A third means is by catalytic activity in which an external agency such as UNIDO stimulates action by *other* international or bilateral organizations which provide the needed inputs. Such activity is being developed in industrial and investment promotion services, industry and management institutes, productivity centers, consultants consortia, and equity capital funds. Other examples are internationally or bilaterally sponsored industrial franchise corporations and repair and maintenance centers. The International Finance Corporation, a subsidiary of the International Bank, serves as a catalyst through its participation in industrial projects and in local development finance companies.

Informational Activity. A fourth means is by informational activities to develop and disseminate relevant knowledge to help local personnel provide needed inputs more effectively than they are otherwise able to do. Such activities include studies and publications, expert group meetings, seminars, and industrial information services. Several international agencies are engaged, or intend to be engaged, in such activity; UNIDO and the OECD Development Center are particularly relevant. Several developed nations have devoted extensive attention to provision of technical documentation and other information to newly industrializing countries.

WHAT TYPE OF INPUT IS BEST?

Although all of the four basic types of external aid programs are useful and even necessary in achieving industrialization goals, some appear to be more effective than others. Direct assistance, such as the provision of experts and consultants, has been emphasized principally to date in technical assistance programs, whether bilateral or multilateral. In the case of bilateral programs, direct assistance may be thought necessary because of short-term political and diplomatic factors or by virtue of the extent of aid that appears to be necessary. For the social and economic purpose of accelerated industrialization, however, institutional and catalytic activities appear to be more effective in the long run in most instances because of their multiplier effects and the increased leverage exercised by indigenous efforts within developing societies. Since the total of external resources available, whether multilateral or bilateral, is always limited, greater attention should be paid to the more enduring contribution made by catalytic and institutional activity.

MULTILATERAL OR BILATERAL ASSISTANCE

Whether the major types of inputs should be on a bilateral or multilateral basis depends upon the particular circumstances of each developing country and the nature of its political relationships with eligible donors. Multilateral activity is frequently more acceptable politically. This view is held not only by most recipients but also by many donors. The competence of multilateral institutions is gradually improving despite initial drawbacks and disappointments. Their resources, however, are pitifully small in relation to the needs of the developing countries.

Some smaller donors, such as the Scandinavian countries and the Netherlands, favor multilateral assistance as a matter of principle. Their own resources are relatively meager. They also wish to develop international institutions and activities to reduce the competitiveness of major bilateral programs. Even though some of the larger donors are showing signs of increasing their reliance on multilateral activity, they are not yet ready to place at the disposal of the international agencies the massive sums required for assistance in industrialization. For the foreseeable future the developed countries apparently will emphasize bilateral programs to meet national objectives in politically sensitive areas.

PUBLIC OR PRIVATE INVESTMENT

While most of the capital necessary for industrialization has come, and must continue to come, from the mobilization of private investment (both internal and external), the World Bank Group and regional development banks also must be sources of capital assistance for several reasons. Private capital is often hesitant to go where the need is greatest. The World Bank, the International Finance Corporation (the member of the World Bank Group chiefly concerned with industrial development), and regional development banks such as the Inter-American Development Bank (IDB), moreover, would appear to have potential for success in exacting performance standards by developing countries. That is, external interference or intervention in many cases is more acceptable and therefore more effective when the agent is a nonpolitical international agency rather than a national government. For this reason, the funds of the International Development Association (IDA), the soft-loan affiliate of the World Bank, should be replenished as soon as possible.

THE PACKAGE-PLANT APPROACH

In financing industrialization projects, international and national aid agencies both should consider the "package-plant" approach on a "turnkey" basis by which training, maintenance, and operations are included for a trial period along with the actual construction of industrial plants. Experience has shown, however, that package-plant projects have suffered from a lack of prior detailed feasibility and market studies.

THE ROLE OF PUBLIC ADMINISTRATION

The experience of both international organizations and developed countries in contributing to the industrialization of the developing countries has underlined the importance of public administration. Developing countries need to create coordinating mechanisms for the effective planning and implementation of industrial programs. Coordination manifests itself as a serious problem at many levels.

First, there is a multiplicity of specialized agencies and programs within the United Nations system. The role of the United Nations Resident Representative in recipient regions and countries could be crucial in helping the recipient country link these activities in a coherent pattern of industrial development. Recipient governments need to know what each of the specialized agencies can provide and should be assisted in relating the contributions of each to its over-all development plan. The World Bank and, in a few instances, regional development banks have been useful in framing such development plans. The coordination task is to instrument properly the varied contributions of several international agencies.

Second, coordination arises as a problem in relating United Nations activities with those of non-United Nations agencies such as the OECD. Some progress has been made in this area. Representatives of the World Bank, for example, attend all meetings of the OECD's Development Assistance Committee (DAC). The Common Market is represented on the DAC by the European Development Fund. National and international officials make increasing use of studies and informational services developed by national and international institutions. UNIDO works cooperatively with many other bodies relevant to industrialization.

A third problem area involves coordination between international programs and national programs executed on a bilateral basis and among the various bilateral programs. Officials in developing countries sometimes are confronted by an array of uncoordinated aid projects, each amounting in many cases to relatively little in a total plan, and each requiring different terms and conditions. The harmonization of aid programs to meet the strategy of an over-all plan and the standardization of the conditions of aid offered by a number of donors are important tasks for the OECD and the United Nations system.

Despite its growing importance, assistance in the field of industrialization is a relatively new activity in public administration. Public administration's importance arises from the fact that industrialization in a developing country extends well beyond industrial technology. Administrative technology is a necessary adjunct if accelerated industrial growth is to be achieved. There are specific needs for assistance in industrial technology, such as an increased emphasis on research and development in plant design, taking into account market size, available resources, and significant local factors, but there is an equal need for administrative services geared to indigenous political experience. There is a paucity of evaluated information concerning the organization, staffing, and methods of operation of national agencies, such as ministries of industry, in developing countries. The tasks of such a ministry are far different from the duties usually performed by the governmental agencies in new nations. They involve such matters as participation in economic planning, development of attitudes and services to promote and assist industrialization, and competence to deal with prospective investors on a modern technical level.

As a follow-up of the present Conference, some institution, such as a university, should undertake more research in the interface between industrial development and public administration. The special role of such governmental agencies as ministries of industry and industrial development banks might be the initial focus of such studies.

14

THE ROLE OF NATIONAL GOVERNMENTS

Principal Paper—K. T. Li
Discussion of the Paper by K. T. Li
Commentary by Warren J. Bilkey
Report of Workshop 11—Robert Norman,
Rapporteur

National governments play a significant role in the concerted effort toward an increased effectiveness of engineering in the industrialization process.

The Editors

THE ROLE OF NATIONAL GOVERNMENTS

Principal Paper by K. T. Li

IT HAS BEEN universally recognized that science and technology play a very important part in laying a strong foundation for a country's economic progress and that scientific and technological research and development are the prime generators of industrial productivity. Engineering technology is especially important to a developing country because it relates directly and very closely to almost every field of industrial activity, be it the construction of a dam or the erection of a fertilizer plant. The effective application of engineering technology, therefore, should be given high priority in all the efforts directed toward the promotion of industrialization.

We all realize that the industrialization of a developing country, especially if it is to be accelerated, could not be achieved without the effective application of modern engineering technology. Yet, virtually all developing countries are facing the same problem—the lack of modern engineering technology. Of course, the necessary technology may be obtained by importing process knowhow, design engineering, and plant equipment from abroad and by engaging foreign engineers for construction and operation. However, excessive dependence on outside knowledge and skills is certainly not a healthy sign in the sense that the so-called technological gap will be widened rather than narrowed. Moreover, technology developed in the context of an advanced country may not be ideally suited to the needs of a developing country, with its altogether different context. One oft-cited example is that manufacturing processes designed for mass production are not economical for the small domestic market of a developing country. The effective adaptation of engineering technology, therefore, must be emphasized and promoted in parallel with the progress of industrialization.

ROLE OF NATIONAL GOVERNMENTS

The government of a developing country can play a very decisive role in the promotion and effective application of engineering technology to industrialization.

Formation of Sound Policies and Action Programs for the Development of Basic Education and Training in Science and Technology. Without a large reservoir of intelligent and well-educated young people, it is impossible to acquire, disseminate, and make effective use of modern technology. In a developing country where the lack of technical and managerial personnel is a serious drawback, the government can do much in the development of manpower by setting up and implementing an effective basic educational system. All children should be afforded an opportunity for at least six years of primary education, progessively increasing to twelve years. The more intelligent and promising high-school students should be given a chance to continue to college and graduate studies, with selections made on the basis of intelligence and ability where facilities for higher education cannot accommodate all applicants. High priority must be given to the selection and training of qualified teachers and to development of modern curricula, textbooks, teaching materials, and laboratory equipment. Curricula at the college and graduate levels should include not only science and engineering, but also courses in management, organization, statistics, marketing, and other subjects related to production and trade. For without modern management and organization and competence in these other areas, the effective application of modern technology could not be facilitated.

In order to develop technical and managerial manpower, education must be closely coordinated with the growth of industry and accompanied by intensive training programs. The government should encourage continuous and close communication and liaison between educational authorities and the industrial sector so that the latter's growing need for technical and managerial personnel can be met. For instance, both the faculty and the students should be exposed to the actual progress and problems of industry, and industrial people should be afforded frequent opportunities to learn of the latest advances in education.

Vocational and apprenticeship training also must be promoted within each individual industry to ensure a constant supply of skilled labor. Here the government can help through budgetary support and by taking advantage of the many training opportunities offered by the United Nations and such exchange programs as may be sponsored by the developed countries.

Leadership by Public Enterprise in the Adaptation of Engineering Technology. Public enterprise usually predominates in the early stages of industrialization in a developing country. The government is thus in a strong position to set good examples in the development and application of engineering technology in the industries directly under its operation. These industries should be encouraged not only to promote the adaptation and development of new technology, but also to provide working opportunities and a research environment for college graduates. The technologies and skills developed within the government enterprises are valuable resources to any program of industrialization. In fact, the government enterprises are often turned into training schools for the private industrial sector to supply them with technical and managerial personnel.

Creation of a Favorable Investment Climate Conducive to Technology Transfer Through Joint Ventures. During the early stages of industrial growth a developing country will depend heavily on outside technology as well as foreign capital. Technical cooperation and joint-venture projects with developed countries provide a significant source of technology. However, prerequisite to achieving such technology transfer is the creation of a favorable investment climate. Among a number of measures that a government may take to improve the existing investment climate are easing of government controls, amendment of obsolete or obstructive legislation, simplification of administrative procedures, improvement of the credit system, betterment of labor-management relations, setting-up of industrial estates, and provision of tax incentives. In short, a stable economy with a healthy investment climate can induce a constant inflow of modern technology that combines with foreign investment either in the form of capital or knowhow.

Promotion of Industry on a Normal Pattern of Growth. The development of engineering technology is not something that happens overnight. Ordinarily, it takes place gradually with the progress of industry. Inspired by national prestige or an over-anxiousness to industrialize, a number of developing countries took hasty steps toward the establishment of heavy industries, all in need of very complex and sophisticated technology, far above the existing level of technology in those countries. Hasty industrialization, plus high-pressure salesmanship typified by the offer of a supplier's credit before a careful project evaluation is made, often result in serious technical difficulties and perhaps even economic dislocation. In this connection, the government can exert very significant influence by mapping out an orderly development program starting with light industries that are not highly demanding of capital and technology and gradually moving into more sophisticated, heavy industries. For example, a general pattern of growth of an engineering industry in developing countries may start with minimal facilities for the manufacture of agricultural implements and hardware items, followed by more sophisticated workshops for the maintenance of imported machinery and equipment. Then after the comparatively lengthy period of time needed for development of skills in using imported tools and semiprocessed materials, various engineering assembly plants for agricultural, food processing, transport, and construction industries can be established.

Promotion of Regional Cooperation to Achieve Minimum Economies of Scale. Many branches of such industries as machinery, heavy electrical equipment and appliances, transport equipment, and petrochemicals are characterized as being highly capital intensive and relying on a growing market to achieve the desired economies of scale. These industries are especially suitable for regional and subregional cooperation, where the government can play a very active role in promoting bilateral or multilateral cooperation based on market sharing or the joint venture principle.

Enforcement of Engineering Standards for Industrial Development. A basic requirement for the production of quality products is equipment which meets certain engineering standards. In a developing country the government needs to establish national standard bodies at a relatively early stage so that various standards, codes, and testing procedures can be provided in the course of industrial development. New standards need to follow as far as possible the recognized international ones. Rigid national standards are a regulatory instrument for corrective application of engineering technology.

Strengthening Cooperation with Developed Countries in Science and Technology and Promotion of an Indigenous Research and Development Program. Research and development are effective means of promoting engineering technology, providing knowledge for more efficient use of equipment, for adaptation of foreign technology to local conditions, for troubleshooting problems, and, above all, for development of indigenous knowhow and technology which a developing country will need to sustain its industrial growth. Because it may take a long time for private industries in most of the developing countries to become research oriented, the government must take initiative action in sponsoring and supporting research and development activities through strengthening cooperation with developed countries and establishing industrial research institutes.

In order to accelerate the development of science and technology, external assistance from developed countries in the form of the services of scientists and technologists can be extremely valuable in the transfer, adaptation, and application of new technology. Such outside assistance can serve as a catalyst to stimulate local research interest, help organize research programs, and greatly shorten the time needed for generation of indigenous know-how and technology.

The government can also help promote technological research and development by organizing industrial research institutes, strengthening research and development activities in government-owned industries, and providing a healthy research environment.

Government Provision of Incentives. In development planning, practiced in varying degrees in most of the developing countries, the government can provide fiscal and tax benefits to all industries to encourage research and development, training of personnel, and application of new technology.

WHAT THE GOVERNMENT OF THE REPUBLIC OF CHINA HAS DONE

Some experiences of the Republic of China may serve to illustrate how government can help in the effective application of engineering technology to industrial development.

Postwar Economic Difficulties and Government Program for Rapid Rehabilitation and Orderly Development. When the province of Taiwan was returned to the Republic of China at the end of World War II after half a century of Japanese colonial rule, it was in a state of ruin and disorganization. All major industries and the infrastructure were severely damaged. The situation was aggravated by the large-scale repatriation of Japanese technical and professional personnel, which resulted in an acute shortage of skilled manpower.

Illustrations of how the effective application of engineering technology has helped the development of some key industries in Taiwan will be presented later, following a few comments on our development strategy.

Initial efforts at industrial development were directed toward the rehabilitation of then-existing facilities with priority assigned to the infrastructure, agricultural-based industries, and important import-saving industries, such as chemical fertilizers and textiles. These industries were principally those related to the needs of the people for clothing, food, and shelter. Subsequent efforts were turned toward the production of more durable goods and industrial intermediates. As industrialization thus moved forth, increasing sophistication and diversification took place as evidenced by the manufacture of synthetic fibers, plastics, and electronics. In the meantime, export-expanding rather than import-saving has become the dominant factor in the allocation of resources. In fact, the whole economy has become increasingly oriented toward the export, rather than the domestic, market. Future efforts at industrial development will be concentrated on promotion of the petrochemical and heavy-machinery industries.

The annual rate of industrial growth during 1953–1967 averaged 13.5 per cent with the major contribution coming from the manufacturing sector which are ranked among the fastest growing industries with an annual growth rate of over 15 per cent.

Another significant feature of our economic growth is the coordinated development of agriculture and industry. The government realized early that agriculture is not only a source of food, but also a source of capital and raw materials. In addition, rural prosperity contributes significantly to a growing market for industrial products. Therefore, a great deal of attention has been given to the development of better irrigation systems, improved farming practices, and more effective application of chemical fertilizers, herbicides, and pesticides.

Extensive Governmental Program of Training Technical and Managerial Personnel. Realizing the need for technical manpower, the government of the Republic of China has spared no effort in the development of human resources. In charge of manpower development planning is a special committee in the Council for International Economic Cooperation and Development, the nation's central economic planning agency. Because projections made by the committee have indicated a sizable shortage of technical manpower in the next few years, an increasing number of vocational schools with an emphasis on industrial skills are now being built. The recent establishment of the National Vocational Training Service for Industry with assistance from the United Nations is expected to bring greater momentum to this effort. Meanwhile, the government has tried to maintain close coordination between educational institutions and industry and encourages public enterprises to set up vocational training programs of their own. But the most important single step taken by the government to meet the new manpower requirement is the recent extension of public schooling from six to nine years. This move was made after much planning and preparation in terms of providing additional teachers and facilities.

In the area of training of employees, a significant number of technical or managerial personnel from industry have been sent abroad every year to receive training or advanced education. We have also made good use of training opportunities provided by the United States and the various United Nations Specialized Agencies. By the end of June, 1968, a total of 3420 technicians and specialists had received such training. Foreign experts or consultants are engaged by the government or through such government-sponsored agencies as the China Productivity Center or the Metal Industry Development Center to conduct seminars or training classes for local industrial personnel.

Creation of a Healthy and Favorable Climate for Foreign Investment. As mentioned earlier, an effective way to acquire modern technology is through foreign investment. About a decade ago the government realized that many of the controls and protective measures which were adopted earlier to cope with a highly inflationary situation were no longer meaningful and had become obstacles to growth. At the same time many of the traditional concepts and institutions and the legal framework originally established for a rural society could no longer serve the needs of industrial development. Consequently, the government mapped out a crash program for economic reform. New investment laws were promulgated providing incentives such as a five-year tax holiday and other tax benefits. The subsequent improvement in investment climate has induced a substantial and continuous inflow of foreign investment. Foreign companies began to set up operations on Taiwan, either with or without local equity participation, for the manufacture of chemical fertilizers, lubricating oils, polyethylene, electronics. Up-to-date knowhow was brought in, sophisticated modern machinery was imported, local engineering and technical employees were given specialized training overseas, and local labor was taught new production techniques, particularly in the fields of electronics and petrochemicals. Moreover, such transfer of technology is a continuing process, since the foreign investors must constantly upgrade their technology in order to remain competitive in the international market. The presence of a foreign firm can also stimulate the improvement and development of local satellite industries in the application of new products and supply of materials, parts, and components.

GOVERNMENT-OWNED INDUSTRIES TAKING AN INITIATIVE IN THE DEVELOPMENT AND APPLICATION OF ENGINEERING TECHNOLOGY

Petroleum and Petrochemical Industries. The development of the petroleum refining industry in Taiwan is a good example of effective application of engineering technology. In the course of modernizing its Kaohsiung Refinery, the government-owned Chinese Petroleum Corporation learned how to develop and utilize its own technical personnel to perform detailed engineering work, fabricate vessels and heat exchangers, and undertake field construction. By doing its own detailed engineering, the engineering fee payable to a foreign contractor can be reduced by almost two-thirds, about 20 per cent of the plant cost. The cost of a vessel or a reactor if fabricated locally with imported materials and fittings can be reduced by as much as 50 per cent below the cost of shipping in a whole unit from abroad. By utilizing local engineering to the maximum, the cost of building a petroleum refining plant or a chemical plant in Taiwan, including ocean freight for imported equipment, is estimated to be only about 85 per cent of the erected cost in the Gulf coast of the United States.

The Chinese Petroleum Corporation is now capable of designing independently such processing plants as crude topping, hydro-desulfurization, products treating, and offsite facilities. Its refining capacity has increased from 6000 barrels per day in 1947 to 110 000 barrels per day in 1968.

The government also is actively promoting the development of petrochemical industries which involve more sophisticated technology. Two principal raw materials will be used, naphtha from imported crude oil and indigenous natural gas. Natural gas is being used as the principal raw material in two existing ammonia-urea plants. Ethane extracted from natural gas will be used to make ethylene as a substitute of carbide acetylene for the local PVC industry. A newly completed naphtha cracking facility is providing a variety of raw materials for making polyethylene and several intermediates, such as acrylonitrile and DMT, for the manufacture of acrylic and polyester fibers. The development of petrochemical industries in Taiwan is a typical example of the process of backward integration in industrial development, as a number of plastics and synthetic fiber industries based on imported intermediates are already established. In this connection, it might also be pointed out that, in a developing country, the government often has to play the dual role of supplier and promoter, as is exemplified in our case of first promoting the extablishment of textile and plastics industries and later serving as supplier of their raw materials.

Electric Power Industry. Realizing that electric power is the prime mover for industrial growth, the Chinese government has placed strong emphasis on the development of the power industry. The government-owned Taiwan Power Company has been expanding its system rapidly from a peak load of only 33 000 kilowatts in 1945 to 1 535 400 kilowatts in 1968. The total installed capacity now is close to 2 million kilowatts, of which about 40 per cent is hydro and 60 per cent thermal.

The biggest thermal unit now in operation, completed only some three months ago, has a capacity of 300 000 kilowatts. Thermal units of this size, I understand, first began service in the United States 8 years ago.

Through the application of modern technology, the power industry has shown marked improvements which may be highlighted as follows:

—Reduction in line loss from over 35 per cent in 1946 to 11.2 per cent in 1967
—Reduction in fuel consumption from 1.48 kg/kWh in 1946 to 0.463 kg/kWh in 1967

—Reduction in number of outages and introduction of the technique of hot-line repair and maintenance
—Promotion of rural electrification; electric services are now enjoyed by 97 per cent of the total population
—Use of computer control

The Taiwan Power Company is also planning to use nuclear energy for power generation. The first nuclear station, with a capacity of 500 megawatts, is scheduled to go into operation by the end of 1975.

Shipbuilding Industry. Shipbuilding plays an important role in the industrial development of the Republic of China, with both shipping and fisheries holding out good prospects for Taiwan's island economy. Moreover, shipbuilding is a labor-intensive industry and requires the assembling of a great variety of machinery.

The government operates the biggest shipyard on the island. As a result of recent expansion, it has begun the construction of 25 000-ton class freighters. A new dry dock is under construction aimed at building 100 000-ton oil tankers under technical cooperation with Ishikawajima-Harima Heavy Industries of Japan. Extensive training of designers, welders, fabricators, and other technical personnel is now being undertaken at the government's shipyard as well as in Japan.

Civil Engineering and Dam-Construction Activities. Marked improvement and application of engineering technology can also be shown in some construction projects in Taiwan.

The Shihmen reservoir project is the first multipurpose water resources development project undertaken by the government and provides such services as irrigation, power, flood control, and public water supply. The construction of all the main structures of the project, which has a storage capacity of 316 million cubic meters, was carried out by utilizing highly mechanized construction equipment and local labor.

Highway bridges are built with unique design and construction methods. For example, the 400-foot Rainbow Bridge on the Taiwan Eastern Coastal Highway, the first long-span prestressed concrete arch bridge built in Taiwan, was fabricated with the cantilever method. The Tahong Bridge, built with a girder-arch structure, also used the cantilever method for erection.

Three water tanks with a total capacity of 64 000 cubic meters were built for the Taipei city water supply. The building of the tanks was characterized by the use of preload steel wire wound around the tank wall to reinforce the prestressed concrete structure.

GOVERNMENT-SPONSORED OR SUPPORTED AGENCIES FOR TRAINING AND EFFECTIVE UTILIZATION OF MANPOWER AND DEVELOPMENT OF TECHNOLOGY

China Productivity and Trade Center. The Center is an autonomous, nonprofit organization sponsored by the government to coordinate public and private industries in order to improve management and quality control, assist in training skilled and managerial personnel, disseminate new technology, and promote industrial design and other activities in the interest of trade expansion and greater productivity.

Metal Industries Development Center. Another autonomous, nonprofit organization initiated by the government, with assistance from the United Nations, is the Metal Industries Development Center. This Center for developing metal and engineering industries and for training technical and managerial personnel at all levels in these industries is well equipped and staffed. In addition to manpower training, its other functions are to give advisory service on the choice of materials, selection of machinery and equipment, and establishment of standards and quality controls; to disseminate knowledge and skills with respect to modern engineering techniques; and to make industrial surveys and organize various seminars.

China Technical Consultants, Inc. Initiated by the government and sponsored by a group of more than twenty leading industries, the China Technical Consultants, Inc., was organized as a nonprofit organization. The main objective in forming this organization is to tap the experienced technical and managerial personnel resources available in large-scale enterprises and make use of them by their rendering engineering, construction, and other technical services to local industry. In the past decade the organization has built a number of industrial plants, including several Sino-American joint investment projects. It has also rendered technical services abroad in Thailand, Vietnam, and Singapore.

GOVERNMENT-SPONSORED PROGRAMS OR INSTITUTES FOR PROMOTION OF SCIENCE AND TECHNOLOGY

Union Industrial Research Institute. This government institute is engaged in industrial research. The government is seriously considering a "Research Park" in the Hsinchu area to be developed around this Institute and its neighboring facilities to encourage research on radio isotopes, electronics, glass manufacturing, food processing, and so on.

Seminar on Modern Engineering and Technology. This Seminar is jointly sponsored by the Chinese Institutes of Engineers in Taipei and in New York and is financially supported by the Chinese government and the Asia Foundation. The objective of the Seminar is to introduce new engineering technology by inviting Chinese specialists now residing in the United States to Taiwan. The first Seminar was conducted in 1966, covering the fields of chemical, civil, and mechanical engineering and electronics. A second Seminar was held in 1968 covering such additional fields as food processing, electrical engineering, material science, and urban development. These Seminars, to be held every other year, have proved instrumental in the extension of new technology.

Sino-American Cooperation in Science and Technology. In order to accelerate the development of science and technology, external assistance from developed countries is needed. The cooperation in science and technology between the United States and the Republic of China provides an example. Conferences between scientists and experts from both countries are held regularly, and emphasis is laid on the sharing of experience and knowledge instead of direct financial aid. Such bilateral cooperation helps formulate policies for developing science and technology, stimulates the improvement of organization and management, and shortens the time required for developing indigenous research capabilities.

BRAIN DRAIN

Lastly, I will comment briefly on the problem of "brain drain," which has become a phenomenon in all developing countries and tends to nullify their efforts to build up techincal manpower, thereby seriously affecting the development and application of science and technology.

Brain Drain Not Conducive to the Growth of Developing Countries. The common causes of brain drain are, of course, well known. Among the more significant are the lack of a favorable environment for research in terms of physical facilities; opportunities for advancement, income and security; and the strong pulls from the advanced countries which offer greater challenge and opportunities together with a high standard of living. Such pulls will always be felt as long as a differential exists between the environments. For the question is not so much "How good are you?" as "How good are you as compared with the best the world has to offer?"

The students of a developing country, after having received advanced education and training in a developed country, constitute an extremely valuable asset to their fatherland. Consequently, as many of them as possible should be encouraged by the developed countries to return to their own countries to work, teach, or do research. However, this is a difficult challenge to the developing countries, because it presents the need for greater incentives, more satisfactory working conditions, better personnel practices, and, most important of all, a willingness to give talented youth positions of true responsibility and authority.

The developed countries must also help alleviate the brain drain problem. They could discourage employment of foreign graduates, on the one hand, and arouse the graduates' interest in the development of their own countries, on the other. If the brain drain of the developing countries cannot be checked effectively, the technological gap between the developed and the developing countries will be widened rather than narrowed, a trend that will not be in the best interest of either the developed or the developing world.

A Suggestion for the Advanced Countries and International Bodies. Therefore, in conclusion, I suggest that something be done by the developed countries and international organizations to improve the present situation.

Today the developed countries, in providing the students from the underdeveloped areas with advanced training in science and technology, are not doing much toward meeting the specific need for skills and knowhow in the developing countries. The more advanced the training, the less its relevance to the context of an underdeveloped economy. No wonder most of our Chinese scientists and engineers, after training in the United States, are lost to us, many forever.

The same problem is also true of the manufacturing processes, techniques, and equipment developed in the advanced countries. In most cases, they need be modified and adapted to the environment of the developing countries if their application there is to be effective.

The advanced countries and international organizations can do much to help redirect the training of foreign students; for instance, attractive scholarships and fellowships could be awarded only to those foreign students who concern themselves with the problems of their own countries and promise to return to their homeland after training and stay for at least a certain period of time. Special classroom and research programs truly relevant to the problems of the developing countries also could be offered.

Regional educational centers at the graduate level could be effective. An example is the Bangkok-based Asian Institute of Technology, which is supported by AID and other organizations and which has an international faculty and an international student body. Such centers promote a greater exchange of ideas and knowledge in an environment in which the realities of life of the developing countries cannot easily be overlooked. The professors recruited from the advanced countries will be exposed, as never before, to the problems of development and, it is to be hoped, will soon learn to reorient their instruction accordingly.

Another arrangement in the interest of effective technology transfer might follow the pattern of the Institute of Technology at Kanpur in India. I understand that it is affiliated with ten technological institutions in the United States.

Special research projects could also be set up and devoted to studies for modifying modern technologies in order that they may be transplanted more effectively to the developing countries. Foreign graduates may well be recruited to work on these projects so that even if they choose to remain in the advanced countries, they can still contribute to the solution of the problems of development in their own countries.

Efforts such as these I have just cited can be as fruitful as other types of technical assistance and much less costly than the shipment of expensive equipment and machinery. I sincerely hope that my suggestions will be given serious consideration by all the aid-giving countries and by relevant private foundations and international organizations.

DISCUSSION OF THE PAPER BY K. T. LI

DR. HUNSBERGER: Minister Li has indicated his enthusiasm for foreign investment and a dependence upon imported technology, which raises two questions: First, what is Minister Li's evaluation and impression of the role of foreign aid? Everybody is impressed with Taiwan's development, but some people try to depreciate it by saying, "Taiwan could not exist without aid from the United States." Second, to what extent have Taiwan's exports been simply a spill-over into foreign markets as a side-effect of development? To what extent have the exports actually created the market in the first place?

Minister Li: In the past decade or so we have depended very much on United States aid, which has helped many aspects of our program. United States officials work closely with their Chinese counterparts. Because policy continuity by our government is maintained, aid to the Republic of China is more fruitful than to other countries. We attach high priority to the effective utilization of American aid, although it phased out in 1965.

One difficult aspect in phasing out United States aid is the severing of relations of educational exchange such as the contract between Purdue University and Chengkung University on engineering education and between Michigan State University and National Taiwan University on agricultural education. In 1967 Dr. Hornig and a team of experts, including scientists, the president of Bell Telephone Laboratories, and the vice presidents of Arthur D. Little and other agricultural experts, came to Taiwan to make a study of our scientific and technological requirements in order to build a bridge between us and the United States. Previously there had been very little communication between the scholars and institutions of my country and the United States. We have many talented, trained people who came to the United States for advanced study and they have not returned. We must find some way to correct what is wrong and build a proper climate or links for their return. I think the links should be set up between government and government, university and university, industry and industry. We should have better technology transfer between the United States and my country.

In reply to the question on export, it is difficult to get our industrial leaders externally oriented in the early years of industrialization. During 1958–60, when I visited industrial plants, I suggested that production capacity should be fully utilized with the probable surplus made available for export. In this way part of the overhead cost can be shared. We have since then also revised our foreign exchange system so as not to penalize export. In the meantime, the government has designed various other incentives toward export; and we have been steadily increasing our exports and the industries have also expanded because they found an overseas market.

To illustrate the recent trend toward an export-oriented economy, during my three years as economic minister 40 per cent of the applications for foreign investment were oriented toward export; last year 70 per cent were entirely for export, with 7.4 per cent for the domestic market and the remainder for a combination of domestic and export trade.

Mr. Miller: Dr. Sabato has pointed out certain aims and goals which are integral parts of research and development. One was emphasis on creating and developing an ability toward innovation, followed by an emphasis on ability toward creation. Could you comment on the emphasis on creation in the experience of the research and development efforts in your country?

Minister Li: Government policy is now oriented toward improving the research climate and building a research program. We support five centers of basic sciences and they are strengthened from time to time with visiting professors from outside to supplement what is available at home.

We must also strengthen our graduate courses. The students have had no exposure to local problems by the time they graduate from college; they just hurry to finish their courses and go to the United States. If they could delay that trip for two years, during which time they would study and perform research on local problems, I am sure they would come to the United States with a better idea of what to study in order to help their country.

In the area of applied research, my ministry is promoting three projects. One is the Union Industrial Research Institute. We would like to find scholars, American or Chinese, to come to this Institute to work on the rapidly developing applied chemical field. The Institute is financed only by public funds but serves the whole industry. Second, we have begun to support exploration and research on mining in the field of coal, natural gas, and geothermal energy. We have quite a potential reserve of geothermal energy and perhaps even some copper mines. The third project is related to the metal industry. Metal and engineering industry representatives indicate that they have many practical problems on which they need some help. We have utilized the facilities of the Metal Industry Development Center which was financed by the United Nations five years ago. A machinery exhibition was held early this year and we eventually will decide to set up an institute , in conjunction with the university, where graduate courses can be provided.

Comment from the Floor: Minister Li has mentioned the desire of his government to have its graduate students in the United States return home. This is not a unique problem for the Republic of China; many other countries have the same problem. Do you agree that to induce scholars, teachers, technicians, and engineers to return to their home, it is essential to have not only physical prosperity, but also a certain freedom?

Minister Li: Our scholars have free access to come and go and we certainly hope some of them will return, but there is not room for all of them to return. We would not have the financial means to support a full program for all of them and they have a better opportunity in the United States.

A compromise alternative would be to have some of these trained men return home from the United States to teach on their sabbatical leaves, thus helping to support a research institute: they also may help other students come to the United States to study and return home. We must develop a program which is feasible and we must have the full cooperation of the universities and research institutions in the United States.

Dr. Kan Chen: As an alien from Stanford University contributing to the brain drain, I would like to suggest the idea of trying to induce American industry to help bridge the technological gap. American industry will have to be convinced, first of all, that there is a very large market for special products. Most of the products that are produced for American domestic consumption are not particularly suited to the markets of underdeveloped countries. If there is such a huge potential market and a lack of new products for such a market, perhaps Taiwan is one of the best places for a research complex. Because the engineers who return to Taiwan know the life styles, tastes, and habits of Asia, they would become a very important resource. If American capital, American engineering ability, and some of these Chinese entrepreneurs and engineers who have lived in various Asian countries combine their talents, Taiwan could become the ideal place to develop the new products such as those from agricultural-based industry that would be particularly suited for use by the less-developed countries.

Minister Li: We are at present trying to set up a research complex in Hsinchu, which is about one and one-half hours' drive from Taipei. We have had technicians from all over the world come to Taiwan to learn about some of the agricultural systems we have developed. The idea of setting up an agricultural-based research institute supported by industry is definitely good, because it will encourage technicians from all over the world to come to Taiwan to learn our system. Such an institute would, in fact, become a laboratory for many companies promoting the use of pesticides, fertilizer, and other new methods.

We also have a small organization called China Technical Consultants, Inc., which was founded in 1959. Instead of calling big consulting firms, such as those in the United States, to deal with the problems of our small-scale industry, we secured company support by getting people on a loan basis from the big companies. In this way, we can build plants with smaller capital for smaller markets. In other words, the minimum economic scale for a certain industry of American engineering standard is different from that of Chinese, and this experience may be very useful for many developing countries. An example is our polyvinyl chloride industry which started with only a four-ton-a-day plant and it has now developed into a big industry.

THE ROLE OF NATIONAL GOVERNMENTS

Commentary by Warren J. Bilkey

THE DIFFUSION of engineering technology involves many considerations of which I will discuss briefly only two: the necessity that the technology in question be compatible with the goals of those who are expected to promote and adopt it, and the problem arising from complementary matters needed for implementing that technology. The first consideration is of obvious importance but often forgotten in practice. For example, a government hardly can be expected to promote a technology unless that technology would further the government's goals. Usually these goals will include increasing employment, increasing foreign exchange earnings, promoting economic growth, and/or improving the social welfare of the people. By the same token, firms could be expected to adopt an engineering technology only if it enables them to achieve their goals, if they are aware of that technology, and if they are able to implement that technology.

The implication of the above propositions is that the starting point for engineering diffusion should be the goals of the government and of the firms in the country in question, not the interest of an engineer in having his innovation adopted. Yet, without an interested engineer, how would potentially interested parties even know about an innovation? It seems that diffusion requires both a familiarity with the needs of firms and governments and an awareness of engineering technology. The team approach probably is the most promising available means for meeting these combined requirements. Unfortunately, it is still but a promise, for interdisciplinary analyses are at a most primitive stage of development. We have not even mastered each other's vocabularies, which is a prerequisite for understanding each other's concepts and methodologies. The problem is far more complex than the management of interdisciplinary teams.

The second consideration with which I am concerned is the complementary relationship between nonengineering matters and the adoption of an engineering technology. For example, a technology cannot be adopted if it requires skills that are not available, if it requires a production volume greater than the country's market can provide, or if it requires more capital than the country's firms can obtain. The engineering technology must be conceived of as part of a "package" which must be adopted *in toto;* otherwise, that technology cannot be adopted at all. In most cases the proportions of such a "package" are flexible within limits; the practical problem is to discover the nature and composition of the "package" in each particular case.

In my opinion, interviewing techniques will be useful for this purpose. For example, firm heads could be interviewed regarding their perceptions of the advantages and disadvantages of a given technology and the obstacles which they perceive to adopting it. Then, by comparing the responses of the firm heads who do intend to adopt that technology with the responses of the firm heads who do not intend to adopt it, clues can be obtained as to which matters are crucial to the adoption of that technology and which matters are of little or no relevance to its adoption. In this way the component parts of the technology adoption "package" can be delineated much more precisely than at present. Research relevant to this technique currently is in progress at the University of Wisconsin.

It seems very possible that any large-scale introduction of engineering technologies into developing countries may require a coordinated international program. The least advanced countries are capable of producing only very simple items, such as processed foods, crude textiles, minerals, and certain agricultural products. They must be able to export enough of those technically simple items, probably to the most advanced countries, to obtain foreign exchange to buy the machinery and materials needed for development. On the other hand, much of the machinery produced by the most advanced countries is too large and complex for the least advanced countries. The latter need machinery for small-scale output, machinery which can be operated by relatively unskilled laborers. This need provides an opportunity for the intermediately developed countries, such as Taiwan, Argentina, and Mexico. They can produce simple machinery but must import whatever highly complex items they need for that production. It seems possible, therefore, to develop a triangular trade relationship along the following lines, with arrows showing the physical flow of goods:

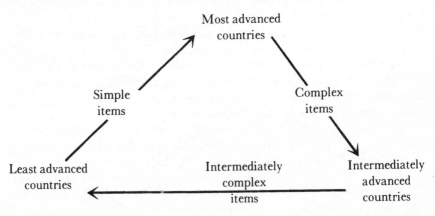

This trade relationship would call for international specialization, with the advanced countries producing only complex items, creating new designs for licensing abroad, and providing international finance; all technologically simple items which they consume—among them bicycles, work clothes, and many processed foods—then would be imported. Unless some such arrangement is developed, where will the least developed countries find markets? According to this reasoning, the most developed countries must change their industrial structure as rapidly as possible so as to provide export opportunities for the least developed countries. The intermediately advanced countries would find their opportunities in terms of technologically intermediate items—simple machine tools, simple textile machinery, motorcycles, and simple canning equipment.

The above propositions are grossly oversimplified. Much research is needed to determine the most appropriate means for stimulating development. My objective is merely to indicate that international structural changes may be needed. We must not assume that the problem can be solved only within the framework of individual countries. A whole complex of new engineering technologies will be needed if international structural changes are undertaken. Research on this matter should be started soon.

Taiwan seems to have reached a transition in its economic development. Mr. Li did not give data on employment and wage rate trends, but it seems reasonable to assume that both are rising. Taiwan's transition from an underdeveloped country to an intermediately advanced country required the availability of different input combinations than were needed at an earlier stage of development. Careful studies should be undertaken to determine, on an industry-by-industry basis, exactly what is required to attract high-wage industries. This necessitates a higher level of analytical technique than was needed earlier. Information must be gathered on an increasingly systematic basis, and the kinds of data gathered must be increasingly comprehensive and exact. I believe that the industrial stimulation studies being undertaken at the University of Wisconsin will be relevant for this purpose.

250

REPORT OF WORKSHOP 11
Robert Norman, Rapporteur

IT IS IN the national interests of all governments, including the technologically advanced ones, to speed the introduction of new technologies to developing nations. It is in the interests of the developing countries to give high priority to new technology in their economic plans, to pay special attention to manpower planning, and, in a variety of ways, to act to speed the process of technological transfer. All governments, those of developed as well as developing nations, must see to it that the current maldistribution of technological skills is righted and that the already enormous and growing gap between the relatively developed and the still developing nations is narrowed.

NATIONAL POLICIES AND PLANS

It is of overriding importance that all national governments be cognizant of the need for encouraging technological transfer and that this understanding be reflected in appropriate policies, priorities, and plans. No two nations are alike: some are highly centralized, others decentralized; some command great resources, others are small and poor; some are federal, others unitary; some have long experience with scientific and technical development, others view science and technology as something wholly new.

Despite the political and social diversity to be found in the world, there are some salient conclusions to be drawn about the role of government in technology. Each national government, and particularly those of the developing countries, should formulate the clearest possible policies and most appropriate programs suitable for various stages of development. Even those countries with vast reservoirs of manpower and little technology must think through the problems posed by technology and equip themselves accordingly. They should work to familiarize public and private leaders with the importance of giving scientific and technical objectives high priority.

The national plan of each developing nation should provide a basic guide as to what objectives technology should serve. The plan should emphasize scientific and technical activity, not as a high-visibility prestige item, but as an integral, indispensable, and effective part of the modernization and industrialization process. There is no easy way for science and technology to be guaranteed high priority in national considerations, but obtaining recognition that they are inseparable from the industrial and economic progress of the nation is a first step. National budgets should then reflect the public resources the governments are willing to commit to carrying out scientific and technical research and dissemination.

National governments can do a great deal to provide a healthy climate for technological innovation. Tax and land reforms, sound patent protection, strict engineering and quality standards, one-stop services for foreign investors, these and a hundred more things will help.

In some cases public-sector industries can help set the pace in research and development; in others, government can work vigorously to attract innovative private investment. Government can do much to strengthen frequently imperfect market mechanisms through sensible tariff policies and other regulatory measures.

In assessing the roles of national governments it is of special significance to clarify and understand who has the power, both within and without the scientific community, to decide what and how much research is to be done. Decisions must be made as to what techniques should be imported and as to where, what, and by whom basic research should be conducted. Governments of developed countries must realize that it is in their national interests to provide policies which will facilitate, not inhibit, the flow of advanced technologies to the developing countries. This spirit of openness on the part of government, often matched by awareness of the limits of planning and the potential of the private sector for innovation, is essential to the spread of technology. National governments must strike a balance between using technology for prestige purposes and neglecting it altogether, emphasizing especially those conditions necessary for creative exploration. Effective technical pioneering requires both the influence and powers of a national government, accompanied by a special climate of scientific freedom.

MANPOWER PLANNING AND PROGRAMMING

If it is the general responsibility of government to provide the framework within which technological innovation can take place, it is the specific and weighty responsibility of government to be concerned for the proper education and training of manpower.

The practical problem is to ensure that the number of engineers and technicians trained in each skill category, either in the country or abroad, is commensurate with the needs of the country. There is no magic way to do this, and again the basic values of the society come into play. In nations where a high degree of personal freedom is honored, it is much more difficult to plan and control the utilization of manpower. And, of course, even with rigid control over what employment men or women may get, estimates of manpower needs may be far off the mark, as has been the case in some totalitarian countries.

National policy toward students studying abroad and the degree of coercion to be used, either by their own governments or by the individuals and institutions with whom they are studying, are hard to formulate. The developing country wants its best scientific talent to return but it may also be reluctant to curb individual freedom completely, especially when the facilities necessary for continued study or research are not available in the country itself. For this reason alone, it is important that the developing nations provide themselves with the best possible institutions of science and technology. All nations have some control over the structure and content of their educational systems and in this way can exert an influence over the careers of their most talented youth in a manner not incompatible with freedom of choice.

Two rather specific things might help insure the return of students leaving for engineering and technical training abroad. First, better selection and orientation of students—particularly at the graduate level—with greater stress on the needs of their own country would excite their interests in the problems of development. Second, technical and engineering institutions in the developed countries should design their programs with an eye to the closer integration of technological expertise and the problems of development.

Beyond the monetary incentive is the incentive of a climate conducive to further intellectual endeavor. There must be an opportunity for successful utilization of technical skills and for education capable of supporting an acceptable minimum of relevant research and development. But even that is not enough, for new discoveries must be adapted to the needs of the developing countries and stronger links forged between academic research and industrial development. To achieve this goal, special attention should be given to encouraging an entrepreneurial spirit on the part of the technically trained elite. Men and women with the motivation to see their discoveries actually tried are invaluable, and their presence makes infinitely easier the task of setting, and then achieving, manpower targets. Men and women with initiative will produce jobs for themselves if government provides them with the necessary opportunities.

MEASURES TO SPEED TECHNOLOGICAL TRANSFERS

In addition to the above suggestions, national governments can do a very great deal to facilitate the transfer of technologies from nation to nation, and this exchange of experience and ideas promises to produce benefits even beyond those provided by the technologies themselves.

The most obvious technical transfers are from the highly developed to the least developed nations. Too little attention has been given by governments and industries in developing countries to the need to modify their techniques of production to suit the actual stage of their development. Recipient governments must give careful consideration to the selection of new techniques to be imported from the highly developed countries to make sure that these techniques are appropriate and will not produce many undesired side effects.

A harder selling job by developing nations directed at the foreign investor is to provide themselves with more options and insure greater freedom to reject technologies which are likely to produce results contrary to the nation's goals and objectives.

Specialized roles may be developed for nations at an intermediate stage of development. Multilateral and regional arrangements would serve the best interests of nations at different levels of development. Even the less developed nations have much to gain from helping one another through the exchange of successful experiences because of the effect such activities have toward mitigating feelings of national isolation and dependence. Government-to-government negotiations will frequently be required to work out the format for these efforts.

National governments at similar stages of industrialization can help their universities to pursue new and creative relationships with one another and with the industries. But perhaps the most important thing national governments can do to speed technological transfers is to encourage the efficient dissemination and exchange of scientific and technical information flows and, where possible, do so through regional information centers. Research conducted in other developing countries has not always been successful; and it would be useful to know why not. There may be an overemphasis, in the beginning stages of development at least, on basic research to the detriment of applied research relevant to the country's particular stage of development.

It is possible, on the other hand, to have too much applied research and there is no knowing ahead of time which research will bear fruit. Nonetheless, there are sound reasons for developing countries to monitor what others are doing and to do some basic research of their own.

Of greatest importance to technological transfer for all nations are governmental policies that will maintain that intangible called "climate," based on openness, freedom, and a flexibility which will ensure receptivity to the findings of others, will be creative in its own right, and will be ever mindful of the need for application and dissemination to technology-hungry nations of the developing world.

15

THE ROLE OF PRIVATE INDUSTRIES
Principal Paper—W. L. Chilton
Commentary—Bax Nomvete
Report of Workshop 12—Hamlin Robinson
Rapporteur

Private industries in the developed nations have a vested interest in the industrialization of the emerging countries. Markets and raw materials are but two
sources for their interest. The role of such industries in the development process is discussed in Chapter 15.

The Editors

THE ROLE OF PRIVATE INDUSTRIES

Principal Paper by W. L. Chilton*

THE PURPOSE of this paper is to examine the role that the private industry of developed countries plays, or can play, in rendering more effective the application of engineering technology for the industrialization of the developing nations. Since this topic has many ramifications, the paper will focus on the following aspects:

1. The direct and indirect contributions made by the profit-oriented firm of the developed nation through its operations in the host country. The emphasis will be on direct investment in manufacturing.

2. Characteristics of the manufacturing sector in the developing countries in response to (a) the widespread governmental insistence on import substitution through local manufacture and (b) the accommodation of the foreign enterprise to mandatory and often rapidly increasing local content requirements.

3. Future business initiatives to sustain or accelerate the industrialization process.

Definitions vary, but it may be sufficient for our purposes to follow recent United Nations practice in classifying economies as "developed" or "developing."[1] There are vast differences, of course, among the developing countries— even within a particular geographic region, for example Latin America— and, to some extent, among the developed nations as well. This initial classification, therefore, provides only very limited support for generalization.

Industrialization, broadly defined, entails a far-reaching transformation of a nation's economy;[2] although the focus of this paper will be on manufacturing (often equated to industrialization), many of the effects of foreign private investment in that sector are of direct or indirect application within the larger framework as well.

The role of the private sector as a whole in providing resources to the developing countries and multilateral agencies such as the World Bank is illustrated by the annual report of the OECD Development Assistance Committee (DAC) (1968). In 1967, the total net outflow of private financial assistance from the 17 DAC member states totaled nearly $4.4 billion or about 39 per cent of the total ($11.4 billion) furnished as public aid and private capital. Even though both amounts were 7–8 per cent higher than those in 1966, prospects are unfavorable for further significant expansion of intergovernmental programs unless required by political or military emergencies.

In many countries, popular support for foreign aid has been eroded by competing domestic needs, some relaxation of international tensions, persistent balance-of-payments problems, and, as the United Nations Secretary-General

*The opinions expressed in this paper are the author's own and should not be construed as reflecting those of the Ford Motor Company which, moreover, assumes no responsibility for the accuracy or completeness of this paper or any part thereof.

observed recently, "a climate of fatigue and disenchantment." (Topping, 1968.) In the circumstances, the developed countries tend to emphasize programs designed to stimulate private financial and technical assistance—a position which is not necessarily welcomed by the presumed benficiaries (Banco Nacional de Comercio Exterior S. A., 1968). A complicating factor is the often inadequate appreciation by the developing countries of the true costs and benefits of various forms of technical assistance. The transfer of skills through governmental programs, although generally free, actually may be very expensive because of the heavy demands made on the time of the few local experts, whereas the potential contribution of well-organized private investment in this area is frequently underrated (Maddison, 1967).

DIRECT AND INDIRECT CONTRIBUTIONS
BY THE FIRM OF THE DEVELOPED COUNTRY[3]

Choice Between Alternative Production Methods. A major difference between the developed nations (especially the USA) and the developing countries is in the pattern of relative factor prices which, incidentally, may or may not reflect fully the underlying relative scarcity of the factors of production—labor and capital in a simple model.[4] Levels of total compensation, including fringe benefits, per employee man-hour generally are substantially lower in the developing countries. This differential underlies the argument that is frequently advanced for the adoption of a more labor-intensive production method in the developing countries than is used in the industrialized economies—to the simultaneous benefit of the firm, through the increased profitability of its foreign investment, and the host country, through the provision of additional employment.

One opportunity for the entrepreneurial choice between alternative production techniques stems from the element of flexibility that is characteristic of at least some production functions. Labor and equipment can be combined in varying proportions to produce a given output, reflecting, within limits, changes in the labor or capital intensity of the technique. In the event that this option is not open to the investor, consideration may have to be given to the much more troublesome alternatives of reviving an obsolete technology or developing a new production method.

Another, and frequently inter-related, problem that compels the investor to review the appropriateness of his customary technological choice is the limited size of the market in most developing countries relative to the production capacity of the smallest installation that is considered economic in the developed nations. It may not be possible to achieve the degree of divisibility or flexibility which ensures harmony between output and absorption capacity at an acceptable level of production costs, necessitating a different approach if the project is to be implemented. These decisions represent a very direct effort to increase the effectiveness of engineering technology for the industrialization of developing countries through adaptation of production methods to local conditions.[5]

The frequent divergence of the actual choice of technology from expectations based on relative factor prices has suggested to some observers that companies operating primarily in the developed countries were either unaware of or indifferent to alternative production methods that would have been more appropriate for use in the developing economies (Chilton, 1962). Similar complaints have been voiced about the design characteristics, notably the labor-saving features, of equipment imported from the economically advanced countries (Kidron, 1965).

These observations suggest that the simple transfer of technology, sometimes called "industrial transplant," from the developed to the less-developed countries is not as profitable to the investor or as beneficial to the host country as it might have been if proper allowance had been made for intercountry differences through technological adaptation.

Actually, an entrepreneur's deliberate choice between available technological alternatives is likely to encompass many factors other than present intercountry differentials in total labor costs per employee man-hour. These factors include quality considerations, the over-all skill requirements of alternative technologies, projections of labor-machine cost ratios, and possible institutional obstacles to subsequent modernization (Chilton, 1962). Differences in average compensation levels fail to disclose the acute scarcity of trained personnel in many less-developed countries. Labor-intensive production methods generally require higher operator skills, a greater commitment to industrialization by the workers, and additional supervisory efforts by management than are needed for a more capital-intensive technique which is machine-paced rather than worker-paced and embodies many of the skills otherwise provided by human intervention.[6]

It is apparent that, at best, the entrepreneurial choice of technology is a complex decision. Examples can be doubtless found where unawareness, indifference, or the cost of study and adjustment resulted in the use of second-best or inappropriate production techniques by foreign investors, even by large companies, from the developed countries. The available evidence, though admittedly fragmentary, suggests that this pattern is now the exception rather than the rule,[7] although there may be wide differences among companies in the major determinants entering the decision-making process and the explicit or implicit weighting systems they use. Finally, the private decision may be influenced and even determined by the host government's preferences, which need not coincide with a choice based on relative factor prices. This problem arises especially in the case of used equipment, which often is viewed with misgivings for legitimate reasons, but is also rejected mistakenly as representing "backward" (ie obsolescent or obsolete) technology (Waterston, 1964)—a view that may be correct within the context of an industrialized country but inapplicable to the requirements of a developing nation.

Education and Training. Increased effectiveness in the application of engineering technology depends in large measure on the nature, extent, depth, and orientation of the educational system[8] and on the availability of the technical skills and specialized training needed in modern business and industry. Shortages of technical and managerial skills hamper not only the efficiency of the firm but are a serious constraint, at times more so than the shortage of capital, on industrialization (Maddison, 1967; International Labour Organization, 1967).[9]

Private foreign investment from the developed countries can play a dual role in breaking this bottleneck by:[10]

1. Importation of skills through the temporary employment of foreign experts until local nationals are able to take their place.[11]

2. Educational programs performing such functions as (a) specific (initial) job training; (b) upgrading, renewal, and, if necessary, transfer of an individual's qualifications; and (c) contributions raising the general level of managerial, scientific, and technical competence within the industry or the community.

The following examples were selected from Ford Motor Company data to illustrate the nature and range of the programs offered in various developing countries either for company personnel or for wider use.[12]

1. *Technical Schools and Apprenticeship Programs.*[13] The Henry Ford National Technical School in Argentina offers an officially recognized six-year curriculum; 30 to 40 students are accepted annually. In 1967, 620 candidates competed for 30 vacancies. The first group to complete the full program will graduate in 1969. Upon graduation, most of the students will probably be employed by other firms or continue their engineering studies.

The apprenticeship program in Mexico has been in operation for eight years. Following recent modifications, a three-year program combining on-the-job training with a new technical high-school curriculum instituted by the Mexican educational authorities now provides training for industrial electricians, toolmakers, technical draftsmen, and automotive mechanics. In 1967, 35 new students were accepted from 1200 applicants. The program basically is geared to Ford Motor Company manpower needs.

2. *Experimental Courses.* Arrangements were made with a government agency to conduct an experimental course in the Brazilian foundry, training a group of precision mechanics as metal pattern makers (a particularly scarce skill) in 60 working days—a great saving in time over the normal on-the-job training period.

A two-year program for selected college graduates in Mexico combines periods of study at IBM of Mexico with practice in the Ford data-processing department.

3. *Public Contests.* An "Industrial Creativity" contest (to be held annually) was organized in Argentina in July 1967. Students of the technical high schools were invited to submit papers on a subject of their choice in the field of mechanical engineering. Substantial prizes were awarded both to the winners and their schools.

Sponsorship of regional 4-H Club contests in 1967–1968 in Argentina followed support of other programs (sometimes jointly with leading industrial firms) designed to raise the level of Argentine agricultural productivity through mechanization and training of experts.

It is not to be inferred that these and other company programs represent the full contribution that might be made to industrialization, broadly defined; this question would require exhaustive study, and conclusions are bound to change with the passage of time. It is suggested, however, that the foreign affiliate can make an important contribution in many respects (Broehl, 1968).

Exchange of Technical Information. A "worldwide feedback program" was started on 1 March 1962 by the Ford Motor Company manufacturing staff to provide for prompt intracompany sharing of new concepts and techniques for manufacture or assembly, material uses, and tools. Eligible suggestions originate primarily in (1) the methods development program of the United States automotive assembly division; (2) project appropriations (divisional cost-reducing programs); and (3) pertinent maximum awards from the United States suggestion program. These items are submitted to the appropriate staffs for review, comment and proposed distribution.[14] The material then is forwarded to the "feedback coordinators" at the designated divisions and foreign affiliates, setting in motion a reporting system as to applicability of the improvement, supplementary-data requirements, and action with regard to its adoption. Although domestic sources account for most of the suggestions, foreign affiliates in the less-developed countries (and, of course, the developed nations) actively participate in this exchange of ideas.[15]

A technical information service, which is also available to the public, describes the present manufacturing standards used by the Ford Motor Company and its suppliers.[16]

Supplier Development and Quality Control. Supplier development generally is a crucial problem when manufacturing operations are undertaken in the less-developed countries in response to local content regulations.[17] Even if the initial requirements are not too burdensome, subsequent increases in the mandatory local content may require very great efforts and large investments.[18] The manufacturer-supplier relationship in the developing countries, moreover, frequently is quite different from the typical pattern in the industrialized economies. The affiliate established by the foreign investor rather than the local supplier is likely to possess or have access to the required engineering and design capabilities (Edelberg, 1963; Kleu, 1967).[19]

The transition by a less-developed country to the complete local manufacture of a major industrial product places a very heavy burden on the economy because of the vast range of components and parts and the complexity of specifications and standards (Baranson, 1968).[20] The systematic development of a supplier network must be accompanied by a corresponding effort to ensure high levels of quality, allowing efficiency in final assembly and protecting the reputation of the product.

Customary quality standards are likely to be low (Surbaugh, 1968; Weatherall, 1968); suppliers in protected markets lack an incentive to improve quality and, even if they would like to do so, they may be preoccupied with production problems and lack the knowledge, equipment, and personnel to ensure acceptable quality.

Vendors, therefore, must be acquainted with the buyer's needs and, initially, extensive assistance may have to be provided in order to prevent defects and hold down rejections.[21] Gradually, these responsibilities can be shifted to the suppliers, permitting a major reduction in the buyer's role.[22] The quality-conscious foreign enterprise is of vital importance to the less-developed country in modernizing its industrial structure and raising its level of international competitiveness. Another important function is the setting of industry standards by committees of experts.[23]

Other Areas. The impact of the foreign affiliate in speeding the transformation of the economy will also be felt in other areas with results conducive to higher efficiency. Temporary assistance may be provided in housing; nutritional standards can be raised in plant cafeterias; and social workers can assist employees unaccustomed to industrial and urban environments. It also has been claimed that the example of foreign engineering experts is helpful in overcoming sociological barriers and inhibitions (Baranson, 1968; UNIDO, 1967).

Host Country Attitudes. The role of private industry of the developed countries in the industrialization of the less-developed nations also depends on private and public attitudes in the host country. Views as to the desirability of foreign investment often differ markedly between capital-exporting and capital-importing countries; its precise significance in many respects is still unknown, but suspicions and objections are encountered frequently (Johnson, 1967; Wionczek, 1968; De Onis, 1968).[24] The investment climate, therefore, becomes a significant factor even though its evaluation is largely subjective (Barclays Bank DCO, 1967; Tazi, 1968).

THE MANUFACTURING SECTOR IN THE LESS-DEVELOPED COUNTRIES

Typical Development. Government encouragement of local manufacturing for the purpose of import substitution is rooted in a variety of economic and political considerations. Imports demonstrated the existence of domestic markets; the high level of per capita income typically found in the industrialized countries and the original emphasis of development theory seemed to recommend this course of action; supply interruptions in times of war and sudden foreign-exchange shortages were additional reasons. It was confidently expected that the new "infant industries" would outgrow the need for protection, stimulate the growth of a modern economy through their requirements for a wide range of inputs, and drastically reduce foreign-exchange outlays in their fields (Lary, 1968).

In view of the limited progress made in the early stages of import substitution when foreign-exchange savings are relatively small and comparatively few employment opportunities are created, progressive increases in local content requirements have been instituted. The resultant frustrations were reviewed by Raúl Prebisch in his advance message as Secretary General to the 1964 session of the United Nations Conference on Trade and Development (UNCTAD).[25]

The extension of import substitution to the suppliers of materials, parts, and even capital goods frequently raises costs throughout industry, increasing the domestic resource cost for the locally produced portion of the portion of the product to a multiple of the local-currency equivalent representing the direct saving in foreign exchange.[26] Once the easy stages of import substitution have been passed, the excess costs of domestic production tend to rise sharply.

National markets in the less-developed countries often are small in size relative to economic scales of production by world standards, raising unit manufacturing costs well above international levels (Lary, 1968; Hung, 1968).[27] These small markets, moreover, usually are shared by a number of independent manufacturers or assemblers,[28] whose product lines often are widely, and perhaps excessively, diversified in terms of grades, sizes, and specifications; types of equipment; or models of a product. Their requirements for materials and parts also may differ considerably.

A reasonable degree of market-sharing, however, may be an acceptable compromise between private and public objectives. The firm, in its former capacity as exporter to, or assembler in, the less-developed country often will prefer to make the required heavy investment in capital, technical, and managerial effort rather than to risk the loss of a traditional market—provided there are reasonable prospects of eventual profitability (Wilkins and Hill, 1964). The host country may prefer a somewhat competitive market structure to the monopoly of one producer in spite of the attendant reduction in the individual firm's scale output; this outcome also avoids the very great political problems connected with the designation of one firm as the sole manufacturer.

Variations in the Pattern. The following departures (some new, some old) from the standard pattern of development of the manufacturing sector are indicative of the potential for improvement in its over-all efficiency. These variants are examples rather than a complete listing of possible modifications and, depending on the situation, advantages in one direction may be offset by disadvantages in other.

Joint assembly facilities have been established in markets where the importation of fully assembled ("built-up") automotive vehicles is subject to prohibitive customs duties. These facilities are operated under a variety of arrangements as, for example, a joint venture by foreign manufacturers from one country or several countries, sometimes with the participations of a local firm; or contractual arrangements with an important dealer who assembles the vehicles of a number of producers.[29] The participating manufacturers provide all required technical assistance for the assembly or partial manufacture of their products.

Standardization of parts and subassemblies permits the supplier industry to operate more efficiently by reducing the design and engineering workload while extending production runs. The economy of the country also benefits from a reduction in the required level of inventories of the interchangeability of parts, freeing resources for other purposes. If components of acceptable quality can be purchased, the parts manufacturers or firms operating joint production facilities may be in the best position to promote standardization (Kleu, 1967). The attitudes of the assemblers of the final product will vary depending on the importance of the particular component for quality, performance, and product differentiation.[30] A large degree of standardization is attainable at times even though some differences remain; concentration on the major features of complex and critical subassemblies has led to substantial "commonization" while retaining characteristics desired by individual producers. Emphasis on standardization, however, can be carried too far if the resultant production economies are more than offset by a decline in operating efficiency of the equipment using the standardized component. Standardization of specifications at the industry level is one possibility; interchangeability between the products offered by the firm is another (Fowler, 1965)[31] which may have very important implications for the international division of labor.

Product adaptation frequently is mentioned as an effective approach to production for the small markets of the less-developed countries; a number of possibilities exist for applying this principle, but it is easy to overlook hidden costs and other disadvantages (Rose, 1968). Some aspects of product adaptation are discussed below:

1. Simplification of product design is intended to reduce investment requirements for special tools and other machinery by relying heavily on standard mill shapes.

2. Changes are made in materials and materials specifications, provided the substitutes are compatible with the firm's quality standards.

3. Differences in emphasis on selected design characteristics reflect the greater importance in a less-developed country of sturdiness, dependability, simplicity, and economy of operation and maintenance.[32]

4. Quality adjustment may mean that a technically superior product is not the most suitable (the best) product under different environmental conditions because of initial cost, operating, and maintenance characteristics.[33] Quality adaptation also could mean a cheapening of the basic design—a lowering of quality in the conventional sense; this course of action raises very serious problems.[34]

A "New International Division of Labor." In view of the acknowledged shortcomings of the typical pattern of import substitution in the less-developed countries, increased emphasis is being placed on proposals for national specialization to serve regional or world markets, with the large international, or multinational, companies[35] playing a key role in the process.[36] Necessary conditions for the success of such arrangements would seem to be:

1. The willingness and ability of these large firms to meet the global demand for their products through carefully balanced procurement and manufacturing programs, entailing a fundamental reorientation of their present operations.

2. The abandonment by the less-developed countries of efforts to achieve self-sufficiency, in the manufacturing sector as a whole or in specific industries, in favor of specialization on a few processes or products.[37]

Since import substitution generally was the outgrowth of persistent balance-of-payments pressures, it appears unlikely that a less-developed country would permit imports of complete units without a commitment by the foreign manufacturer to purchase an equivalent amount of locally produced materials, parts, or assemblies.[38]

3. The acceptance by the developed countries of important changes in the composition of their trade and, possibly, in their trade balances, reflecting the inflow of components from foreign countries and increased exports of the complete product.

Large-scale implementation of the proposed "new international division of labor"[39] raises formidable problems that appear to be susceptible only to very gradual solution.

Governments of developed and less-developed countries alike can be expected to follow with great concern the balance-of-payments and employment effects of such arrangements. The developed nations, as a group, have been hesitant to improve greatly the accessibility of their markets for the manufactures of the developing countries.[40] The fears, rivalries, and political pressures that have slowed or doomed so many efforts at economic integration probably will continue to impede progress.

For the multinational companies, a rapid transition to the new sourcing pattern would entail (1) basic decisions (eg the conversion and even abandonment of facilities); (2) the development of a highly complex interchange of products and components[41] together with new and sophisticated managerial and operational techniques to ensure its smooth operation; and (3) additional problems in the field of government and public relations.[42]

The operational problems alone of implementing such a program can be forbidding if we assume that a component previously was purchased or manufactured by the multinational firm in the country of final assembly (eg the United States or a West European nation) and now is supplied by a less-developed country.[43] The possibility of supply interruption is more worrisome in view of the greater complexity of shipping arrangements and environmental differences that may be understood only imperfectly. Greater distances often entail a transportation cost penalty and are likely to require larger inventories, raising carrying charges, because of the difficulty of obtaining additional deliveries on short notice. Instead of the supplier assuming quality control and rendering prompt technical assistance, the buyer may have to provide these services—the cost of which is increased by distance and, often, differences in culture, language, and law.

There appears to be considerable scope, however, for imaginative thinking and useful initiatives. An important first step could be the maximum use of identical components of uniform quality throughout the firm's manufacturing operations (if not worldwide then on the broadest possible basis) to set the standards and provide the markets for eventual international production sharing.

A very different approach, which may have significant implications for the efficient industrialization of developing countries, is the appointment of specialized firms in the developed nations to apply techniques of systems analysis and management to the promotion of economic growth.[44]

FUTURE BUSINESS INITIATIVES

This concluding section outlines several proposals that are designed to draw on the special capabilities of private industry in the developed nations for the support of industrialization in the less-developed countries. These proposals are intended to supplement and expand, not replace, existing programs which, wherever possible, should be broadened in terms of coverage and sponsorship, and further strengthened.

Access to Technology. Low levels of economic development place a burden on small- and medium-size companies in trying to keep abreast and make use of technical changes relating to their product and manufacturing methods. Even though this burden is eased gradually as industrialization progresses,[45] the small firm often is at a disadvantage compared to large companies because of the difficulties of gaining access to foreign technology or the relatively high cost of preliminary studies (Wionczek, 1968b). *It is proposed, therefore, that programs be devised by firms or industries in the developed nations to facilitate access to such data by small- and medium-size companies in the less-developed countries.*

A starting point for such a program could be the approach followed by the Industrial and Chemicals Division of the Ford Motor Company in offering to potential users certain of its processes.[46] This plan, of course, would have to be expanded greatly in terms of product and process coverage and geared to the low-volume requirements of the developing countries.

These efforts should prove beneficial in a number of ways. Improved access to technical information combined with attractive arrangements for the transfer of this technology will raise the industrial capabilities of the new users, act as a stimulus to technological advances by other firms, and ease the problem of supplier development should the need arise. An important intangible benefit would be the demonstrated willingness of private industry in the developed nations to lend assistance on very reasonable terms.[47]

Education and Training. An even more specific commitment to industrialization can be envisaged. Major operations by large international firms in less-developed countries frequently give rise to a wide range of programs of direct or indirect significance for the industrialization process, especially in the fields of education and training, in the broad sense of the term. *It is suggested that these activities be reviewed periodically from the viewpoint of the contribution they are making and could be making, without large additional outlays, to the industrialization of the host country. Prompt and full intracompany sharing of the findings and of new programs or methods should be stressed.*

The review mechanism might take the form of regular staff conferences— first, at the country level to deal with problems peculiar to each affiliate and, subsequently, at a regional or "global"[48] level to allow maximum scope for crossfertilization of ideas and free discussion. These objectives would be furthered by the participation of outside experts in at least some of the sessions.

Since the large international firm has special competence in modern business management, it can play a very important role in establishing or supporting suitable educational facilities in the less-developed countries which, in general, are very short of qualified personnel in this field. Graduates of these institutions will enter many professions, including engineering, and assist directly and indirectly in raising the prevailing low level of efficiency in the utilization of resources. *We suggest that firms able to contribute equipment, funds, or staff time participate in the establishment or the support of business schools that provide rigorous professional training.*

The interest of the firm in aiding the host country's industrial progress can be demonstrated also by supplying financial and, if necessary, technical assistance to specialized nonprofit institutions in such areas as economic research, economic development, or advice to small businessmen.

International Division of Labor. Assignment to qualified less-developed countries of production responsibility for part or all of a corporation's global requirements for certain parts, assemblies, or even specific product lines, instead of the present national objective of increasingly uneconomic selfsufficiency, raises many difficult and potentially costly problems. Current unit production costs for these items, moreover, typically are considerably lower in the developed nations than in the less-developed countries, but this situation need not be an unalterable condition (Kleu, 1967). Even if the gradual reorientation of the firm's customary sourcing pattern entails a moderate over-all cost penalty, it may be compatible with long-term profit maximization.[49]

The complexity of this question suggests, however, that special arrangements should be made to ensure that it is given adequate consideration in the corporate decision-making process. *It is proposed, therefore, that a high executive be designated at corporate headquarters to examine on a continuing basis the actual and potential production capabilities of the less-developed countries and to par-*

ticipate as their informal spokesman in all decisions pertaining to supplier selection and manufacturing investments.[50]

A gradual change in the present international division of labor also would provide an auspicious opportunity for some decentralization of research and development.

NOTES

1. The United Nations *Statistical Yearbook 1966* classifies as developed countries: "countries in North America, Europe and Oceania, together with Japan and South Africa." The terms "developing" and "less-developed" will be used interchangeably in this paper; no distinction is intended between more developed and less-developed "developing" countries.
2. Harry G. Johnson (1967) notes in this connection:

> In more specifically economic terms, the establishment of a modern economy requires 'industrialization.' By this term, however, is meant something different from the establishment of 'industry' (the production of manufactured goods) as distinct from and in replacement of 'agriculture' (the production of commodities from the soil). Industrialization properly speaking involves the organization of production in business enterprises, characterized by specialization and division of labor both within and among themselves; this specialization is based on the application of technology and of mechanical and electrical power to supplement and replace human effort and motivated by the objectives of minimizing costs per unit and maximizing returns to the enterprise. . . . So conceived, industrialization is an economy-wide phenomenon, applying to agriculture and the service trades as well as to manufacturing; the essence of it is not the production of the products typically considered as 'industrial' but the rational approach to the production process itself that it embodies.

See also United Nations Industrial Development Organization (UNIDO), "Issues and problems in manpower development for industrialization," Item No. 3(c) of the Provisional Agenda for the International Symposium on Industrial Development in Athens (November 29–December 20, 1967). The distinction between industrialization and the growth of manufacturing industry is emphasized in paragraph 13, as follows:

> It would be inappropriate to equate the needs of skills for industrialization by looking exclusively to the needs of skills for manufacturing industry. . . . Manufacturing plays a central role in the industrial system, analogous to the role of the assembly line in a modern factory. But just as the assembly line requires support from the rest of the factory organization. . . . so the development of manufacturing on a truly viable basis requires the parallel development of a great many ancillary and supporting activities. . . .

3. The examples cited in this section generally reflect the experience or initiative of a particular company rather than of the "average" firm, however defined. Given limitations of time and space, an exhaustive survey clearly was impractical. If the company in question is a large international concern, this fact does not detract from the over-all significance of the example since such companies account for a very large share of U.S. (and foreign) private investment in manufacturing industry abroad. If the firm happens to be the Ford Motor Company (as is frequently the case), it reflects primarily the accessibility of such formation and carries no implication as to the novelty, extent, or value of such programs compared with those undertaken by other firms (large or small) in any of these areas. Without a detailed survey of company practices, it cannot be inferred that a given program instituted by one firm represents the norm for the industry or even a major segment (eg large firms) of the industry.

4. Labor is not a homogeneous commodity and the abundant supply of unskilled workers (often total strangers to the market economy) in many developing countries is in marked contrast with the

266

pronounced shortage of skilled and even semiskilled personnel which gave rise to an exceptionally wide inter-industry wage dispersion in the early stages of industrialization. Recently, however, interferences of one kind or another (notably minimum wage legislation) have tended to narrow wage differentials much more rapidly than indicated by the upgrading of the labor force. See Hal B. Lary, *Imports of Manufacturers from Less Developed Countries,* New York: National Bureau of Economic Research, 1968, pp. 109, 112–113.

The contrast in many Latin American countries between an ample (if not abundant) labor supply and the acute shortage of highly skilled workers is discussed by W. E. Swanson (Director of Personnel Department, IBM Corporation) in "Manpower and compensation planning," Thomas A. Gannon, ed., *Doing Business in Latin America,* New York: American Management Association, 1968, pp. 96–98.

Open or disguised subsidization of capital costs (eg through the extension of long-term loans on unusually favorable terms) is another source of structural distortions in the pattern of relative factor prices which may result in the adoption of a more capital-intensive technology than would have been chosen otherwise. See Nuño F. de Figueiredo, "Arrangements for the Transfer of Operative Technology to the Developing Countries. Case Study of Brazil"; study included (as Annex I) in the Progress Report of the Secretary-General to the 44th Session of the U.N. Economic and Social Council, March 4, 1968.

5. See (London) *Times,* "How Philips Links Trade and Philanthropy," September 8, 1966. The article notes,

> The company is able to combine business with philanthropy in its pilot plant in Utrecht which is devoted to the task of building tiny production lines capable of turning out modern equipment in small numbers and with a maximum use of labour and a minimum of capital investment. The reversal of the usual trend for industrial development is tailor-made for the less developed countries. Philips claims it is the only way of introducing an electrical industry into less developed countries with low levels of skill and small markets. . . .

This approach is discussed in greater detail in a letter to the author from Mr. H. Verster, N. V. Philips Gloeilampenfabrieken (Utrecht, June 30, 1967), who makes the following points:

(a) Products must be of recent design to enable the manufacturer to secure or retain a worthwhile share of the highly competitive market in consumer electronics.

(b) Design characteristics should permit the use of highly mechanized production methods. Component improvement has progressed so far that the construction of radios, record players and television sets (which are the items primarily assembled in the Utrecht pilot plant) is rather simple, requiring little assembly time even if relatively labor-intensive methods are used.

(c) Pure assembly operations abroad, based on imported materials and components, result in only small savings of foreign exchange and very limited employment creation, while costs of the complete units remain high. These problems are eased through the local production (with the manufacturer's technical assistance) of wooden cabinets and plastic components.

(d) Special research and the development of new manufacturing methods (and equipment) now permits local production of such components as loudspeakers, rf coils, etc. with minimum investment and without impairment of quality. For example, the heating facilities required for glueing or cementing can be provided by a smoothing iron or an electric cooking plate instead of the usual (and much more costly) induction heating or tunnel ovens.

6. Van Court Hare jr., "The horse that can save more than a kingdom," *Columbia Journal of World Business,* May–June 1967, pp. 55–62. The author notes (p. 55):

> The power of automation comes when intelligence, processing skills, and control features are built into the equipment, and need not be added by human intervention at the time a product is made. The more intelligence is packaged into a machine to inexpensively supplement or provide otherwise scarce or unavailable production control skills, the

greater the opportunity to employ large numbers of unskilled workers who, without the skills the machine provides must remain idle and unproductive.

7. The very process of creating an international network of manufacturing or assembly operations provides many opportunities for a firm to develop a group of engineering and management experts, attached to a central staff, who are called upon to assist in the establishment, initial operations, and subsequent problem-solving of new foreign affiliates. It is in the interest of the company to assign to such tasks well-qualified personnel experienced in these matters (eg low-volume operations).

A clear distinction must be made, however, between this situation and the importation of equipment and knowhow by an independent firm of a less-developed country from a supplier in a developed nation. As pointed out by de Figueriedo (1968), the importing enterprise, and especially medium-size and small companies, may be unable ". . . to formulate its requirements properly and to make a well-considered evaluation of the alternatives offered by foreign technology in respect of production processes and equipment. . . ."

8. UNIDO, "Issues and Problems in Manpower Development for Industrialization." The role of education is described in paragraph 7:

> Education is the first step in the generation of skills. Furthermore, it is an instrument of social transformation and modernization. It has been often stated that the modern industrial system is a highly complex organism and not merely a collection of machines and the skills to operate them. To industrialize successfully in an environment where economic-social-political features of traditional society are still strong, educational programmes must do much more than create a technically qualified labour force. They should assist in liberating minds, broadening people's outlook, etc. Nevertheless, machines are part of industrial life and skills are needed to use them.

9. The International Labour Organization study of "Skill Requirements for Industrialization" refers to the provisional findings of a statistical analysis undertaken by the Unit for Economic and Statistical Studies on Higher Education of the London School of Economics. In this study, levels of skill formation and educational achievement of the labor force in a number of countries were compared with economic growth rates, suggesting the existence of a systematic relationship between productivity and occupational composition. A more detailed study by Northeastern University (Boston, Massachusetts) arrived at the conclusion that "variations in the proportion of professional and technical workers are a major determinant of productivity in almost every industry. . . ."

10. UNIDO Industrial Development Board, "Report of the International Symposium on Industrial Development" (Athens). The point is made in paragraph 93 that ". . . foreign investment is a valuable source for the provision of industrial skills and that training programmes undertaken by foreign-financed industrial enterprises in developing countries are of considerable value in increasing local resources of skilled manpower."

11. Direct investment, of course, is only one of several channels through which private industry in the developed countries can assist industrialization in the developing nations. Alternatives include licensing agreements, management contracts, the provision of technical services and knowhow. It is possible, however, that the entrepreneur's involvement in a direct investment is sufficiently greater than, for example, in a licensing agreement that the affiliate in the developing country has a significant advantage over the licensee in terms of the technical assistance it receives.

12. The various country programs discussed in this section do not represent a complete listing of the educational and training facilities provided by or through the Ford Motor Company in any of these countries. Moreover, the facilities available for these purposes differ from country to country, reflecting local conditions, size, and function of the affiliate (eg extensive manufacturing operations in Argentina, Brazil, and Mexico, but only assembly in Peru).

13. Part of the operating cost is recovered in countries imposing special taxes to finance outside training programs but providing for refunds to taxpayers whose own efforts meet the official requirements.

14. In 1967, 246 items were received for review and about 60 per cent were approved for distribution. This relatively small number reflects in part the ineligibility of suggestions based simply on "good engineering practice" or environmental differences. Approval, however, is not confined to major or complex improvements; suggestions were accepted (and found useful by a number of affiliates) for such basic ideas as the modification of step-ladders and the development of multilingual posters for plants employing workers of several nationalities.

15. The crossfertilization of ideas is carried one step further when the original suggestion results in further improvement by one of the recipients (which is disseminated again).

16. Ford manufacturing standards are divided into 23 classifications, each covering data relative to a specific phase of manufacturing processes, materials, methods, industrial equipment, and tools. Subscriptions may be taken out for any of these classifications including supplements and revisions issued during the year. About 2300 outside subscriptions are serviced at the present time, not counting educational institutions which receive this material on a complimentary basis.

17. "Local content" refers to the portion (by weight or value) of the product which must be of domestic origin, the definition of which varies widely, depending on a country's regulations and their interpretation.

18. For passenger cars, local procurement typically will focus at first on (a) paints, oils, and greases; (b) tires and batteries; (c) soft trim; and (d) seat springs and frames. The first two product categories usually can be supplied by the affiliates or licensees of U.S. companies, while the other items can be produced by relatively labor-intensive techniques. Additional local content requirements eventually necessitate investment in such costly facilities as a foundry or engine plant, and, perhaps, stamping facilities.

19. Edelberg (1963) observes "While in the United States, it is the supplier who frequently has the 'know-how,' in Mexico it was the assembler who had such know-how as existed in the country, or at least the access to it." Kleu (1967) comments:

> There was a general awareness in South Africa among assemblers and importers of the need for assisting suppliers, but it was really only the two large firms which had worthwhile assistance programmes. Ford had the most elaborate programme, for which it was highly praised by suppliers. . . . The Company not only supplied vendors with specifications but gave them a detailed statement of the requirements with respect to facilities, techniques and procedures, laboratories, gauges and testing equipment, manpower and performance and quality control records to comply with specifications. . . .

Although South Africa is not classified as a less-developed country, some of the problems encountered in meeting local content requirements for the auto industry resemble those found in the major developing nations.

Foreign affiliates often make an important, even if indirect, contribution to the improvement of technology in the host country by (1) establishing contact between prospective licensees in the less-developed countries and suppliers of the requisite knowhow in the developed nations and (2) inducing traditional suppliers to their parent companies to perform the same function abroad.

20. In "Automotive industries in developing countries" (unpublished paper, May 31,1968), Jack Baranson notes:

> There are literally thousands of elements that go into a single vehicle. A small British car averages 2500 major parts or assemblies. . . . A standard diesel engine consists of 750 parts. . . . Components and parts are manufactured from hundreds of different types of iron and steel and other industrial metals and materials including rubber, plastic and glass. Mass production of standardized components and parts demands a rigid uniformity in materials specifications and manufacturing tolerances. . . .

21. In discussing the supplier assistance program of the Ford Motor Company, Kleu (1967) notes:

> Under the Company's quality assurance programme it made available to vendors the services not only of quality control men but also of manufacturing engineers for im-

proving processes and material control experts to help them with programming of production. In 1965 Ford had thirteen permanent quality assurance engineers in the field working with vendors. These engineers were resident in the area for which they were responsible. . . .

22. In Argentina, for example, the expansion of automotive manufacturing operations from the end of the 1950s led to:

(a) Establishment (in May, 1960) of an automotive research center, jointly sponsored by ten auto producers; following the manufacturers' withdrawal (in 1963), these laboratories have performed tests for the auto supplier industry.

(b) The Ford supplier assistance program in effect between 1959 and 1964 has been reduced largely to quality control in subsequent years, and vendor responsibility is emphasized under the program "partners in quality."

When the Ford Motor Company establishes assembly or manufacturing operations abroad, a group of great importance is the "source development and supplier assistance" staff. As these problems are resolved, this group is reduced in size and ultimately absorbed into the normal Ford purchasing function.

23. The Society of Automotive Engineers, for example, at the request of its members in Mexico, recently completed a Spanish-language handbook of selected vehicle standards (using also the metric system), based on the annual U.S. edition. This handbook was distributed in 1968 on a trial basis.

24. Johnson (1967) notes:

The strength of economic nationalism in the modern world, and the irrationality of which it is capable, is nowhere more evident than in the extreme hostility and suspicion with which private direct foreign investment is generally regarded by the 'host' country. . . . The deepest hostility appears to be aroused by the large international corporations engaged in the extractive industries . . . and the mass-production, technically-most-advanced manufacturing industries. . . .

25. Based largely on his close observation of the Latin American Region in his former capacity of Executive Secretary of the United Nations Economic Commission for Latin America, Prebisch found ". . . that the 'easy phase' of import substitution had about reached its limit in the countries which had followed that course, and that it could not go farther without considerable waste." He also found that high tariffs to protect narrow national markets had "encouraged the establishment of small uneconomical plants, weakened the incentive to introduce modern techniques, and slowed down the rise in productivity."

26. Baranson (1968b) estimated that, for Argentine cars, it cost, on the average, $3922 in January, 1967, at official exchange rates, to produce foreign-exchange savings of $1782; the corresponding figures for small Mexican cars were $1440 and $516. Local cost figures are based on annual production runs of 20 000 to 30 000 vehicles (higher volumes would result in more favorable comparisons), while foreign-exchange savings are the *difference* between the c.i.f. (cost, insurance, and freight) price, the Latin American part of the complete U.S. vehicle, and the U.S. components that continue to be imported.

See also New Zealand, House of Representatives, *The World Bank Report on the New Zealand Economy 1968,* Wellington: Government Printer, 1968. In the section on the automotive industry, estimates are made of the excess costs of domestic production which may be on the order of 150 per cent (paragraph 78). New Zealand, of course, is not a less-developed country, but some of the problems of its automotive industry resemble those encountered in the developing nations.

27. Lary (1968) cites the following excerpt from the report by Rául Prebisch to the 1964 UNCTAD session:

Thus, a real vicious circle has been created as regards exports of manufactured goods. These exports encounter great difficulties because internal costs are high, and internal costs are high because, among other reasons, the exports which would enlarge the markets are lacking. Had it been possible to develop industrial exports, the process of industrialization would have been more economical, for it would have made possible international division of labour in manfacturing.

28. Baranson (1968b) observes:

The worst case on record for Latin America is that of Chile, where approximately 7800 vehicles were assembled in 1964 by 22 firms at four times what it would have cost to deliver a comparable vehicle to a Chilean port. Since only 40% of the vehicle is produced locally, this meant a domestic value added cost about 8.5 times international costs. . . .

The IMF *International Financial News Survey* of July 19, 1968, reported on the automobile industry in the Republic of China (Taiwan) as follows:

(a) The Yue Loong Motor Company, which began operations in Taiwan in 1953, was the only automobile manufacturer on the island until last year. Since then five new manufacturers have been licensed, all of which are cooperating with Japanese concerns. Some have started already to produce cars, and others are constructing plants.

(b) Government regulations require that in the initial year of a new industry at least 40% of the parts to be produced by the factory concerned or purchased locally. This ratio rises to 50% in the second year, 60% in the third, and 70% in the fourth. . . . When an existing plant reaches a self-sufficiency ratio of about 40%, a new manufacturer must do as well. Yue Loong is now 60% self-sufficient in parts.

(c) When the five manufacturers are in full operation, production will reach about 27 000 cars. The island produced 8315 cars last year. . . . If demand does not increase appreciably, there will be a large surplus for export.

A subsequent report in the *International Financial News Survey* of September 27, 1968, stated that the Taiwan government had decided on September 12 to lift the ban on the import of "compact-sized" automobiles. The government-owned Central Trust of China was designated as the sole import agent, with Japan, the United States, and Western Europe declared eligible to compete in the Taiwanese market. The significance of this decision for the viability of the domestic automobile industry would seem to depend on the structure of import duty rates, the excess costs of domestic production, and the pricing policies of the Trust.

29. American Motors Corporation (AMC) participates in a number of such operations. In Mexico, assembly and partial manufacture is handled by Vehiculos Automotores Mexicanos, a majority interest in which is held by a Mexican company, with AMC and Kaiser Jeep (in that order) as the minority stockholders. In Peru, assembly facilities are owned jointly by AMC and Renault. In Venezuela, ownership is shared by AMC, Renault, and a Venezuelan firm. In Costa Rica, a local company in which AMC has a financial interest assembles and distributes AMC cars but also has a contractual arrangement for the assembly of vehicles from Toyota and Ford Werke A.G. (Ford of Germany).

See also *Oriental Economist,* "Malaysia—Progress seen in industrialization," August 1968, pp. 23–24. One assembler of cars, the Asia Automobile Company, is a joint venture of a local firm, Asia Motor (which owns 27.2% of the capital); two Japanese companies, Toyo Kogyo and Sumitomo Shoji (with 31.8% and 4.6% stock ownership); and Peugeot of France. Another assembly operation is conducted by Associated Motor Industries Malaysia (a dealer) for vehicles of BMLH, Ford, General Motors-Holden, Renault, and Rootes. A third group, Champion Motors, is reported to handle the assembly of vehicles manufactured by Mercedes-Benz, Toyota, and Volkswagen.

30. Kleu (1967) concluded that "Automobile producers traditionally manufacture certain assembles themselves in order to keep close control over quality. These are the engine. the transmission and rear axle assembly and the body shell. The reason lies in the importance of product differentiation as a competitive weapon in the automobile industry." Similar observations were made to the author in recent interviews—especially with regard to standardization of the body shell and engine.

31. The problems and benefits of instituting such a program are discussed by Cyril F. Fowler,

Parts Plans Coordinator for Massey-Ferguson Limited, in "Parts interchangeability world-wide," *M. F. View,* November-December 1965. Particularly relevant are the following observations:

The Massey-Ferguson program has developed over the past eight years to the point where not only the centre (axle) housing (of a tractor) but almost the entire transmission is fully interchangeable between 90 per cent of our tractor production. For example, a transmission produced in France can be assembled with a rear axle produced in the United Kingdom to form the transmission train of a tractor assembled in Detroit with a U.S. built engine.

Another typical example of full interchangeability is the heart of the Ferguson System, the hydraulic pump. This is interchangeable and used in many models manufactured in a number of locations around the world. . . .

Interchangeability applies not only to tractors, but also to combines, balers, ploughs, drills, mowers, industrial products and most importantly to diesel engines. . . . As a typical example of this development, the pistons of 3 cylinder, 4 cylinder and 6 cylinder engines, while of different total capacities, are fully interchangeable. Other items such as rockers, bearings, valves and many other components are fully interchangeable between many units manufactured in such markets as the United Kingdom, France, Brazil and Italy.

Another important application of interchangeability is the design of components for new models to permit the servicing of units no longer in production.

32. Design characteristics of a product may suggest adaptation but, in fact, be explained by conditions in the country of origin. Relatively poor road conditions in Japan made durability an essential car design feature very suitable for the developing countries, while European designers had fewer problems in this respect.

33. If no alternative product is available and objections are based primarily on the price of the item, redesign still may be ruled out by the high costs of product adaptation for a small market. Moreover, even if alternatives exist (eg a Jeep compared with a passenger car), the car-buying public will not be satisfied indefinitely with basic transportation.

34. A deliberate lowering of quality in selected countries is unlikely to be acceptable to companies whose products enjoy an international reputation. Even if this policy is appropriate for a particular market, there is no assurance that its effects can be restricted to that area, in view of possible export sales, use or purchase by tourists, and the consequent damage to the company's image.

Another aspect is the critical importance of quality for a country's export competitiveness. The establishment or expansion of manufacturing industry to replace imports barred by prohibitive tariffs already poses a grave threat to quality, necessitating very great efforts to maintain internationally acceptable standards. In the circumstances, compromising quality may be a disservice to the longer-run interests of the host country.

35. Definitions vary of the term "multinational"; some writers virtually equate multinational companies to firms with large international operations, whereas others insist that decision-making processes should take account of international alternatives. An even more rigorous definition requires truly global ownership and management, of which few examples can be found.

36. Baranson (1968b) mentions the following opportunities for specialization in automotive products by the less-developed countries: "(1) manufacture of specialized components and parts; (2) responsibility for a particular vehicle line; (3) specialization in low-volume replacement parts for obsolete models; or (4) reconditioning of engines and parts. . . ."

37. Progress in this direction has been made in some cases, at least for limited periods of time, through special arrangements between the government of a host country and the foreign affiliate, permitting partial fulfillment of local content requirements through exports of parts or assemblies already manufactured locally when offical content targets could not be reached within the stipulated time limit.

38. The comments of the IBRD Mission to New Zealand (1968) are pertinent, even though the suggested arrangements probably would be of an inter-governmental nature. Reduction in the

272

diversity of domestically produced types of steel to lower unit production costs is to be achieved by specialization. The Mission notes "Access to overseas markets could perhaps be obtained by offering access for steel products which New Zealand should not make because of small volume."

39. This term also is used in a different context, namely in connection with the Prebisch proposal that the developed countries grant tariff preferences on manufactures to the developing nations.

40. Lary (1968) pointed out that

> . . . greater accessibility would mean the scaling down of the tariff rates of developed countries, particularly the 'effective rates', on goods of which the less developed countries are actual or potential suppliers; the progressive loosening of quantitative restrictions, both those imposed by the importing countries and the 'voluntary restraints' exercised by the exporting countries; and the identification and removal of other, less obvious impediments to imports. . . .

41. A prototype of such arrangements (for developed countries) was the IBM program for electrictric typewriter manufacture in Western Europe in the late 1950s or early 1960s. Production in one country for export to the other Western European nations was considered impractical because of the protection granted to local industry. The IBM "interchange plan" was a production-sharing arrangement which allocated the company's total requirements for certain parts and supplies to one of the eight participating West European countries; Canada also participated. (Robinson, 1964.)

This program apparently was discontinued according to a letter from Mr. Allan Smid, Information Department, IBM World Trade Corporation (16 September 1968).

42. International specialization requires difficult decisions as to the countries that would be assigned production responsibility for specific items. These decisions are likely to become the focus of strong private and public pressures which may not be confined to the countries immediately concerned. In addition, existing demands on the firm to play its role of good corporate citizen may well be intensified.

43. Some of these problems are mentioned in a letter to the author from Mr. J. de Vries, Economic and Market Analyses, Westinghouse Electric International Company (September 30, 1968). Mr. de Vries comments:

> With regard to . . . feeder operations, you are right in assuming that operational and organizational problems are serious in this particular aspect. It is not only a matter of internal company organization, but also of passing through a large number of customs barriers and of transportation rates. except for automobile manufacturers, I do not know of any American company that tries to inter-relate production of components in a number of developing countries.

44. A well-known, and probably the largest single, contract in this field is the agreement signed in May, 1967, between Litton Industries, Inc., and the Government of Greece for the economic development of Crete and the Western Peloponnesus.

45. Industrialization is accompanied by growing appreciation of the significance of research and development, increased availability of trained personnel, and wider acceptance of modern engineering and management techniques.

46. The "electrocoating" process, for example, which was patented and is extensively used by Ford Motor Company (to paint vehicles and parts), has applications in many industries; the "electrocure" process (for rapid curing of liquid coatings) is still at the pilot plant development stage.

47. This policy could provide an effective answer to charges that foreign companies exact a very high price for their technology and knowhow. Such complaints are made by Kidron (1965) and cited by Wionczek (1968a).

48. "Global" might be defined as all the countries in which the firm has such interests or only the countries classified as "less-developed."

49. Long-term profit maximization, of course, is a very elusive concept, which may make allowance for such intangibles as corporate social responsibility.

50. International production sharing may be accomplished through a variety of organizational arrangements, ranging from wholly owned facilities to long-term purchase contracts with independent suppliers. The absence of a direct financial interest by the (foreign) firm may be helpful in avoiding charges of foreign domination of local manufacturing industry.

THE ROLE OF PRIVATE INDUSTRIES
Commentary by Bax Nomvete

IT IS MY interpretation that we are really considering the "role of private industry in the developed countries in the structural transformation process in developing countries," structural transformation meaning in this context the transmission of the capacity to absorb and initiate new technological processes of production, leading to an increasing share of manufacturing in both output and employment, to an extent where this share, as in all developed countries, exceeds that of agriculture and mining. Our problem is to consider how private industry in developed countries can accelerate this process. Engineering technology is available to developing countries through various sources:

1. publications, at relatively little cost;
2. public, ie governmental aid and technical assistance programs;
3. purchase of patents and licences, including purchase of nonpatented knowhow where it can be obtained separately from capital and management; and
4. knowhow transferred jointly with capital and management through direct investment.

Technical publications and technical assistance with regard to the creation of a manufacturing industry would be more effective where the absorptive capacity of the developing countries concerned has reached a fairly high level of sophistication in the sense that there is a nucleus of industrial enterprises already in existence that could absorb and apply the new knowledge, and there is also a nucleus of technical and managerial skills and an entrepreneurial class, private and/or public.

Where this is not the case (eg in the majority of African countries), the transmission of technology through publications and public aid will run into difficulties. This makes it necessary to consider how, in addition to these other measures, direct private investment could be attracted and utilized to the advantage of developing countries.

Direct private investment brings with it in one package, capital, modern technology, managerial and technical skills, and marketing expertise. Direct investment by international corporations has the added advantage of bringing with it the technological and managerial innovations of the parent company. Direct private investment, however, poses certain problems which have to be faced by both the developing and the developed countries. These problems are more serious today than they were during the nineteenth century.

Foreign capital inflow in the nineteenth century was mainly in the form of loans and only a small proportion in the form of equity. Today, private international bond investment is very small, and public credit or aid has taken its place. The overwhelming majority of what is today called private investment is direct investment in equity. Remuneration of equity investment is in general between

15 and 25 per cent before taxes and 10 to 15 per cent after taxes. Bond credit costs from 5 to 6 per cent. In other words, risk capital expects a higher rate of return than that normally applied to investment by way of loans. Private capital expects to earn as much in a developing country as it can in a developed country, plus some additional margin for the risk element in unfamiliar climates. Additional remuneration of managerial and technical personnel and the combination of consulting firms and suppliers' credit results in expensive equipment. The net effect is that equity investment carries a higher transfer burden. Higher rates of remitted profits generate balance-of-payments problems and reduce the amount of reinvestment, slow down transformation and, consequently, the transfer of technology.

Another problem is that foreign private capital is traditionally, in Africa at least, invested in extractive industries such as mining, oil, and plantations, mainly for export; this creates enclave economies with limited linkage effects. Besides extractive industries, foreign capital goes to commerce, sales organizations, and assembly and packaging plants, in order to increase exports from the developed countries, thereby compounding the foreign exchange problem. As in the case of extractive industries, this concentration of direct investment on commerce and semiprocessed products slows down the transfer of technology. When developing countries want to establish domestic industries to replace the imported finished manufactures, the foreign investors consider that such products compete with their import business; accordingly, they resist the creation of an integrated manufacturing sector which would, through forward and backward linkage effects, induce a much greater transfer of technology by stimulating national investment in domestic industry and trade.

Finally, there is fear, on the part of developing countries, that private foreign capital will dominate the economic and political life of the recipient country and compromise its independence. One should not forget, of course, the argument of private industry in advanced countries when invited to participate in developing manufacturing industries in developing countries. It is often argued that the investment climate is unfavorable. This is a nebulous concept meaning many, sometimes different, things to different private investors.

Investment climate seems to boil down to:

1. political stability
2. inadequacy of externalities, etc.
3. inflation
4. devaluation
5. nationalization

I would suggest solutions to these problems, mainly in the African context.

Since private direct investment in equity form is expensive, it is necessary to establish priorities, ie encourage direct private investment to move into those sectors of industry where its technological benefits will be maximized and leave the other sectors of industry either to public aid or to domestic savings or management contracts.

In this connection, a distinction may be made between three types of industries:

1. Industries where technology is well known, standardized, and generally accessible (eg mining and public utilities); public aid may be sought to develop this sector.

2. Industries where technology is complicated, where plant design and management vary greatly, and knowhow is not easily accessible. Most of these will be in the field of capital and intermediate goods. These might be selected for direct private investment.

3. Industries between these two categories, ie the intermediate sector in which plant design and management are not completely standardized but in which design options are limited; for example, steel mills, oil refineries, and some consumer goods industries. This group might be developed by the use of management contracts.

This seems to suggest giving priority, as far as private foreign industry is concerned, to the development of the producers' goods sector (capital and intermediate goods). It may be argued that this is against conventional wisdom, which teaches that in these countries it is the simpler and labor-intensive industries that ought to be encouraged. The answer to this would be that the major source of growth and technological advancement in industrial production is import substitution in respect to intermediate and capital goods.

When we consider prevailing technology and its improvement in developing countries, we tend to consider mainly why underdeveloped countries have not developed labor-intensive technology appropriate to their factor endowment. This bypasses the role played by the producers' goods sector in technological advancement. A major source of technological progress is improvement in the efficiency of capital goods production. Most of the major technological innovations in developed countries have emerged in the capital goods sector. One of the most significant propelling forces in the growth of high-income countries is the technological dynamism of their capital goods industries which maintains the marginal efficiency of capital at a high level. Underdeveloped countries with little or no capital sector cannot make capital saving innovation because they lack the necessary capital goods industry and, therefore, the technological base of engineering knowledge upon which further technological progress can be made.

Establishment of priorities should be accompanied by a reexamination of the ownership problem and training arrangements.

The general desirable pattern for foreign equity investment is a partnership with eventual majority-holding or national ownership.

Technology will not always be the scarce factor in developing economies. Newly developed processes are at first scarce and gradually become part of common knowledge. The maximum contribution in overcoming the technological gap is in the early process of industrialization. Therefore, majority-owned foreign equity could be limited in time.

It is feasible that:

1. There could be agreement between the developing countries and foreign investors that foreign investment, in the complicated sectors of industry, may start with 100 per cent or majority equity ownership, then offer the majority share, after an agreed period of time, to nationals or sell all the rest of equity to nationals. This would mean that the high price paid by the nationals for technology and management during the early years of production will ultimately accrue to national ownership.

2. In sectors where the main contribution is management rather than technology, the majority share of the foreign investor might not be required or required only for a relatively short period of time.

3. In cases where dependence on a continuous supply of new research and foreign technology is vital, majority foreign ownership might be required for indefinite periods. The advantage here, if technology is critical, is that knowhow will be transferred on a continuous basis. There may be a charge on the basis of royalties on sales, but parent companies are more likely to take a more relaxed attitude toward wholly owned or majority-owned subsidiaries than toward joint ventures, when fixing royalty, share, and dividend policy and may even assign a larger export role.

The trouble, of course, with joint ventures, is that some foreign companies are reluctant to enter them because local shareholders would resist investment, their time horizon is short, problems arise over pricing, imports of machinery, markets. In management contracts where technology is not a crucial issue, the problem is that fees are usually high for a developing country, and there is no guarantee that management will be good. A possible solution is for the foreign firm to offer credit to the national firm covering a percentage of investment cost, or take a minority share so that it has a stake in the enterprise.

There are other forms of joint ventures which might be considered: (1) coproduction agreements, whereby a national enterprise acquires equipment and technology and pays for it by exports; or (2) purchase of licences, trademarks, and patents. The trouble here is that the purchaser of the patent may not have the right to penetrate the market of the advanced country or may be confined to selling in his own country in order not to compete with holders of the same patent in other developing countries.

The flow of private investment would, of course, especially in Africa, be facilitated by regional integration or multinational economic cooperation to provide adequate markets and scale economies for industries, especially those producing capital goods. Subregional cooperation would also strengthen countries in negotiating with foreign investors.

All this does not really solve the major problem—direct private investment is costly. In general, it might be argued that the evaluation of foreign private investment cannot be based on straight comparisons of the inflows and outflows of foreign exchange in the short run. Many factors are involved, including the recipient country's projections of its short-run and long-run foreign exchange gap and the over-all contribution to long-range economic development. In short, a price has to be paid for development.

On problems of investment climate, all that could be said is that unfavorable climate is a symptom of underdevelopment and could be solved by increased investment from the developed countries. Therefore, governments in developed countries could assist by setting up a system which would ensure against the operating losses that a private might incur—preferably through international institutions such as the World Bank.

REPORT OF WORKSHOP 12

Hamlin Robinson, Rapporteur

WORKSHOP 12 was concerned with the role of private companies in the USA and other economically developed nations in assisting the industrial growth of the developing countries, including both the introduction of modern technology and the development of an indigenous technological base within these countries.

It must be recognized at the outset that generalization is difficult in this area; each situation must be evaluated separately with due regard to the conditions prevailing in the developing country under study and the characteristics of industry and product. It is acknowledged, however, that private foreign companies have a very important role in the process of transferring and adapting modern technology. This role will differ, of course, among the various industries. The development of a technological base within the developing countries will depend basically on two factors: the existence of educational opportunities in scientific and technical fields, and vocational and research opportunities to apply the new knowledge and skills. The first depends primarily on the developing country, whereas the second can be affected substantially by the entry and growth of companies from the industrializing nations employing advanced technology. Clearly, however, the two factors are interrelated, and progress in one area will prove beneficial to the other.

It was agreed that, for the industrialization of the developing countries, the key element is the human factor, ie the availability of an increasing number of highly trained technical people and of a nucleus of entrepreneurship. It is imperative, therefore, that countries desiring to apply modern technology for the achievement of their developmental objectives should strengthen their educational systems in science, engineering, and related subjects. For advanced training, smaller countries, in particular, may find it more efficient and economical to rely on regional engineering and technological centers. The developing countries should endeavor to identify their long-term needs for scientific and technical manpower at all levels, which requires thorough analysis and an appreciation of their comparative advantages. The educational opportunities must then be provided, realistically geared to employment prospects if the graduates are to be retained, through appropriate national priorities and funding. Private firms can assist this effort through scholarships, financial assistance, and donations of equipment and expert advice.

This approach will facilitate the creation of an indigenous technological base and enhance public understanding of the requirements and discipline of industrialization and technology. Foreign manfacturing enterprises using advanced technologies will be attracted to the country that has ample trained manpower and, hence, actual or potential engineering and scientific capabilities. The availability of trained personnel and its employment in positions making use of this training, lays the basis for domestic research and development, a priority objective of many developing countries. These considerations will operate as a first and major screening device for the location decision of the foreign company; investment incentives will enter the decision-making process at a later stage when the choice has been narrowed down to a few alternatives. The prospective investor is likely to be quite flexible in this respect.

Two other important factors, at least for high-technology industry, are the relative stability of the political and social environment within the developing country and favorable prospects for sustained long-term growth. The emphasis is not so much political stability as such, but on reasonable predictability with regard to the directions of social and political development. Where this situation does not obtain, the growth of modern technology may be impeded seriously, deterring entry of firms from the industrialized countries.

One of the distinguishing features of the developed nations, especially the United States, has been the continual rise of entrepreneurs in the society. These people generally combine some technical knowledge or skill, a desire for independence, and a willingness to take great risks in new enterprises. A striking example, but by no means a unique one, is the Hewlett-Packard Company of California, which had its origin 30 years ago in a backyard enterprise with an investment of only $600 and which now employs some 12 000 people in 17 plants, manufacturing a very wide range of precision electronic measuring devices. It is extremely important in the less-developed countries that vigorous efforts be made to seek out and assist those promising individuals who are likely to provide the entrepreneurship needed for dynamic growth.

Successful entrepreneurs of this type should not be regarded as exploiters of society, but should be given recognition for their contribution to the economic and technological growth of the country. Political leaders and the general public in the developing nations frequently lack an adequate understanding of the importance of the entrepreneurial function that result-oriented private enterprise can perform. Entrepreneurs can be found in all countries, even though their number or their level of achievement may be relatively modest; better public appreciation of the role of the private sector must come through the demonstration effect of a creative sector rapidly expanding exployment opportunities and incomes.

The fact that financial assistance to industrial and commercial enterprises is now made available primarily through banks and financial institutions can be a real barrier to the expansion of entrepreneurial activity. Financial institutions are likely to insist on security as the primary criterion for extending loans, and to limit their loans to those who can provide the necessary collateral in the form of real estate, plant, and equipment. Some of the most promising entrepreneurs, on the other hand, may lack such collateral and have nothing but their own ideas, skills, and drive. Methods need to be found for reaching these individuals; and in this effort, both local and foreign private enterprises can play an extremely important role, especially if channels of communication can be opened and maintained between government and industry.

The availability of financial resources for such ventures appears to be less of a factor than is generally assumed. Too much reliance is placed on the institutional flow of capital and too little emphasis on the provision of risk capital by high-technology firms of the developed nations to support entrepreneurs in similar or related industries in the developing countries. There is reason to believe, however, that this is receiving growing recognition.

Those companies which realize the importance of providing support to local entrepreneurs and the profit potential, in spite of high risks, of such ventures should take the initiative to determine how the business community can assist in identifying and supporting entrepreneurs in the developing countries in ways which are beyond the scope of the more institutionalized sources of capital and other assistance. This approach would provide an additional important channel for the transmission and use of technology. Efforts along these lines will require a clear mandate from the top management of the firm and may require that a high-ranking executive be assigned the responsibility for the development and implementation of such a program. It is strongly recommended that this proposal be explored further in small informal meetings of internationally minded business leaders in an effort to devise broadly based, long-term arrangements.

Although their objectives differ, there is a wide mutuality of interests between the high-technology firm and the less-developed country; both seek growth and prosperity. Moreover, the company with world-wide production and marketing activities can play a key role in identifying and promoting particular industrial projects that capitalize on a country's comparative advantages. These companies have the necessary technology, are prepared to use it, and, if necessary, to modify it; they market their products in many countries; they know or can determine the technical and economic feasibility of local production; and they can be very helpful to national planning organizations in pointing out promising development oportunities and in realizing such opportunities.

Whether foreign companies enter a developing country on a joint-venture basis or through wholly owned subsidiaries is less important than whether they make an investment, although eventual local participation in ownership as well as management is highly desirable, if not essential, in the long run. The high-technology industry, however, requires very specialized management and it often may be advantageous not to include local participation in ownership until the enterprise is well established, fully qualified local managerial personnel are available, and the local partners or stockholders understand the requirements for its growth. On the other hand, many companies regard joint ventures with local partners as highly desirable and as an important factor in identifying the enterprise with the country in which it is located. Other forms of participation also may be

281

appropriate in some cases, such as management contracts—often accompanied by an equity or other financial interest in the enterprise.

It is in the foreign company's own interest to understand the motivations and aspirations of the host country. The company often is in a vulnerable position merely by being a foreign-controlled enterprise because the people and governments of developing countries may be fearful of domination by large foreign concerns, may resent the ability of outside interests to undertake projects beyond local means or capabilities, or may misunderstand the company's problems and the nature of its operations. These and other open and latent fears and suspicions must be taken seriously by the foreign investor who has to inform and educate the public in order to avoid friction and unwarranted charges.

Similarly, countries desirous of attracting direct foreign investment should understand the objectives and preferences of the companies or industries they seek in order to compete effectively for their attention. Rigid policies as, for example, a fixed proportion of local ownership, may drive away high-technology enterprises that are so essential to broadly based economic development.

Government agencies and other organizations concerned with industrial growth need to develop their own capability to select and analyze the industries in which their country has a comparative advantage or which appear promising for other reasons. They will then be in a good position to interest foreign companies and to obtain their views and commitments.

Obviously, it is impossible to legislate attitudes, either for the host countries or the prospective investors but, ideally, investment situations will be approached on a case-by-case basis with flexibility in regard to individual arrangements and emphasis on the mutual interests of both parties.

REFERENCES CITED

Banco Nacional de Comercio Exterior S. A., "La crisis de la asistencia externa," *Comercio Exterior,* August, 1968.
Baranson, Jack, "Automotive industries in developing countries," unpublished paper, May 31, 1968.
————, "Will there be an auto industry in the LDC's future?", *Columbia Journal of World Business,* May–June 1968.
Barclays Bank DCO, "Private foreign investment in developing countries," *Overseas Review,* May, 1967.
Broehl, Wayne G. jr., *The Case Study of the International Basic Economy Corporation.* Washington: National Planning Association, 1968.
Chilton, Werner L., "The choice of technology for United States direct investment in Latin American manufacturing industry and its implications for economic development," Ph.D. dissertation, New York: Columbia University, 1962.
Edelberg, Guillermo. *The Procurement Practices of the Mexican Affiliates of Selected U.S. Automobile Firms.* Boston: Harvard University, June, 1963.
De Figueriedo, Nuño F., "Arangements for the transfer of operative technology to the developing countries. Case study of Brazil," *Progress Report* of the Secretary-General to the 44th Session of the United Nations Economic and Social Council, March 4, 1968.
Fowler, Cyril F.,"Part interchangeability world-wide," *M. F. View,* Massey-Ferguson Limited, November-December, 1965.
Hare, Van Court jr., "The horse that can save more than a kingdom," *Columbia Journal of World Business,* May–June, 1967.
Hung, G. Nguyen Tien, "Economies of scale and economic integration," *Finance and Development,* No. 2, 1968.
International Labour Organization, "Skill requirements for industrialization," Provisional Agenda of the International Symposium on Industrial Development, Item No. 3 (c), Athens, 1967.
International Monetary Fund. *International Financial News Survey,* July 19,1968.
————, *International Financial News Survey,* September 27, 1968.

282

Johnson, Harry G., *Economic Policies Toward Less Developed Countries*. Washington D.C.: The Brookings Institution, 1967.

Kidron, Michael. *Foreign Investments in India*. London: Oxford University Press, 1965.

Kleu, Sebastiaan J. *Import Substitution in the South African Automobile Industry*. Boston: Harvard University, June, 1967.

Lary, Hal B. *Imports of Manufactures from Less Developed Countries*. New York: National Bureau of Economic Research, 1968.

Maddison, Angus, "The supply of skills to the industrial sector in developing countries," Background paper prepared for the International Symposium on Industrial Development, UNIDO, Athens, 1967.

New Zealand, House of Representatives. *The World Bank Report on the New Zealand Economy 1968*. Wellington: Government Printer, 1968.

OECD, "Development assistance—1967 and recent trends," press release, Paris, July 4, 1968.

Onis, Juan de, "Latin lands, troubled by 'challenge' of U.S. business penetration, seek a new stance," *New York Times*, September 17, 1968.

Oriental Economist, "Malaysia—Progress seen in industrialization," August, 1968.

Robinson, Richard D. *International Business Policy*, New York: Holt, Rinehart and Winston, Inc., 1964.

Rose, Sanford, "The rewarding strategies of multinationalism," *Fortune*, September 15, 1968.

Surbaugh, Norvell E., "Marketing and distribution in Latin America," Thomas A. Gannon, ed., *Doing Business in Latin America*. New York: American Management Association, 1968.

Swanson, W. E., "Manpower and compensation planning," Thomas A. Gannon, ed., *Doing Business in Latin America*, New York: American Management Association, 1968.

Tazi, Abderrahman, "The world-wide opportunity for private capital," *Finance and Development*, No. 3, 1968.

Times (London), "How Philips links trade and philanthropy," September 8, 1966.

Topping, Seymour, "Aid to developing nations shifting to private sector," *New York Times*, August 5, 1968.

United Nations, *Statistical Yearbook 1966*.

UNIDO Industrial Development Board, "Report of the International Symposium on Industrial Development," Athens, 1967.

United Nations Industrial Development Organization, "Issues and problems in manpower development for industrialization," Provisional Agenda for the International Symposium on Industrial Development, Item No. 3(c), Athens. November 29–December 20, 1967.

Waterston, Albert, "Good enough for developing countries?", *Finance and Development*, September, 1964.

Weatherall, Ernest, "India goads auto firms on quality," *Christian Science Monitor*, June 6, 1968.

Wilkins, Mira and Frank Ernest Hill, *American Business Abroad: Ford on Six Continents*. Detroit: Wayne State University Press, 1964.

Wionczek, Miguel S., "La inversión privado norteamericana y el desarrollo de Mesoamerica," *Comercio Exterior*, August, 1968.

——————, "La transmisión de la technologiá a los paises en desarrollo: Proyecto de un estudio sobre México," *Comercio Exterior*, May, 1968.

16

THE ROLE OF NATIONAL PRIVATE INDUSTRIES

Principal Paper—G. P. Kane

Discussion of the Paper by G. P. Kane

Commentary—Warren S. Hunsberger

Report of Workshop 13—Robert Krueger, Rapporteur

Private industries in the emerging nations obviously have a strong interest in industrialization and development. Their interactions with the industries of other nations and the governments of the developed nations of the world are important to the development process.

The Editors

THE ROLE OF NATIONAL PRIVATE INDUSTRIES IN INDIA

Principal Paper by G. P. Kane

HISTORICALLY, India represents a country where traditional life and society flourished continuously for several centuries. Merchandise from India, including fine textiles, was renowned in all parts of the old world. However, the intellectual elite in India remained unaffected by the new era of machines that swept over Europe during the Industrial Revolution. The result was that the country was overrun by vigorous invaders overland from the Northwest, and by the sea-route from Europe, until British rule was established throughout the country at the beginning of the 19th century. In the subsequent century and a quarter, until the transfer of power to the Indian people in 1947, the deliberate policy of the alien rulers was to confine Indian production as much as possible to agricultural commodities and naturally occuring minerals. However, the availability of traditional skills and low-cost labor in the country attracted adventurous rulers to embark on agro-based industries such as tea, jute, and cotton textiles; their example was quickly followed by prosperous Indian merchants and landowners. The bitter experience of blockade in Britain during World War I, and the need to create a supply base in the East during World War II, compelled the British rulers not only to lift existing restrictions on the free movement of production such as salt from one part of the country to another, but also to offer special inducements for the establishment of industries such as sugar.

A notable feature of the Indian situation has been that, all along, Indian entrepreneurs have been available who could appreciate the financial and social gains that could be reaped from the establishment of industrial activity in the country. Such entrepreneurs would not necessarily wait for government to offer special inducements for setting up industries. They would act according to their own judgment and, when necessary, employ all methods of persuasion, including public opinion pressure, to obtain protection from government. Among them, an outstanding personality was Jamshedji Tata. At the beginning of the present century, he planned many industrial enterprises including textile mills, a steel plant, hydro-electric power plants, and mills for producing vegetable oils from copra and oilseeds. He visualized the need for an elegant residence for travelers and an appropriate center for social gatherings in the city of Bombay and built the well-known Taj Mahal Hotel. Jamshedji Tata was also far ahead of his time in realizing the importance of scientific research for the development of the country, and established the India Institute of Science at Bangalore with a magnificent donation of Rs. 4 million in 1908. His benevolent activities pervaded so many spheres of national life that, at the celebration of his centenary, in describing him, Prime Minister Nehru said that Jamshedji Tata appointed himself as a one-man Planning Commission for the country and proceeded forthwith to implement his plans. The House of Tata has continued in its pioneering role. Prominent among its later activities are development of a successful internal as well as international airline; establishment of the largest soda ash works in the country; creation of a cancer research center support in initiation of the Fundamental Research Institute in Bombay under the inspiration of the late Dr. Bhabba; and a recent contribution for organizing a center for preforming arts in Bombay.

Another factor that ultimately proved to be of significant assistance to the establishment of industries was the decision of British rulers to orient education in the secondary and higher stages according to modern methods through the medium of English, rather than traditional, training in the classics inparted in local languages. With familiarity with the English language, information about world literature and the progress of science became available to Indian intellectuals. The rulers realized also that, for insuring stability of the regime, it was necessary to gradually extend the scope of employment to educated Indian personnel. Facilities for professional education in engineering and medicine were soon provided; the first two engineering colleges celebrated their centenaries a few years ago. Towards the end of the 19th century, Indians became eligible for appointments in the higher civil and medical services. Recruitment was made through examinations held in London and gifted young men started going abroad to appear for qualifying examinations in these fields, as well as for the study of other subjects, such as law, which would lead to lucrative careers at home. Their ranks soon swelled as the number of students going abroad for training and research in natural and applied sciences increased rapidly. Some of them went abroad for technical studies in the hope of pursuing an academic or research career on return; others were fired with missionary zeal in response to the declarations of political leaders that training and its application to industry were an essential part of the agitation for political emancipation. Many such students went abroad with limited funds scraped together by hopeful relatives and supplemented by loans from philanthropic organizations. On return, some of them faced bitterness and disappointment, since there was no demand for their acquired skills and their expectations remained unfulfilled. Others persevered against heavy odds, either on their own or in association with progressive entrepreneurs, and set up industrial units to meet some of the demands in the country. Often these units served as nuclei for substantial industrial growth in the postindependence period. Although an accurate record of the number of such trained people is not available, it is safe to assume that there were several thousands of trained men available in the country by 1947.

Between the two World Wars, the Indian chemical industry was in its infancy. Usually, the chemicals chosen for production were those which had a local demand and which could be made without investing large funds: alum for water purification and sizing; magnesium chloride for sizing to maintain the moisture content of yarn in the textile industry; Epsom salt, galenicals, and spirituous extracts of materials from medicinal plants for medical purposes; and naphthalene for insect repellent and road tar, obtained by the distillation of coal tar. Even for these products, competition from imports was severe, and the procedure for obtaining tariff protection was lengthy. The producers flourished only when scarcity appeared, as during the two World Wars when imports were irregular owing to the sinking of ships by enemy action. Sulfuric acid was the only chemical with natural protection against imports because of its corrosive nature. Therefore, production of other chemicals usually was organized as an adjunct of a 5- or a 10-tons per day sulphuric acid plant. Basic chemicals like caustic soda ammonia were not made at all. A plant for 50 tons per day of soda ash was set up, but it suffered from technical difficulties as well as severe competition from imported natural and synthetic soda ash.

Scarcities prevalent during the two World Wars provided ideal conditions for attempting the production of chemicals that were usually imported, because readily available products fetched prices several times higher than the normal. The situation was attractive to traders whose import business was restricted but who knew the needs of the market from past experience. Manufacturing activities were planned with the minimum expenditure on plant and equipment to ensure that the investment would be recovered from the high profit margin on sales long before the restoration of normal trade. Very soon it was evident that the new class of entrepreneurs regarded a low turnover with a high profit margin—made possible by the prevalence of a seller's market under conditions of scarcity—as the primary requisite for developing domestic production of new articles. Inevitably, the private entrepreneurs agitated constantly in the years after independence to maintain these conditions through protective tariffs and import control, as well as by their efforts to underestimate requirements and to exaggerate domestic capacity for production in discussions on plan targets.

However, considerable ingenuity as well as initiative were displayed by entrepreneurs in their efforts to organize production of chemicals during emergencies. When magnesium chloride required for sizing by the textile industry could not be imported from Germany during the first World War, bitterns from salt works containing about 9 per cent of $MgCl_2$ were considered a suitable alternative source of the material. The bitterns were collected by being lifted manually in mugfuls from the discharging ponds into movable steel tanks and transported a few miles to a factory for concentration in directly fired open pans to elimate sodium chloride and magnesium sulfate. Initially, the concentrated liquor was supplied as such to the textile mills; later on, a fused product in drums containing 46 per cent of $MgCl_2$ was placed on the market. Although the process of manufacture remained unchanged, the operation was so economical that, a few years after the end of the war in 1918, a few thousand tons of fused magnesium chloride were exported from India to Western Europe, including Germany. During the second World War, calcium chloride required as a cooling medium by ice factories was produced by the treatment of a magnesium chloride solution with lime. When the need for a few thousand tons a year of bichromate for khaki dyeing became urgent during the second World War, more than ten small companies undertook its production. After the war, many of the companies dropped the activity, but three units survived and grew to such size that, after meeting the needs of the country, bichromate could be exported whenever the prices were favorable. Other chrome compounds, including pigments, are also made now. When, during 1940–1944, components intended for the equipment of a soda ash unit under construction were lost at sea by enemy action, more than once the company obtained drawings from abroad and set up its own foundry especially for the purpose of fabricating the components. A few years later, under conditions of drought, the same company used treated sea water instead of fresh water for maintaining the operation of its soda ash plant. The dyestuffs industry began during the second World War when supplies from abroad were erratic and prices rocketed sky high. The activity started with the preparation of mixture of dyes and diluents that would give a given weight of fabric the exact shade desired by the customer. Gradually the simpler dyes and textile auxiliaries were made from penultimate intermediates, and the manufacturing program was extended backwards to the primary raw materials. Sometimes such extension took place only as a result of insistence by the government, as every increase in the number of manufacturing steps required further investment per unit weight of the final product, and the entrepreneurs were not anxious to incur such additional investment on their own.

The enthusiasm for chemicals production generated among Indian entrepreneurs during the years 1940–1944 continued unabated in the postwar years. The activity was confined .even then to making materials for replacing products that were imported to meet existing needs. But the scale of operation and the sophistication of processes adopted for manufacture increased rapidly. The first commercial plant for fertilizers with a capacity of about 25 tons of ammonia per day, based on the novel process of gassification of wood for making synthetic gas, was planned by a private entrepreneur with financial support from a state government. Projects for rayon filament yarn and staple fiber raised the magnitude of investment in individual chemical enterprises to approximately $10 million. Electrochemical and electrothermal industries were introduced into the country with units for caustic soda, hydrogen peroxide, and calcium carbide. A beginning was made towards utilization of byproduct chlorine by organizing the production of bleaching powder and benzene hexachloride. By 1951, the country became selfsufficient and ready to enter export trade with edible as well as industrial salt.

Industrial development in general, and chemical industries in particular, registered a further spurt of activity with the advent of the Industries Development and Regulation Act of 1951. The licensing system under the Act was designed to channel the limited funds available for investment into industries that were regarded as national priorities in the program for achieving import substitution as well as selfsufficiency in essential goods. Import control and actual user licenses introduced simultaneously provided the licensed industries an assurance of off-take of their goods immediately after achieving production and access to imported raw materials at reasonable prices. In this favorable environment, Indian companies participated with enthusiasm in the unprecedented expansion and diversification of chemical industries that took place between 1954 and 1962. Some companies operated their plants with the knowhow obtained on payment from overseas collaborators; others succeeded in persuading well-known overseas companies to share in the investment for new projects, even though the scale of operation and/or the source of raw materials were such that the projects were regarded as uneconomical by Western standards. Production of the synthetic plastics, polystyrene, and PVC was introduced into the country by such companies. Initially, the capacity for polystyrene was 5000 tons a year and the styrene monomer was imported. Capacity was increased three-fold after styrene monomer was made in the country from indigenous benzene and alcohol-based ethylene. Later the same group organized the production of SBR synthetic rubber in a complex that included facilities for making butadiene and styrene from alcohol and benzene, with a total investment of about $20 million. The first plant for PVC had a capacity for 3600 tons a year, based on its own production of chlorine and acetylene from calcium carbide. Two other plants were set up with somewhat larger capacity, one employing acetylene from calcium carbide and the other ethylene from alcohol. Recently, a 20 000-tons-a-year PVC plant using petrochemical ethylene has been established. It is expected that the older plants will expand very soon to achieve similar capacities and, in doing so, change over to the use of petrochemical ethylene and acetylene. Units for nylon yarn, set up with an onerous condition that they must earn the exchange required for import of caprolactam by the export of yarn, have proved to be very profitable undertakings. A company making insulating enamels finds that its products have been received so well abroad that in the near future more than half of its expanding production will be exported.

Whenever government initiated schemes for the development of individual sectors of industry, there was an immediate and enthusiastic response from the entrepreneurs. For instance, the Alcohol Committee recommended in 1956 that, to insure full utilization of molasses from the sugar industry, the production of industrial alcohol should be stepped up from about 10 million gallons to 40 and 60 million gallons by 1961 and 1966, respectively. It was also suggested that, as circumstances were not yet favorable for setting up petrochemical industries, the first units for the production of organic chemicals might be planned with the use of alcohol as a raw material. Before publication of the report in 1958, entrepreneurs had obtained licenses for the production of alcohol as well as all the chemicals recommended by the Alcohol Committee. Plans for the greater utilization of byproduct chlorine by organizing the production of stable bleaching powder, pesticides, PVC, and chlorinated solvents followed rapidly. As a result, the utilization of chlorine is 63 per cent, notwithstanding the fact that in the last 15 years the annual production of chlorine increased eight times. In the report of the Petro-Chemical Committee submitted to the government in 1960, it was recommended that since there was a prospect of surplus naphtha for quite a few years, the time was opportune to establish petrochemical complexes in the country for large-scale production of organic chemical products at low cost. Before publication of the report in 1962, an Indian company obtained a license to set up an integrated petrochemical complex in collaboration with well-known overseas companies. Its plan envisaged the production of high-density polyethylene, PVC, ethylene oxide, butyl and octyl alcohols, butadiene, and benzene by full utilization of all product streams from a naphtha throughput of 240 000 tons. The complex, with a total investment of about $75 million, has recently gone into production. Since the announcement of a government decision three years ago permitting fertilizer producers to sell their products without control on prices for seven years, Indian companies have entered the field and initiated projects that require investments of $50–75 million each.

Expansion in the capacity of individual units and total production in the country of basic and other chemicals have increased considerably in the last fifteen years. The earlier plants made 10–25 tons of sulfuric acid a day. Now 300-ton-per-day plants are regarded as normal and future plants based on pyrites are likely to produce nearly 1000 tons of acid daily. Annual production of sulfuric acid has increased seven times to nearly 1 million tons. As for soda ash, instead of the former 50-ton plants, one factory now makes 500 tons a day and another expects to approach a similar figure in about two years. The annual production of soda ash has increased nearly seven times to nearly 350 000 tons. With caustic soda, instead of the former 3- to 10-ton plants, the preferred capacity is 100 tons. There are indications that, with the growing demand for chlorine, the capacity of some of the plants may increase to 300 tons a day. The annual production of caustic soda during 1968 is likely to be 300 000 tons. The country is selfsufficient with respect to calcium carbide, with an increase in annual production from 3000 to about 60 000 tons. A major portion of the sodium sulfate required by the paper and other industries is recovered as a byproduct of the rayon industry. The existing production is adequate to meet all demands in the country for hydrogen peroxide, precipitated calcium carbonate, sodium hydrosulfite, borax and boric acid, industrial phosphates, and cryolite. Indian industry in the private sector can claim credit for a major share in this achievement.

The earlier industrialists had no difficulty in identifying areas for investment, because there was enormous scope for making products that were developed abroad and for which the existing demand in the country was met by imports. Such opportunities no longer exist as a result of the developments that have taken place in the last fifteen years. On the contrary, the rapid growth of industrial activity has been responsible for the creation of a new problem: the availability of industrial raw materials that are not found in the country. For example, fifteen years ago the annual bill for importing sulfur was less than $3 million; today it is nearly $40 million, and there are signs that by 1973 it will rise to $125 million. The cost of imported rock phosphate is likely to increase in the same period from $1.5 million to $120 million. If the rising demands are evaluated for the unavoidable imports of other materials such as the nonferrous metals copper, lead, zinc, tin, and nickel; petroleum crudes; and mercury and asbestos, the annual value of such imports alone may amount to $1 billion or more by 1973. It is also likely that, even if such amounts can be made available (which is highly improbable in view of the present imbalance between exports and imports), the raw materials may not be available in adequate quantities in world markets. Therefore, industrialists must begin to take an increasing interest in developing products and processes that can use indigenous instead of imported raw materials. This means that in the future stress must be on internal development rather than on mere application of what happens elsewhere.

So long as a rapid increase in production was urgent for minimizing imports in the shortest possible time, the cost of product to the consumer was of secondary importance. The rigid application of import control had created a seller's market for most products with the result that the consumer had to pay prices that were often exorbitant, even in comparison with the landed prices of imported materials after payment of import duties at high rates. The practice introduced under British rule of charging import duty on a raw material or a component at a rate higher than that charged on the finished product, survives as an anachronism in some cases and accentuates the position. It became almost an axiom that products made in the country cost substantially more than the corresponding materials imported from abroad. This situation was a deterrent to the drive for organizing an export trade of manufactured articles. The industrialists felt, first, that while a seller's market prevailed, there was no need to export; and second, that if they did have to export under compulsion from the government, the difference between the internal price and the f.o.b. realization on exports should be made good, either as a cash subsidy or equivalent assistance in some other form. The situation has begun to change, however, because a surplus of some chemical products is now available as a result of a temporary decline in demand owing to recession. More surpluses will occur in the future since it has been realized that matching licensed capacity for production exactly with the estimated demand is the safest way of ensuring the continuance of a seller's market. Exemption from the licensing provisions of the Industries Act to an increasing number of industries, and the greater availability of machinery in the country, are likely to help create more surpluses and therefore a competitive market. Industrialists must adjust themselves to the changing conditions and readily accept an obligation to export even when the realization on exports is lower than on internal sales. This happens elsewhere all the time because it is understood that in the initial years exports help to keep a plant of higher capacity in full production and thereby reduce the cost of production. Simultaneously, a cushion is provided for meeting rising internal needs in subsequent years against competition from more modern and larger plants.

The per capita consumption of manufactured products is still low in India and amounts to no more than 1–2 per cent of the corresponding figures in the United States. The low off-take results from consumption are determined primarily by the relatively small wealthy section of the population, mainly in the urban areas. How small their numbers are can be judged from the fact that the total number of income-tax payers in the country is well under 2 million even when an annual income of about $500 is liable to tax. However, the number of consumers is likely to swell by a few million every year with the growth in opportunities for employment and prosperity in the agricultural sector that is expected from the country's plans for economic development. So far the relatively affluent minority has been prepared to pay high prices for consumer goods. Prices must come down a great deal if the goods are to reach the large numbers of new customers. Production has been organized in units of a size that would meet existing needs, and it has not been necessary for the manufacturer to exert himself by promoting sales. Strange as it may seem, when large units are set up to insure production of basic materials at low cost, producers may have to face the problem of off-take unless they plan and develop the use of such materials for the making of diverse and unconventional end products.

This situation has been reached already with PVC. There is ample scope for diversification as the demand is growing rapidly for structurals, apparel footwear, detergents, cosmetics, household appliances, packaging for processed foods, fruits, and medicines. Conventional materials are either unsuitable for modern requirements, or their supply is inadequate. Industry cannot expect to solve these problems without involvement in research and development.

There is a growing feeling of resentment in the country that Indian industry has taken very little interest in research and development. In the 1950s, when new products were to be made by employing sophisticated processes in Indian companies that had no experience with such activity, it was natural that they should request process knowhow and engineering services from abroad. Such requests have been considered sympathetically by government for the past several years in the hope that, when profits eventually build up, the companies would undertake research and development in their own as well as in the national interest. Perhaps this has not happened because the manufacturing companies have become so used to operating in an assured, protected market that they do not consider investment in research as necessary for their survival. In the draft outline for the Fourth Plan published in 1966, the Planning Commission estimated the current annual expenditure on research by government, including amounts provided for the Department of Atomic Energy, at $80 million, and similar expenditure by companies in the private sector of 5 per cent of this figure. Even though the annual sales value of some of the chemical companies has increased to $25–50 million, with the occasional exception of products such as grade pulp dissolved from bamboo, production programs rarely include developments arising from their own research. Sponsoring research programs or establishing research professorships in technological institutes and the universities are activities that are rarely supported by industry. Only recently, a few companies have started taking advantage of the incentives for research offered by the government through tax concessions. The Planning Commission has rightly concluded that "research and development has not made adequate contributions to economic growth so far. India remains weak in design and development, and much too dependent on the import of foreign design and technical knowledge."

The existence of the situation described above has given rise to a feeling that industry is not interested in research carried out in the country. Today the larger chemical companies do maintain research cells, and some of them can claim credit for developing processes for commercial production such as dissolving pulp from bamboo and reactive dyes. But it must be conceded that the over-all involvement in research is small. Scientists employed in the research laboratories/institutes set up by government after independence for the declared purpose of fighting poverty and hunger by utilization of natural resources available in the country feel frustrated that their work remains unutilized by industry. Simultaneously, there is criticism that the scientists are working in isolation from industry and are engaged either in repetitive research or in the investigation of problems that are of very little interest to industry. This controversy has been the cause of some drastic suggestions recently, including the proposal for a compulsory levy on all output of industry for research, propagation of a view that intermediate technology is more suitable than the most advanced technology in a developing country, and agitation for restricting the use of technology imported from abroad for promoting research within. In the national interest it is important for industry to do all it can to resolve this controversy.

Involvement of Indian industry in research and development is essential, not merely to maintain the profitability of industry under the various strains arising from rapid expansion, but also to enable it to penetrate competitive world markets for exports. Simultaneously, industry will make its contribution towards arresting the "brain drain." According to the draft outline to the Fourth Plan, the number of graduate engineers in the country was about 93 000 in 1965–1966 and, in the same year, the fresh annual intake in engineering institutes was 23 315. In the current year, the number of engineers qualifying for degrees will be 15 000 in comparison with 35 000 for the United States. Precise figures of Indian engineers working abroad are not known, but it is unlikely that they will exceed a few thousand. From these numbers it could be said that the anxiety about "brain drain" is somewhat exaggerated, particularly in view of the recent decision to reduce engineering enrollment slightly, consequent upon a recession in the engineering industry. The anxiety about emigration of Indian engineers arises because recently the number of Indian engineers going abroad for postgraduate training and research, followed by employment abroad, has risen sharply. The shortage of engineering personnel in Australia, Canada, and the United States, and the establishment of new institutes of technology at Bombay, Madras, Delhi, and Kanpur, with substantial academic and financial assistance from the Soviet Union, West Germany, Great Britain, and the United States, respectively, providing opportunities for personal overseas contacts, have helped to accentuate the outflow. This problem is not peculiar to India. In a recent paper in the *Chemical Engineer* on "Industrial research and development," Hopton (1968) stated that, during 1966, the number of engineers and technologists who emigrated from the United Kingdom was 4200 representing 42 per cent of the new supply three years earlier. He ascribed this to the professional engineer being more highly regarded and better paid in the United States than his counterpart was in the United Kingdom, as well as to the vast concentration of research and development resources in a few sectors of American industry which results in centers of outstanding value. To counteract these attractions it is necessary to create more challenging opportunities in the United Kingdom, particularly in industry, for young engineers, technologists, and scientists.

The conclusions are applicable even more to the situation in India, as well as in other developing countries, because of the vastly greater disparity between emoluments and opportunities available to a professional engineer in these countries in comparison with the United States. Further, it is apparent that Indian industry is generally unaware that Indian engineers with postgraduate training and industrial experience abroad are attracted more by jobs in research and development than by those in production. Industry would find it profitable to attract such young men home by creating opportunities for them to assist in solving some of the pressing problems that face the country. Prominent among such problems are developing methods for the supply of fresh water in large areas where at present muddy or brackish water alone is available; increasing the supply of proteins and other nutritive foods by adoption of better agronomic practices as well as new synthetic processes; preventing waste of materials and energy; reducing the drudgery of household and other work; developing synthetic fibers with properties similar to those of popular natural fibers; and producing at low cost newer drugs and medicines to insure good health and many consumer products to enrich the life of the people.

The possibility of obtaining a satisfying job with a good income is certainly an inducement for a promising young man from a developing country to prolong his stay in the United States after completion of his training, but it would be a mistake to assume that the predominant reason is one of personal financial gain. When a young man in his most impressionable years lives in the United States for some time, he learns that time is money and quick decisions are inescapable. When he returns home, he is appalled by the waste of time inherent in the traditional way of life and the delayed decisions of administrative machinery inherited from colonial times. After his experience working for a few years in a country where there is almost full employment, the young man is bewildered by import control and licensing procedures at home, as well as by the reservation to the small-scale sector of certain industrial activities that are necessary for the planned development of a country with limited resources. He is disappointed when he realizes that there is very little change to utilize at home the special skills he has developed abroad in a sophisticated technological field. And he feels

294

frustrated in the absence of any orientation or insight into the basis of planned economic growth of a developing country. These factors, rather than the motive of material gain, are probably most responsible for the so-called "brain drain."

At the UNESCO-sponsored Conference on the Application of Science and Technology to the Development of Asia (CASTASIA) held in New Delhi in August, 1967, the Director General, René Maheu, said that too often scientific or technical assistance to underdeveloped countries comes down to a simple transfer of knowledge and knowhow, accompanied by some supply of equipment. Maheu stated further that

the results of this sort of aid are neither deep nor lasting, giving little weight to the understanding of the reasons and the explanations, or the setting up of structures designed to encourage or facilitate creative work. Such aid does not enable people to assimilate properly or to achieve the intellectual and social prerequisites for technical progress.

In the last fifteen years, the United States, the Soviet Union, the Federal Republic of Germany, and the United Kingdom have given substantial assistance through UNESCO for the establishment of institutes of technology with the object of creating centers of technological training and research in India. It is distressing to observe that soon after graduation about a third of the graduates of these institutes proceed to the United States, Canada, or other advanced countries for postgraduate work. It is a cause for concern when this cream of Indian talent seeks employment and remains indefinitely abroad.

There is evidence that many of these young men have a deep-rooted desire to return to India. When a suitable position is available, quite a few return home on salaries in rupees that are *numerically* equivalent to their dollar earnings in the United States ($1 = Rs. 7.50). What is required is an acceleration of the return movement, motivated by greater understanding of the influence of technology in development planning. This might be done by orienting the training and research in such a way that, while investigating a most sophisticated problem in an institute in the United States, it becomes obvious to the researcher that the same outlook and methods of technological inquiry can be applied to the tasks confronting a developing country. At this stage, it is also important to emphasize that the apparent conflict between the traditional concepts in an undeveloped country and the outlook of modern technology can be resolved if people who have experience and understanding of both undertake the task. It might inspire them to do so if, during their stay in the United States, students in the engineering and technology faculties have frequent opportunities for association and discussion with engineers who have had the good fortune to be involved in the rapid industrialization of a developing country, and learn from them of the heartbreaks and joys of such endeavor.

DISCUSSION OF THE PAPER BY G. P. KANE

THE PHRASES "modern," "old," or "intermediate" technologies cause difficulty since they always bring an element of superiority or inferiority as well as confusion into any talk. Perhaps the phrase "profit" technology might be better and avoid subjective evaluation of development technology. The most appropriate technology could be a technique that it is 1000 years old or it could be the most recent. The most profitable technology is the one which gives the highest efficiency, whether that technology be old or new.

The most "efficient" technology in economic terms would be the one that, as in any system, gives the highest output-to-input ratio, that has the most capital efficency.

Multinational cooperation is the most convenient system by which technological efficiency can be achieved. It is desirable to organize multinational cooperation for production by directing production, in one country, of certain parts at a low cost of other parts in another country, and by then combining them. It is important, however, to recognize that multinational interplay so organized can conflict with national sovereignty in the sense that individual countries want to control their own internal affairs economically and not have production decisions made about their employment and their production with reference to what is going on in an outside market. This is, in effect, a conflict between the country's desire to control its own economy and its desire to achieve the economies of scale by sharing in international trade with other countries.

PRIVATE ENTERPRISE IN INDUSTRIALIZATION
Commentary by Warren S. Hunsberger

AS AN ECONOMIST, not an engineer, I wish to make a few points about these two professions and their relation to the industrialization of low-income countries. In the formal sense of a technical discipline, especially as an academic field, economics originated with the Industrial Revolution in England. As with many other specialties of industrial societies, economics is now divided into a growing number of subspecialties. The latest edition of the *Handbook* of the American Economic Association, dated 1964, lists 15 major subject-matter groups in economics and a total of 46 subdivisions.

Engineering operations are, I suppose, as old as civilization. I immediately think of such engineering works as the Egyptian Pyramids and the Great Wall of China—to mention two examples from countries called underdeveloped or developing. And today engineering as a profession may be subdivided into even more subordinate specialties than economics.

According to many—though not all—economists, the central concern of economics is scarcities. When resources are scarce, men have economic problems. But the scarcities are not necessarily objective facts. What counts is whether the scarcity is felt by human beings or human organizations. If people do not know that they have a vitamin deficiency or air pollution, there is no scarcity—so far as human wants and decision-making are concerned—of vitamins or of pure air. If people have never heard of Coca-Cola, they have no scarcity of it and no economic problem related to this almost universal American product. But there can be serious scarcity of sea shells or gold if men want more of these commodities than they have, in which case there is a real problem.

Engineering is quite different. The capacity of a bridge or of bridge-building materials is a matter of objective fact, not just of human perception or wants. Whatever men may know or care about the engineering facts and principles concerned, the bridge will fall when overloaded. So, it is possible to have a shortage of adequate bridge-building materials even if a people are unaware of the problem and thus feel no scarcity in the economic sense.

If this distinction between economics and engineering is valid, perhaps it has some pertinence to the topic of national private industries and their role in increasing the effective application of engineering technology to industrialization. Private industries in low-income countries are for the most part small, since such countries usually have both limited capital and quite limited means for combining the capital resources of many small investors or lenders into large private enterprises. I shall consider only small industries, even though there are such large private enterprises as the famous Tata Iron and Steel Company in India.

Small private industries may be completely traditional handicraft activities with no engineering problem other than the application of traditional technology and no economic problems other than those involved in acquiring traditional raw materials by traditional methods, using traditional credit practices and marketing by traditional means. As more and more small industries are finding new economic problems, pressures, and possibilities, engineering problems frequently arise. Vast numbers of such small firms are unsuccessful in making significant changes, especially in India, Burma, Indonesia, and other countries where the scope for private enterprise has been limited by circumstances, state policy, or both.

But in a growing list of countries and a spreading range of products, especially where United States import demand has been a factor, small private enterprises have succeeded in making new products, wholly or partly new, in quantities requiring rapid increases in firm size along with substantial introductions of new technology and machinery.

The process began in the 1950s in Japan, a country no longer in the low-income class—that is, no longer called developing, despite the fastest growth rate the postwar world has seen. Buyers, mostly from the United States, arrived in Japan with samples of merchandise looking for suppliers. First they wanted women's blouses, then a variety of other textiles and clothing, then sundries, optical goods, electronic goods, and an ever-widening range of finished products, parts, and components.

The buyers soon began to look beyond Japan, first because of cotton textile export quotas imposed by Japan in January, 1957, under pressure from the United States. Hong Kong soon joined Japan as a supplier of textiles, clothing, and a spreading array of other products, especially for the United States market. Then Taiwan, Korea, Singapore, and other countries began to enjoy rapidly rising export sales of products formerly not exported or never before produced. In some cases producers did not even know what they were making.

The American buyers and, to a substantially lesser extent, buyers from other industrial countries did not merely bring a market to the door of private producers in the countries concerned. These buyers also brought specifications and standards; in some cases a great deal of technical advice; credit, especially in the form of advance payments; quality control; and other supervisory and innovative functions.

The supplying firms in almost all of these cases are private. The countries where such business has boomed are countries where private enterprise is allowed some leeway. Governments have even assisted in a variety of ways in the successful countries. The Asian countries with the most direction and control from their central governments, the countries most strongly interested in public industry—India, Burma, Indonesia—have done very little of this innovation.

If India, for instance, could somehow remove the impediments that have kept Indian firms from sharing in such business, Indian industry might begin to move in a way that would not only boost Indian production; it might strain the tolerance of the importing countries, especially the United States, for competitive imports. But up to now import restrictions have not prevented dramatic successes in Korea, for example. Korean exports, mostly of small manufactures produced by private enterprise, have risen by a full 40 per cent a year on the average for ten years.

My understanding of the impediments that have afflicted Indian private industry and caused foreign buyers to leave empty handed after visits to India is that the impediments are economic and administrative. The domestic market is too atractive, import and export procedures are discouragingly numerous and difficult, and the technical level of would-be suppliers is too low. The engineering and other technical problems are, I believe, the least and easiest to solve. These have given way elsewhere when the economic and administrative circumstances have been right.

REPORT OF WORKSHOP 13
Robert Krueger, Rapporteur
ECONOMIC AND ENGINEERING DIMENSIONS OF THE TRANSFER OF TECHNOLOGY

THE TRANSFER of technology from developed to underdeveloped countries has both engineering and economic dimensions. Technology can be transferred to some countries by grafting a new product and the techniques necessary to produce it onto the existing economy, as in the case of American businessmen who persuaded the Japanese to produce and export blouses, cameras, and electrical equipment. In other countries, however, both engineering and economic factors may prevent such a development.

The interrelation of technological and economic factors also is apparent in the question of what constitutes an "appropriate" technology for the developing nations. In the United States, it makes economic sense, because of high labor costs, to use disposable hypodermic needles. These needles represent the latest technology, but it does not follow that they are necessarily desirable for India or Africa. In these countries the cheapness of labor relative to capital would suggest technologies which are labor intensive. This argument rests solely on the private costs borne by economic units utilizing needles; social costs—the possibility of greater likelihood of disease from the older needle—should also be examined in the process of making decisions about introducing new techniques.

A successful example of the application of engineering and economic understanding to the introduction of new technology is found in the recent development of a stove in Colombia, where peasants had spent half their day gathering wood for fuel. An understanding of the engineering and economic aspects of this problem led to the development of a cheap portable stove which burns an available fuel. Last year 1 million of these stoves were sold in Colombia.

Technology transfer in an underdeveloped country might be facilitated by the availability of a number of case studies which show the engineering, economic, and cultural problems other countries have had in the introduction of new techniques. Also, insofar as possible, economic and engineering advisors to private firms in the developing countries should live with the operation or design they have proposed. Far too common is the practice of giving technical-economic advice, with the advisor having no responsibility for implementations.

THE ROLE OF GOVERNMENT

Generally, government should set up an environment which is favorable to the introduction of new technology by the private sector. Specifically, government can do this by providing the infrastructure, by developing monetary and fiscal policies and institutions aimed at stimulating new innovation, and by creating special agencies to promote economic development.

The question of where government activity is desirable is pragmatic; the criterion should be: "Will the benefits of the anticipated government activity outweigh its costs?" In the past, government has played a larger role in the economies of the underdeveloped countries, and it probably will do so in the future. Indeed, if the history of Western economies is examined, it will be seen that government played an important role in their early economic development.

Government, in its role as a stimulator of economic development, might consider the following proposals:

—initiation of the development of new export markets (as in the case of Japan);
—use of P. L. 480 funds to finance the exports of one developing country to another;
—development of ways of averaging the demand for agricultural products, thus removing wide price fluctuations and the entrepreneurial uncertainty that such fluctuations cause.

300

THE PROBLEMS OF LARGE AND SMALL FIRMS

Large firms in the developing countries should be encouraged to utilize the smaller firms as suppliers, as has been done in both Japan and India. This could eventually lead to the possibility of combining the modern industrial technology of the large firm with the traditional skills of the small peasant craftsman-proprietor.

LINKAGES

There are some cases of strong linkage effects being created in developing countries. A brewery in Mexico spawned a host of supplying industries, including kegs, bottles, and labels, and in turn these industries created a need for other suppliers. However, small markets often prevent strong linkage effects. When a developing nation must make choices about which industries to support, it should choose those with the greatest linkage effect. Of even greater importance is the need for government to stimulate the development of industry with strong linkage effects.

IMPORT SUBSTITUTION INDUSTRIES

Many development economists feel that the creation of import substitution industries has been pushed too far. Such industries are highly oriented to the domestic market, have high prices because they receive tariff protection, and, therefore, have a small market, with the result that their impact on the economy is small.

ENTREPRENEURSHIP

Crucial to the development of the private sector and its utilization of technology is the encouragement of entrepreneurial activity. The power of indigenous entrepreneurship should not be overlooked. The usual picture of the development of the Japanese economy has been biased toward the role of government; what has not been seen are those cases where government operation of industry failed while private businessmen made remarkable successes.

The social and political environment is important in securing entrepreneurial talent. Some development economists have suggested the importance of minority groups as sources of this talent. In Japan, nationalistic prestige may be related to the high levels of saving and investment.

REFERENCE CITED

Hopton, G. U. "Industrial research and development," *Chemical Engineer,* April, 1968.

17

THE ROLE OF UNIVERSITIES IN THE UNITED STATES

Principal Paper—B. R. Teare jr.

Discussion of the Paper by B. R. Teare jr.

Commentary—Merton Barry

Report of Workshop 14—Edward Stuart, Rapporteur

Universities throughout the United States have interests and activities relating to the multifaceted problems of the emerging nations. University faculties in the United States find natural associations with colleagues in the universities of other countries. The effectiveness of United States institutions in the assistance of universities in other countries is discussed in Chapter 17.

The Editors

THE ROLE OF UNIVERSITIES IN THE UNITED STATES

Principal Paper by B. R. Teare jr.

ONE OF THE key phrases in the complete title of the dicussion I was invited to lead—"The role of universities in the United States toward an increased effectiveness in the application of engineering technology to the industrialization of the developing countries"—is "increased effectiveness." This rightfully infers that there are on-going programs and that we are concerned with what the universities can do to make them more effective.

That the universities have an important role is clear. Modern industrialization is accomplished by a team of professionals—engineers, scientists, and managers. It is the function of universities to educate these people. As universities in the developing country advance and mature, they will assume the responsibility for the education of their professionals. The role of universities in the United States is to assist in building and strengthening the universities in the developing countries and in helping them to achieve the kind of programs that will be most useful in applying technology to industrialization.

The professionals in the industry team are backed, of course, by a corps of technicians. It may or may not be the function of the university to train these workers; in the United States, technician programs are found in some universities but exist mainly in technical institutes.

It is my plan to discuss my topic in terms of its problem structure and to suggest ways of dealing with the problems. I shall focus on three that I think are very important. However, since these problems arise in the context of the mechanism by which universities in the United States provide help, it may be well to state first as a premise the nature of this mechanism.

In one phase, the universities provide advice and counsel by sending faculty and administrative staff to the university in the developing country for varying periods. Usually the visiting faculty teach classes because there is no better way to become acquainted with the institution they are seeking to help. It may be better to demonstrate by example than by words, but their major function and more important contribution is to offer advice in matters of curriculum, courses, policies, procedures, faculty building, and the purchase of equipment and library materials.

Still, it is clear that the responsibility for decisions should rest with the institution receiving the aid, for on it alone will depend future growth and progress after the period of assistance has ended. As a sample illustration, the equipment for instruction or research should be selected by the professor who will use it; if selected by the advisor, it may not be used after he leaves.

In another phase of the aid mechanism, young faculty from the developing country are supported in graduate programs in universities of the United States. If the major function is to counsel and educate young faculty, it may well be asked—what kind of counsel and what kind of education—and this leads to a number of important specific questions. I would like to single out three of these for discussion:

1. Should the curricula in engineering, science, and management be directed towards the immediately useful or towards the theoretical; should there be graduate work and research programs as in the United States?
2. How can technological education be related closely enough to industry and government so that it can contribute most effectively to the growth and strength of the whole industrial enterprise?
3. Is there a kind of graduate education better suited to the faculty of the developing country who come to the United States for advanced study than the kind we offer our own students?

It may be of interest to our friends in other countries, and humbling to us, to realize that we face these problems ourselves and do not always agree on what the best answers are for our country. Sometimes working on the educational problems of another society helps us to find new solutions for our own.

A consideration that must underlie our thinking in dealing with these questions is that of lead time. Professional education in technology requires four, five, or more years, and it must be useful to the professional ten, twenty, thirty, and forty years after graduation. This period will be one of great change in the industry of the developing country—greater than the corresponding change in the United States if the developing country is truly to catch up. It will be a period in which the professionals will continually seek new and better solutions to problems of developing industry. At any one time, these solutions must be matched to the requirements of their own country and they may not be identical to the solutions of similar problems that occur in the United States.

The long lead time of education over practice has several implications for education: namely, the student must learn how to go on learning during his entire professional life, and he must also learn to solve new problems or find new solutions to old ones, not only to keep up with the changing technology of his field, but also to help create the changes.

Thus one major component of education must be theory since an understanding of sound fundamental theory is the basis both of extension of learning and for dealing with new problems. Technology changes rapidly but fundamental principles remain the same.

What is the implication of lead time as far as courses in techniques and practice are concerned? I believe it is that these should be held to a minimum—the minimum a graduate needs to hold a job. One should be especially wary of teaching techniques useful in the United States now or even those found useful when the United States was in a state of comparable development, not only because techniques obsolesce rapidly in any country but also because techniques that were good at one time in one country may not be suitable in another. I have heard a very descriptive phrase from an educator in India who said, "Our graduates will indeed have to solve your 19th century problems but they will use 20th century methods."

I have seen building construction in Asia in which wicker basketsful of wet concrete were carried on the heads of laborers who clambered up bamboo scaffolds. My first reaction was that this was pretty primitive in an age of labor-saving machinery. But, upon reflection, I am not sure that this was necessarily the wrong way to do the job in a country where capital is scarce, labor cheap, and unemployment considerable. At the very least, one should not come to a hasty conclusion. In the United States, railrods were built before airlines. Does this mean that a developing country should also build railroads first or that railway engineers should be turned out before aeronautical engineers? Or more generally, is the 20th century solution to the transportation problem in a developing country the same we adopted in the 19th century?

Reducing or eliminating technique courses does not mean, however, that engineering applications should be ignored. In fact, there is a great need for applications courses, but they are not the descriptive treatment of equipment and methods that used to be common in engineering. Urgently needed are courses in which the student learns to apply engineering science to problems that are new to him. The problems should be current real-life problems in his own country and, in dealing with them, he does incidentally learn something about equipment and practice. But he has to discover solutions for himself instead of having them given to him; any area of practice is sampled rather than "covered." Experience in the United States shows that such courses are feasible in engineering and management; that they do much to develop understanding of theory; that they do fairly well as to practice, much better than might be expected from a sampling procedure. It turns out that what is really practical in the long run is not a recital of current practice but the mental equipment to devise practice.

In addition to theory and the special kind of application courses just referred to, another major stem has been found desirable in professional education in the United States, and that in the social sciences and humanities. They are needed not only to help the student become a better citizen with a richer life of his own, but also to equip him to deal with economic, human, and social problems that he faces when practicing his profession. Such problems are, if anything, more complex and difficult in a country undergoing an accelerated industrialization; hence, it would be expected that social sciences and humanities would be needed even more in professional education in these countries than in the United States.

What is the place of graduate education in a developing country? One sometimes hears the question, "Why have graduate work in a country where the crying need is for technicians?" The answer is that there is a need for personnel educated at all levels, through the whole spectrum of technicians, Bachelor's, Master's, and Doctor's degrees. Leaders are just as important as followers, if not more so; and they are harder to come by. Twentieth century methods simply cannot be mastered in undergraduate programs alone. Graduate education serves other ends, too; it helps to make a university attractive to prospective faculty (and so helps induce a reverse "brain drain") and also to stimulate faculty to grow intellectually.

University research is desirable for many of the same reasons. Like education, research should be directed towards the problems of the developing nation itself. This means that research should not necessarily be transplanted from the United States; it may take an unusual professor from the United States to assist in establishing the right kind of research there. It also points to the urgency of developing a national-need orientation on the part of the home faculty.

This leads to a consideration of the second question: How can technological education be closely related to industry and government so that it can contribute most effectively to the growth and strength of the industrial enterprise?

Experience in the United States may be helpful here—the experience embodied in the Boston Route 128 concept, the symbiosis between industry and technological education that geographically locates research and development laboratories near universities, as has been done along Route 128 near MIT and elsewhere. Industry chooses this location to facilitate the use of professors as consultants, and to make it easier to use the university's libraries, computers, and special laboratory facilities. Proximity also makes it easier for engineers in industry to participate in conferences, seminars, and short courses offered at the university and to undertake graduate work that leads to Master's and Doctor's degrees on a full- or part-time basis. The opportunity for graduate work is an especially strong attraction in company recruiting. The university benefits from the relationship, too, through the consulting opportunities for its faculty by having a nearby reservoir of lecturers and support—both moral and material—for students in graduate programs, for placement of graduates, and in other needs. Perhaps the greatest benefit is one that is not so obvious: interaction with industry helps to shape education and make it more relevant to the industry it serves. In many ways, this is parallel to the hospital-university relationship that has been so productive in the area of medical education.

What has been said about relations with industry applies equally to relations with government laboratories for advanced technology.

It may be noted, however, that the relationship that can be so fruitful can also be misused, as it is when the university sponsors low-level programs, when professors undertake consulting that is subprofessional, or when the university lowers its standards of academic performance to accommodate its friends in industry. Also, there is an obstacle to the establishment of a strong relationship if the university faculty prefer to remain in their ivory tower, untainted by partnership with commerce. This, I think, is relatively uncommon now, but I know from experience that some faculty have to be convinced that the work they do in organizing intensive short courses and conferences pays them rich dividends in professional stimulation, contacts with new people, and new ideas.

If we carry the Route 128 concept to the developing country, the professional schools of the university in the area of technology can be strengthened markedly by close collaboration and partnership with industry and government technical agencies. A relationship is sought in which professors consult with industry and/or government and become cognizant of real problems by working on them. The professors have to be good enough so they can make genuine contributions to industry and command its respect; moreover, they have to be truly interested in the real world. Such abilities and interest become requirements in faculty recruiting and development; they are not necessarily any harder to meet than are other requirements for academic excellence.

The university builds the kind of library that can serve industry and government at professional levels and goes a little more than half-way in rendering service. The university provides leadership in new areas. For example, it may establish a computer center, make it available to outside engineers, and provide short courses to develop proficiency in its use, all for reasonable fees. If the country needs to be surveyed or mapped, the university develops a center of excellence in this area; if the properties of indigenous materials such as timber and soil are not very well known, studies are undertaken at the university to determine them. If the country is to develop an electronics industry, the university might establish a solid-state and even an integrated-circuits laboratory. These examples, by the way, are real, not imagined.

What is most important is that the faculty who undertake activities which are relevant to national development, should also teach and thereby bring to their students an understanding of the real world.

The desirable strong relationship between the university and industry and/or government is not likely to exist without conscious effort. However, it is well worth cultivating; indeed, helping the developing country to find ways to do so can be one of the most productive aspects of the role of the university in the United States.

The last question deals with the role of our universities in offering graduate programs to the faculty and potential faculty of developing countries. A great many such faculty are now studying here and, while the work that is offered is good, it can be made more suitable to needs.

Graduate work in engineering in the United States has grown very rapidly since the end of World War II and much of it has focused on engineering science and preparation for research. Engineering science has an important place but if it is to be useful, it has to be related to the real world. In practice, a professional engineering task force starts with the need for something and, in trying to meet the need with due regard to costs and the marketplace, it encounters problems to which engineering science provides partial answers. These answers are synthesized into engineering designs or decisions that result in meeting the original need. Critics of present programs, of which I am one, feel that in concentrating on the middle stages of engineering science, we fail to do justice to the important first and last steps—the ones which connect science to the real world. Moreover, many of our engineering teachers are products of such graduate programs and have had little experience with the engineering process as a whole. Subjects of doctoral research are often narrow and sometimes esoteric.

I hasten to add that there are universities in this country where there is a reasonable balance between the esoteric and the relevant, and that there is a growing recognition that the function of engineering must meet a real need. Yet there are still debates at national meetings on whether analysis and design are as acceptable as research for Doctor's theses in engineering.

Thus, while there is even some question as to whether the graduate programs in engineering are appropriately balanced for our own country, it seems clear that faculty education for a developing country should place much more emphasis on real problems if the faculty are to be prepared to participate in a partnership with industry and government.

Yet, improvements might be made without a drastic change. For example, there would be much merit in just two courses, a problem and a project course which deal with real situations drawn from the developing country of the student or at least from some developing country. Thesis research should have the same kind of relevance. Total time would not have to be added to the program if two of the less relevant discipline-oriented theoretical courses were given up in favor of the problem-oriented work.

There are relatively few professors in our universities with sufficient understanding of the technology of the developing country or interested in achieving it. Some might, however, be found among those who have served in developing countries and who have brought back the requisite knowledge and interests. They could be concentrated, at least temporarily, in a few of our institutions that would offer strong special programs for graduate students from developing countries. The concentration of students in a few places would be desirable because, large as they are in numbers, these students are spread thinly over many departments in many universities and ordinarily they are treated the same as the graduate students from he United States. Concentration would justify special courses and special consideration.

Our faculty knowledgeable in the problems of developing countries could be augmented by visiting professors from these countries as well as by engineers from their industry and government.

Another possibility would be to establish excellent programs in a few of the developing countries; these would be oriented towards national needs and would be used as centers for the production of needed faculty.

In summary, let me say that universities in the United States, in fulfilling their role of advising and assisting universities in developing countries, face three very important problems: (1) the balance of emphasis between theory and the immediately useful in the curriculum, (2) the relations with industry and government that will contribute most effectively to industrial development, and (3) the kind of graduate programs offered to their faculty who came as graduate students. I recommend that the routines and practices of immediate usefulness should be minimized to the lowest level consistent with holding a job; that there should be a balance between theory on the one hand and learning how to apply it to the real problems of the developing country on the other. There also should be a strong component of social science and humanities. Graduate work and research are just as necessary in the developing country as they are in the United States, although not necessarily in the same proportions. Ways should be sought to develop close ties between the university and/or government that will be as beneficial to each as the ties that exist in the United States. Graduate programs for the faculty in engineering should emphasize the application of engineering science to real problems as well as the engineering science itself.

These patterns in education, I believe, are ones that would increase effectiveness in applying engineering technology to the industrialization of developing countries. In any case, the primary role of the university in the United States is not to dictate patterns of education but to help their counterparts in the developing countries to determine and achieve their own goals.

DISCUSSION OF THE PAPER BY B. R. TEARE JR.

MR. HAMILTON commented that faculty members who help foreign universities often try to institute a curriculum designed to prepare all students to enter graduate school in the United States. He pointed out the error of this system. A foreign student who is in the United States for graduate work is indiscriminately assigned an advisor who does not have the necessary overseas experience. As a result, the student is often educated far beyond the capabilities required when he returns to his homeland. Mr. Hamilton suggested as an example a student trained in advance microwave technology, who returns to his homeland to find that he has no opportunity for research or teaching, and no one to talk to. The student becomes dissatisfied and begins to search for a way to return to the United States. He concluded that counselors of graduate engineering students must be very careful to consider the student's country of origin in conjunction with his ultimate goals.

Mr. Lador spoke of a problem of recruitment in his country, which has been receiving an ever-increasing stream of requests from other countries for advice and expertise in various fields. University professors are unwilling to respond to these requests, fearing the loss of contact with their home university, as well as the possibility of loss of academic advancement.

Mr. Teare agreed that recruitment of experts from universities is a very real problem, and he stressed the necessity of finding the best people to send. He pointed out some of the pros and cons in recruiting professors. On the one hand, professors probably will be unable to do research in a developing country and, consequently, will not be writing papers. On the other hand, among the incentives that lead people to go to developing countries is the strong desire to serve, as well as the more selfish desire to see other places and travel. Another motivation might be the intangible reward of serving in a developing country, working under totally new conditions, and receiving an education impossible in the United States, perhaps one that would help the professor become an administrator. A case in point was that a faculty member at the Massachusetts Institute of Technology who became a head of that school's largest department after his return from Kanpur.

A comment from the floor attempted to present an answer to some of the problems cited by both Mr. Lador and Mr. Teare. It was suggested that the way to get the bright, young faculty to participate in these development programs was to have them present the same courses they have developed at their own universities in the form of short courses abroad. The point was made that these faculty, devoted to the frontiers of new technology, are usually extremely busy; they have research students who depend upon them and on-going research problems that they cannot simply quit for a year. In addition, they have difficulty getting research grants after their return. Consequently, participation in programs abroad can be extremely difficult for such bright, young people.

On the favorable side, these people are usually very idealistic and would be willing to participate abroad. They could, for example, take off a month or two during the summer to teach a class of 30 professors in a foreign country and talk to 30 students from that country. Furthermore, a great deal could be done in the United States to assist professors overseas. Stanford University had a program on a professor-to-professor basis with a former student. Lectures were tape-recorded at Stanford and sent to a young professor who was trying to start a similar new course at West Virginia University. It took very little additional effort to hang a microphone around the lecturer's neck and then send off the tape and source material. A similar plan could be used with professors at foreign universities.

The concluding suggestion from the floor stressed the desirability of a travel period for American professors giving short courses abroad. These men should spend a month or two traveling through developing countries, meeting with teams of two or three professors at various universities to discuss their problems, answer questions, review laboratory equipment they have set up, and generally help them over the rough spots.

THE ROLE OF UNIVERSITIES
IN THE UNITED STATES

Commentary by Merton Barry

IN MY VIEW, it is the purpose of contemporary secular education to help prepare human beings to interact with one another and their environment to mutual benefit. The university and the engineering school should be organized and should function to fulfill this purpose. That the university or school is not perfect in either its organization or function does not detract from its central purpose.

We are concerned here more specifically with the role of the university in interdisciplinary aspects of application of engineering technology to industrialization. The Conference has focused much attention on the brain drain and questions of the proper training of the foreign student within our universities. Focusing our attention on these problems tends to obscure the fact that the major universities in the United States are now world universities. That is not to say that only United States universities are world universities, nor that only major universities are worldwide in their outlook and the clientele they serve. That approximately 30 per cent of the graduate enrollment in engineering schools are composed of foreign students is known. This is further testimony that the university in the United States currently plays a significant role in the subject of this Conference.

There are many barriers to labor mobility, including mobility of professional engineers and managers as well as of other professionals. I believe we can say with reasonable safety that the higher the skill or expertise, the greater the potential and actual mobility. This being the case, we should look at the role of the universities in developing the world talent pool. In discussions of the brain drain not enough attention has been given to the notion of a world talent pool. It should receive the same kind of attention and research effort as do global studies of natural resources.

Except for natural phenomena with their impact on man, all things of concern to us are done by people. The things we do in the universities, the structure of our curricula and programs, will eventually greatly affect development. Since the productive peak for most university graduates comes between 15 and 30 years after their graduation, the university's role in long-range application of technology to development is surely great. We must necessarily concern ourselves with the distant horizon and realize that the effect of the universities' major function—teaching—will peak around the turn of the century for the students now completing their training. In other words, by preparing people to think and act in certain ways, the university contributes significantly to the inevitability of future events. The role the university can play in interdisciplinary approaches to problem solving is great; the impact of systems analysis and design is only dimly perceived as yet.

In the short run, interdisciplinary approaches to the application of technology to development will, I believe, be made by professional practitioners rather than by persons within the universities. Compare the difficulty of the collaboration of many specialists in preparing feasibility studies for, say, the World Bank, with the working together of a group of academicians in a university. Even in a university as permissive as my own, it is evident that we shall have to await the maturation of young scholars now in training before full interdisciplinary collaboration will be an actuality within the university. I tend to think that engineering, with its problem-solving-oriented curriculum can, and probably will, play a key role in the eventual flowering of an interdisciplinary approach within the universities.

In this regard, I feel that foreign graduate students should be fully prepared and involved in future interdisciplinary studies. Those who return home should carry with them this concept as well as the concepts of engineering sciences.

Much has been said of the worldwide corporation at this Conference. Although many reservations about it have been expressed, it does exist. Its use as an institutional technique for man to meet some of his problems is inevitable. In assessing the United States university's role in applying technology to development, we must recognize, and prepare to adjust our own institutional framework to take advantage of, this inevitability, learning from experience in the industrial sector. We have in recent years made some progress in this direction. First, we have borrowed faculty from each other to meet talent requirements for technical-assistance contracts and grants; and second, we have formed the consortium of several universities to focus their energies and resources on a mutually desired end.

I believe that the third step will be to form international consortia of universities to focus an even larger talent and resource pool on some of mankind's major problems. As universities or individual faculties and institutes within universities in developing countries increase their capabilities, the true consortium can come to fruition. The lack of profit motive or profit necessity within the university structure means the absence of many of the emotional and psychological problems that confront the international corporation, which must be profit oriented. The university in the United States has not in the past taken advantage of the reality of the presence of the international corporation in its own efforts at technology transfer. In this we must improve. Perhaps international consortia of universities can best react with the international corporation for the mutual benefit of humanity.

We in the universities, as in all other fields, have learned much from our experience in the past 15 to 20 years. Looked at from the perspective of 1950, we have come a long way in our commitment to the notion of a more equitable life for all. This Conference is a testimony to the fact. If we can avoid trampling each other to death, I think we shall do much better in the future.

312

REPORT OF WORKSHOP 14

Edward Stuart, Rapporteur

WORKSHOP participants focused their solutions to a variety of problems on two broad areas—a better statement of objectives and provision for better preparation. Although they should appear at different levels, there is an absence of a statement of objectives in many necessary areas by the donor and host universities, government, and industry. Preparation for the present system of faculty donations also takes on a tripartite role. Gaps can be found in the preparation of the individual faculty person and of the donor and host universities.

Questions and conclusions by the Workshop members are presented first, followed by a summary of comments made by Mr. Baker.

QUESTION AND CONCLUSIONS

1. *What type of curriculum should be recommended for the host university? Should it be immediately useful or highly theoretical?*

This question can best be answered by a statement of the immediate objectives of the host country and institution. Our board objective should be one of providing increased technological education for the host faculty since this is more efficient than just educating the engineering student. There may be local objectives that should be stated early and met if possible. Coursework with immediate applications will increase the confidence of local industry in the program. Each country's objectives will vary greatly. The broad concept of educational or institutional experimentations on the part of the Indian Institute of Technology system is an example of a unique local objective.

2. *What about graduate work and research?*

Both are very necessary to satisfy the objective of providing good faculty at the host institution.

3. *How do we relate to industry?*

Industry should be involved early and deeply in setting the objectives of the development of the host institution. Its early involvement may help again to gain confidence in the faculty of the host institution, giving the faculty the continuing rapport with industry necessary for their continuing education and their own professional development. The research institute is another solution to the problem of industrial involvement. A research institute will allow the development plan of the country to concentrate on specific areas of research, while the university faculty can maintain its freedom of research direction. If then the objectives as set by the government and industry are too confining, the research institute may act at the interface between these two and the university. Donor institutions should be prepared to recognize this need in their own planning.

4. *What about providing graduate education for the faculty of developing universities?*

There was agreement as to its necessity but caution that preparation here on the part of the faculty person is necessary. Faculty should be well oriented before they come.

5. *Is there a third-country role?*

Yes, the successes of the Technion in Israel and the Asian Institute of Technology are examples. Here the objective of teaching the teachers comes to the surface at a very high level.

6. *What kinds of visiting professors, in terms of background, are needed?*

Whether the development plan calls for theoreticians or practitioners, there is a greater need for more preparation on the part of these people. To be effective, they should have more knowledge of the economic, cultural, ethnic, and labor relations problems. Added to these must be some formal preparation in institutional or managerial development.

7. *What about recruiting problems?*

It was agreed that the best faculty should be recruited, but this plan calls for a very high level of preparation on the part of the donor university. To provide the best faculty for these programs, the donor university must be prepared with an institutional commitment to provide the incentives for proper faculty recruitment. Of course, establishing consortia has helped but an in-depth commitment by the donor universities and a faculty preparation plan by the consortium are still needed.

8. *Do we want an advisor or an expert?*

Again, the objectives are chosen by the host government, industry, and university. The broadest objective would suggest the advisor since institutional development and faculty development are more important than teaching class. Experts have been found useful for short-term teaching programs. At this level, the host institution may use these people for their faculties' continuing education.

9. *How do we handle language difficulties?*

This problem can be again solved by better preparation on the part of the individual faculty member. Lectures would best be given in a language in which technical literature was available.

10. *How do we establish objectives?*

The problem of the immediate objectives seems to be the subject for research. The tripartite agencies—government, industry, and university—all must contribute. But there is a question of *how much* each is to contribute.

11. *Are there generic characteristics of the host university mitigating against the technology transfer?*

This is possible and is part of the donor universities' preparation problems. A major policy should be made to provide incentives for the faculty to participate in the technology transfer.

COMMENTS BY MR. BARKER

1. United States faculty advise on curriculum, policies, procedures, faculty building, administration; they use teaching only as a stop-gap measure. However, the majority are only interested in (and capable of) teaching and research.

2. United States training of host nationals is usually motivated by a natural tendency to encourage a student to attain the highest educational level allowed by his capability regardless of his country's needs or his country's capacity to absorb the resulting skills. It is not wrong for a student to do basic research or a Master's thesis or a doctoral dissertation; on the contrary, it is good training. But we must not start juices that cannot be satisfied.

3. The characteristic of the United States engineering education which is needed in less-developed countries and for export is its methodology (inquiry, empirical verification, problem formulation, experimental design). Most of this viewpoint is gained subconsciously by United States students who focus on the substance of the new math only now being introduced in high-school science.

4. It is perhaps over-ambitious to hope to "equip him to deal with economic, humanistic, and social problems." However, the student should be sensitized to these variables and parameters sufficiently to know when they come to play and to be able to work with specialists in these fields so that problems can be addressed jointly. A relationship should be established with other professional schools, particularly those for public administration and education.

5. United States universities should involve some participant trainees in a basic training program for graduate engineers in selected basic industries. This internship for United States engineers is missing in less-developed countries and must be accounted for somehow in their training.

6. Western technology has obscured distinction between the scientist and the engineer; clearer distinction may still be appropriate for some less-developed countries.

REFERENCE CITED

Kerr, Clark. *The Uses of the University.* Cambridge: Harvard University Press, 1963.

18

THE ROLE OF THE NATIONAL UNIVERSITIES, GOVERNMENTAL AND PRIVATE

Principal Paper—Antonio Salgado

Discussion of the Paper by Antonio Salgado

Commentary—Mordechai M. Levy

Commentary—William D. Van Vorst

Report of Workshop 15—George E. Klinzing, Rapporteur

The universities of the emerging nations are, like their counterparts in the developed countries, instruments for social and economic change. Their interactions with other institutions in their own countries and with universities in the developed world are the topics of Chapter 18.

The Editors

THE ROLE OF THE NATIONAL UNIVERSITIES, GOVERNMENTAL AND PRIVATE

Principal Paper by Antonio Salgado*

I SHALL TREAT the proposed theme by using the Ecuadorian university as a reference. In doing so, one can generalize, within certain limitations, about other developing countries and about Latin America, fundamentally. If we understand the development process as the process by which per capita income increases, we conclude that progressive industrialization constitutes one of the bases that sustains development. The Latin American countries have understood this reality and have come to recognize great forces for the procurement of their industrialization. Mexico, Brazil, Argentina, and Chile have arrived at the intermediate stage of industrialization and have striven to reach their industrial structure by superior development. Other countries, such as Ecuador, Bolivia, and Paraguay, of lesser relative economic development, find themselves in the initial stage of the production of consumer goods and desire to proceed toward more advanced goals of industrialization.

Following this desire, the Latin American countries created the Latin American Association of Free Commerce, ALALC, in the Treaty of Montevideo. ALALC, similar to a Common Market, among other things, aims to stimulate and make more technical the process of industrialization of its member countries.

At the same time, the United States of America and the Latin American countries at Punta del Este promised to enact a joint effort for "accelerating the process of a rational industrialization in order to increase the global productivity of the economy. . . ."

Internally, the developing countries are stimulating private enterprise by systems of protection, concession, and subsidy that permit industrial development. The effort that is being made to procure successful progressive industrialization is definitely evident. One thing, however, has been forgotten which fundamentally causes delay of "rational industrialization"—adequate preparation and capacity of those who must be placed in charge of executing the development programs. I do not want to analyze whether the internal or external political economy of our countries is now on an adequate road to obtaining the industrial development Latin America desires. I do, however, want to mention that, whatever the strategy taken, for this strategy to be well oriented, no satisfactory results will be obtained if the professionals in charge are not perfectly capable.

Industrialization, like applying technology to agriculture and protecting human capital, is one of the pillars that sustain the economic development of a country by procuring a means of life in accordance with human dignity and

*Ing. Salgado's paper was written in Spanish. This translation was prepared by Dr. G. E. Klinzing, Assistant Professor, Chemical and Petroleum Engineering, University of Pittsburgh.

education. One cannot speak unilaterally of one factor of development without binding the others that must move in parallel so that the process has a normal rhythm. Consequently, if we speak of developing our countries toward definite goals of industrialization, we must refer to an integral process that includes the works of infrastructure in which professionals of different specialties must cooperate. These specialists must be highly capable in the stated process to obtain satisfactory results.

Here is where the university intervenes since it has the assigned educative function to prepare researchers and professors to solve all the problems related to national development. In final terms, the university constitutes a laboratory in which a country's development must be conceived. For the university to accomplish this goal, it must change its structure to one that aims for service toward national progress.

The engineer, a product of the university, has a preponderant role in the development process, especially in industrial development. Under his direction, the country executes almost all the programs of economic infrastructure and industrial technology.

The modern world has made science more and more applicable to technology and thus to industrial technology. It has converted the engineer into the fundamental pinion of the complicated gear of industrial technology. Therefore, these professionals have to orient their responsibility to the process of industrial development and look for solutions that agree with rational utilization of the natural and human resources which each country places at their disposal.

I have already explained that the engineer is the product of the university; consequently, to a great extent, his function depends on the efficiency with which the university imparts its teachings. Is the Latin American university, or more concretely, the Ecuadorian University, complying with the objectives that enables it to give the country's engineers not only a technical knowledge for advancing the development of the country but also the knowledge of the country's social and economic reality?

If we want to answer this question, we have to analyze carefully the role which the engineer has come to perform inside the structure of the country and how he has responded to the tasks set before him.

In retrospect, we find that the engineer has shown marginal interest in executive functions and, therefore, has had very few opportunities to perform at a deliberative level. He has been given predominantly technical responsibilities, for which he digests the information and supplies it to other professionals who make the decisions.

Undoubtedly, this phenomenon has its origin in the nature and type of preparation that the engineer until now has been receiving in the university. In the majority of cases, the engineer's technical and scientific preparation has ignored the national reality and made him a basic man in production but not the executive, planner, or manager which he logically should be.

It is well known that to be able to accelerate the industrialization process of the developing countries, parallel effort must be exerted in programs related to works of economic infrastructure, highways, electrification, irrigation, transportation, communications, well being, and health.

In planning, programming, and executing these works, the intervention of a team of specialized professionals in fields such as economics, sociology, agronomics, veterinary medicine, and anthropology, is necessary. It is the engineer, however, who holds the major role in these tasks. Thus, his preparation must be comprehensive.

If we establish as a premise that the development and industrialization of a country depend directly on the capacity and degree of preparation of professional engineers, we must conclude that the university plays a definitive role.

Consequently, we must analyze how the university should structure itself to take advantage efficiently of the disposable resources so as to supply engineers who completely comply with the responsibilities which the nation confides in them.

It is vital that the professional engineer, within the process of his university education, acquire a clear concept of his country, his socio-economic reality. He must be aware of the available natural resources available and the possibility of taking advantage of them. He must familiarize himself with the national program of development and its goals. He must have exact vision of his part as a professional in the development process. In short, he must know the role of his profession as a service to the socio-economic development of his nation. This is the task of the university. The university can do this job effectively if it assumes the directive function in the development process and identifies with the national programs.

Unfortunately, the Latin American university, and consequently the Ecuadorian, has followed a policy of political isolationism. I consider this to have been definitely prejudicial. The university has defined its autonomy as a mechanism which permits an institutional life of closed doors, making it an impermeable organization to the national needs. I consider that being autonomous is the greatest asset and foundation of the university's personality, but the university must know how to use, defend, and reinforce this autonomy always for the service of the country.

Accepting this reality, we must admit that the efficient application of engineering technology to the industrialization of the developing countries depends largely on the degree of qualification and preparation that the professionals receive from the universities. Fundamentally, this means the possibility of research which the university would be able to offer its students and graduates.

It is essential that we analyze the university's ability to comply with these propositions, noting that all the Latin American universities—governmental, state, or private—confront an almost unsurmountable barrier impeding the most rapid development which the needs of these countries require: the economic factor. Consequently, the university needs to find means of adequate financing so it can accelerate its development.

Some Latin American universities are interrelated with the public and private sectors that perform programs demanding research. Collected experience on this allows us to conclude that institutions of higher learning can be financed on the basis of services they are able to offer.

Admitting in principle this means of financing, the university has to prepare itself with adequate physical space, laboratories, and researchers. It has to establish a program properly coordinated with the sectors of production and united with industry, permitting the university to become involved in situations that favor private and state enterprise and, at the same time, increase its field of research. Universities cannot continue to relegate research to a second plane because Latin American universities either have not begun research or have begun it on a very limited scale.

For the moment, I believe applied research must have room in our universities. Applied research is exactly what we propose to suggest as a way of improving the preparation of our engineers. During their period of training at the university, they must actively participate in research programs that are in progress at the university. That is even more important if we consider that applied research constitutes the basis of engineering and industrial technology.

With this basis of analysis, we must admit that, in an infinity of cases in countries such as ours, research must not be outside the university. If research is outside, the public sector and private enterprise that are related to engineering projects must have large investments in laboratory equipment and in salaries for the researchers to carry on their programs.

There is the risk that the laboratories will remain in disuse when the research terminates and that the researchers, with their acquired experience, must perform routine functions in the organizations or businesses that employ them. On the other hand, the universities need to equip teaching laboratories which also contain those basic elements required for applied research in engineering and industrial technology.

Will it be possible to admit to the thesis that countries with limited resources need to duplicate facilities for research, or will it be possible for the universities, state organizations, and private enterprise to make a profound analysis of the problem and find a successful solution? The solution is that applied research in set fields be placed under the responsibility of the university. Various seminars related to the studies of engineering in Latin America have asked this question and arrived at the conclusion that, as one of its fundamental functions, it is necessary that the university intervene with the presentation of services. This is considered to be the only mechanism by which research can take place. It is necessary, however, for the university to create an atmosphere of confidence in order to gain the concurrence of the public and private sectors in combined programs.

In this manner, a more solid structure of the university must be obtained. It must demonstrate to private enterprise and industry, in particular, that whatever investment is made to assist in the formation of national researchers is recoverable in a short time, and that benefits will be derived for that same industry. Such politics would bring the university, with its students, professors, and researchers, to solutions of national problems—solutions that will be strictly ours and in agreement with our reality.

Governments and private enterprise in Ecuador have resisted acknowledging this class of integral programs. They say that the universities have been so involved in politics that leaving these responsibilities to the universities would be dangerous to the execution of such programs. This thesis may have much truth, but it owes its existence to the relation of the university to process of development. If the structure of the university is radically changed, and if it assumes the directive function which belongs to it, it will be an active part of such a process and a determining factor in the decisions made. The university would be responsible, if you like, for success or failure. The activity of the university thus will change.

I have mentioned here the true sentiment behind university reform—the university in service. This is the basis of research and the manner in which the university employs its resources.

If we give the university the research task, it would have to endow the physical and human means for making this research possible. The governments ought to proportion the mechanisms that permit the channeling of research through the university. They must establish within the engineering works programs, budgetary divisions that finance the research and, in the same manner, provide a possibility for study. These divisions will partially finance the university, and the university will compensate with the presentation of services.

In this respect, it is interesting to note that in developing countries the major part of engineering works in the industrial programs are completed by external financing. This financing, without a doubt, endangers those countries' debt capacity. This fact makes a combined effort of the institutions and the university even more necessary for the major use of the resources.

The best way in which to take advantage of these resources would be to have the university participate actively in its research and consulting work for the programs. Another source of financing for the universities of our countries, then, would be to grant loans that finance engineering programs. In these loans would be stated the obligation to employ a division for research. This would make possible funds for acquiring equipment for laboratories and scholarships for professionals and researchers.

Emphasizing the imperative need to prepare our own researchers—a task that will take time—we must, in the interim, use foreign professional technicians and researchers of a high level. Advantage must be taken, as I have already indicated, of funds provided by external loans that finance engineering programs, a procedure that is facilitated when the conditions of the international credit agencies contain a contractual obligation to use the services of foreign experts who must advise on studies and execution of the projects. Why not consider the possibility of also including, under the conditions of the loan, researchers who work at the university in the field of research and teaching?

It is advisable that the national organizations that promote development, just as the agencies of international credit that finance programs of development of this "third world," understand that we cannot develop ourselves if we do not establish the basis for our own research. This basis is precisely what promotes the satisfaction of such a requirement.

This necessarily results in the mentioned agencies including funds for research in their financing. It makes possible the arrival of experts to direct the university's research programs.

Finally, I ought to mention the need for our university to maintain an interchange of professors and researchers with the universities of the developed countries for the purpose of initiating and increasing research. It is fundamental to understand the true scope that this intellectual interchange must give and advisable that our professors travel to study in North American and European universities. Fundamentally, this is necessary both to make them capable in fields in which their country needs experts and to initiate basic research for industrial development. This investigation would be directed by eminent researchers of the developed countries. They would be able to apply this research to concrete solutions which our country requires.

To cite an example, think of what we would gain by the industrialization of the banana. The research required could be directed through a foreign university with Ecuadorian researchers and overseen by North American or European scientists; or with North American or European researchers who would come on their sabbatical year to work in our universities. We would offer them remunerations that would make their absence for decisive periods attractive. In this manner, the quality of expert professionals and scientists that visit our country would be guaranteed.

We agree then that we need advice and technical help. Help, however, is not needed to the point of deceit and exploitation represented by the coming of pseudo-experts, disguised as scientists who have remunerations incompatible with their contributions to the development of the country. The underdeveloped countries cannot continue to support the tremendous load represented by the payment of the salaries of these so-called "foreign experts."

I know of an infrastructure program that has just terminated in my country that had advisors with monthly remunerations of $2000 to $3000. Their number was such that their total monthly salaries equalled the budget of the professors of the Faculty of Engineering of our university. How beneficial it would be for our country to have, instead, a team of capable professionals with a $3000 monthly salary, who would work in those same projects which would be financed with foreign capital. They would, however, with the university, help with the teaching and formation of our researchers.

But, as we have come to realize, the problem is rooted not only in the efficient preparation of professionals, scientists, or researchers. It is fundamental for us to procure and retain in our country our own professionals, scientists, and researchers.

For a long time, we have been tolerating what is called the "brain drain." The professionals most prepared, most gifted, and most capable, who have initiated research, emigrate to more highly developed centers looking for better opportunities In the majority of cases, they leave for very advantageous reasons, offered justly by international organizations that propitiate the development of our country. In this international market that has opened for the professional, one finds a true paradox. Professional engineers of various specialties are hired to serve as experts in advising countries other than those form which they originate. Would it not be more logical for these professionals, loaded with knowledge and experience, to be employed in the milieu which they know? Would it not be preferable to create some special incentive so that they do not take up root in other countries? Ought not the agencies for development and international credit that finance these programs understand that the policies they are carrying out in technical assistance are creating an inoperable and prejudicial international bureaucracy? Should not these organizations, which are diminishing the value of the specific function of the professional, be shown that they are converting him into a special diplomat rather than an advisor?

These are questions whose obvious answers give solutions to one of the most critical problems before the countries on developmental paths—the flight of the professionals. It is advisable also to admit the need to continue with the specialization of engineers in the different fields required by industrial development. That will have to be done in more advanced centers so that they can later intervene in our programs. They must be employed under advantageous economic conditions that assure that they stay in the country. If this is not done in such a manner, these same countries will patronize the flight of specialized professionals. At the present time, it is normal practice that the national expert not be offered the best opportunities to serve his country.

There are cases where even the universities have not taken advantage of the opportunity to stimulate specialized professionals that have returned. It is even sadder, as is evident, that decisions of the government are taken with respect to political criteria or trust to eventuality or empiricism without employing the properly qualified expert. As has been confirmed by history, this failure to employ qualified professionals has resulted in complete failure of those projects.

This yields a conclusion that the organizations of public and private character which employ these professionals must offer them the best opportunities of work with remuneration comparable with that which technicians and men of science represent. At the same time, the universities must agree with the inconvertible truth that teaching bodies must be integrated with the most qualified professionals. By doing this within the proposed plan, the professionals would assume the function entrusted to them—working in applied research and consulting for the benefit of the private and public sectors; presenting services that would permit remunerations that guarantee their staying in the university, and consequently, in the country; and aiming to establish the basis on which the nation rests its general and industrial development in the process of creating its own technicians and researchers.

This entire explanation can be summarized in the following terms:

1. The efficient application of engineering technology in the industrialization programs of the developing countries is a function, among other things, of the integral preparation of engineers. Besides technical and scientific preparation, the engineer must have a profound knowledge of the national reality, of the national plan of development in his field of specialty, of the goals which are fixed, and fundamentally the role in which the technician is going to take charge. He must always think of aspiring to the level of director or executive.

2. Only with the conquest of science and technology based on research will one have an efficient, industrially progressive development. It is the universities which are responsible for the advancements of scientists and technologists in order to succeed in defined goals in industrial development by means of the capable and integral preparation of the engineers. The university must plan in this sense. This will be possible if the public and private sectors concur in helping to integrate the university in their respective programs of general and industrial development. They must use appropriate means for research that such programs demand. Finally, this presentation of services, conveniently supported, finances physical space, laboratories, professors, and researchers which the development plan of the universities requires. Clearly, for the proposed case to succeed, the university must revise its programs and direct its forces toward fields of professional teaching which the country requires. We have to change the university's structure, transporting it from what has been called "cultural archipelagoes" toward the formation of an academic unit which prepares men of vast vision and integral culture. Concretely, for the case we are considering, it is necessary to train engineers with an appreciation of human dignity.

3. It is imperative to prepare our own researchers, who are oriented to our industrial development, with a convenient utilization of our human and natural resources. Researchers who will be able to prepare the basis of interchange of experiences with industrialized countries are necessary. Its universities must work together with true technical assistance, seeking financial support through international credit organizations.

4. The agencies of international development, the entities of international credit, and, more concretely, the centers of regional and national development must manage their programs of industrial development, looking for collaboration with the universities in the research tasks. In this manner, their scientists, researchers, professors, and students will be able to take part in the programs of industrial development. They will also contribute all resources to the solution of the national problems and provide a mechanism for the self funding of their own development.

5. These services must not be interpreted as removing from the university its specific function of teaching. We are proposing in this Conference to look for a way to elevate the level of teaching in our universities, to obtain a more integral preparation of our engineers, to initiate them into research, and to increase the same by the preparation of services.

We think that in following these plans, we shall succeed. The university will be able to contribute positively to the efficient application of the technology of engineering for the industrialization of the developing countries.

DISCUSSION OF THE PAPER
BY ANTONIO SALGADO

1. We are all familiar with students in developing countries who come to the United States for graduate studies and then, upon their return, cannot find the jobs commensurate with their training. They will then return to this country, if they cannot find a teaching job there.

The programs discussed in Mr. Salgado's paper seem to indicate that universities in the developing countries must establish graduate programs. To what extent should universities in these countries commit themselves to graduate programs? Do they really need to graduate Ph.D.s in those countries? Is it possible that when these Ph.D.s graduate, they will find no work, no place to be assigned? Perhaps they will generate work for themselves, strike out on their own, and thereby speed up the development process?

Mr. Salgado: It is a financial problem and such financial problems should be covered first, with international loans. There are international agencies that give monetary help to developing countries and provides experts from Europe or the United States to the developing countries. These experts should not only advise on the building of a highway, for example, but also do some research in the university.

2. The United States, through its involvement with UNESCO and with the International Labour Organization, has encountered this problem. On the one hand, there is a problem in choosing experts to be sent to underdeveloped countries. On the other hand, there is a problem in the receiving country or in the receiving institution in trying to use such people. For example, when selecting an expert, a university will often insist on a Ph.D. and, when an agency, such as UNESCO, submits a very qualified person having a Master's degree, he may be turned down; a Ph.D., who can be second-rate in terms of the requirements of that specific position, is accepted.

In addition, the receiving institution often is not able to use the man or the team that is best qualified, and cannot furnish counterpart faculty. Often, there is no attempt to get laboratory equipment and, when it is there, there may be no effort to use it effectively. Too often—not in all cases but too often—the receiving institution just is not able to use these experts. Such disappointments are then spread around at home. How can this problem be overcome? What can the requesting government and the requesting institutions do to make this type of assistance more effective?

Mr. Salgado: To answer this part of the problem, two principal points should be considered. The first point concerns the lack of language communication. In Ecuador, for example, there are many experts who went to the university not knowing how to speak Spanish; there was a language barrier that had to be overcome. The experts that were assigned to Quito could not make themselves understood and, thus, much time was lost until they were able to communicate. The other point to be considered is the economics of this type of assistance. Local institutions are supposed to provide a counterpart but, in international program funds, there is often no provision for the local counterpart and a full-time staff member is required to be the counterpart of the expert who is visiting the country, necessitating a special provision in the budget. The low income of the local institutions is then a major problem. Some provision so that the local counterpart could be paid by the international loan could be a first step towards the better use of experts in the program.

THE ROLE OF THE NATIONAL UNIVERSITIES, GOVERNMENTAL AND PRIVATE

Commentary by Mordechai M. Levy

AS I SEE IT, the national university—in our context, a university located in a developing country—should be contrasted with a foreign university. Though within this wide complex, the universities of the United States are a very important example, they are not exclusively representative. Therefore, before I begin to discuss the role of national universities in the framework of our general subject, I would like to make a few remarks about the role of foreign universities.

The early phase of a more enlightened rule of the colonial powers over their possessions, which developed mainly between World Wars I and II and shortly thereafter, was characterized by the expatriate training of small numbers of carefully selected native senior civil servants, tribal chiefs, and other community leaders. This schooling typically took place in the metropolitan countries. Study in other countries, for instance in the United States, generally was not encouraged and was even frowned upon by the colonial authorities who, as a deterrent, did not recognize degrees and diplomas acquired there. And indeed, as in these other countries, students had not been "carefully selected government scholars;" many returnees from the United States and the Soviet Union later became the leaders of the national liberation movements.

With the approach of independence and in the first years after it had been achieved, the trickle of students and trainees outside their home countries turned into a torrent and pervaded into any country that permitted entry, particularly into those that offered scholarships. To give you a more concrete idea of the numbers involved, I refer to a study I undertook in 1966 on behalf of the United Nations Economic Commission for Africa. I concluded that, at the time and from that continent alone, the total number of persons studying and training outside their own countries approached the 100 000 mark. It must be noted, however, that the distribution of this enormous number over the various courses of study and training was not at all in agreement with the economic and general needs of the countries concerned, mainly because of the lack of appropriate guidance and scholastic preparation.

The study of engineering was never actively promoted by the colonial powers—neither during the period of their actual rule nor after it had ended. Even when they helped to establish university engineering departments in their former colonies they still envisaged a very limited size and enrollment, mainly in civil engineering. We can safely assume that this policy resulted from the former colonial powers' fear of losing large engineering enterprises they held in these countries. These were staffed mostly by expatriate engineers—even if, in the course of time, a certain amount of control had to be transferred to local managers. Although national governments are now trying to develop their own engineering schools, for many years to come, because of the lack of adequate local facilities, a large number of future engineers from developing countries will have to look to foreign universities for all their training, or at least for its advanced and more specialized stages.

Government agencies therefore should be set up in every country carefully to guide their youth to the most suitable institutions abroad and to follow up their scholastic progress. One of their main objectives should be to forestall the estrangement of their young nationals abroad from their original environment and culture, the indiscriminate adoption of foreign value judgments, and the confusion of standards. To a great degree, these aims have proven to be attainable by means such as contact with education officers attached to embassies, promotion of national student associations, provision of assistance for spending vacations at home, and up-to-date information on suitable job openings there. Because these pitfalls were not avoided in the past, many students decided not to return to their home countries or left them again after they found that they had lost contact and were unable to find a common language with their own people.

In recent years, several technologically advanced countries have initiated special university-level specific engineering courses to answer the needs of developing countries. As examples I cite courses in tropical architecture in Great Britain, and postgraduate programs in building, hydraulic and sanitary engineering, and photogrammetry organized by the Netherlands Universities Foundation. Another example, and one I am particularly familiar with, is a course in agricultural engineering for students from developing countries established by my university—Technion-Israel Institute of Technology. It is a full-fledged four-year course leading to the Bachelor of Science degree, although the following features distinguish it from the regular Technion course in the same subject.

1. It is given in English and not in Hebrew.

2. In the first two years, it has enriched course content in mathematics and physics to accommodate students with slightly inadequate preparation.

3. It provides instruction in subjects, the syllabi for which are adapted to the students' home countries, ie arid or humid climate, specific conditions of soils and building materials, and unavailability of sophisticated machinery and repair facilities.

4. The subject of the fourth-year project to be prepared by every student is taken from the agricultural situation of his own country, either based on personal work experience of faculty members or on their correspondence with local authorities.

Because of the success of this course, plans are underway at the Technion to set up, with the help of a foundation, a similar course on the graduate level and a course for agricultural teachers, with particular stress on agricultural machinery. The latter is on the behalf of UNESCO.

Israel is thus an example of those countries not yet fully developed themselves that offer training and study facilities to students from other developing countries. While this scheme might offer certain drawbacks, it also offers specific advantages over study and training in highly developed countries. The gap between the respective stages of economic and technological development in the host and the home countries and differences in specialization and sophistication, as well as in the availability of resources, are not as unbridgeable and awe-inspiring in developing countries as they often are to students in the highly industrialized countries, where the study process may be handicapped by feelings of inferiority and frustration. The host countries also often offer more familiar climatic conditions, both from the student's personal point of view and from that of subjects of study such as medicine, agriculture, and architecture.

THE ROLE OF NATIONAL UNIVERSITIES

FIRST, I would like to reply to the question implicitly asked by the organizers of this Conference when, in formulating the topic, they suggested a distinction between government and private national universities. I venture to guess that they made this distinction on the basis of experience in the United States, the Philippines, certain Latin American countries, and a few other countries. I would submit that, for the greater part of the developing world, this division does not exist. This is true if we exclude from our discussion purely profit-making institutions and consider only those private universities which have been established by private or public bodies for the furtherance of the same aims as those generally promulgated by government-sponsored universities. Such institutions may even have the advantage of operating without the limitations often imposed on state universities that depend on legislative and fiscal machinery. There then remains no reason here to distinguish between the two categories.

How, then, does a university in a developing country fulfill its role of increasing the effectiveness of industrialization by applying engineering technology? Or even, how does it assist in laying the very groundwork for an industrial economy, as is still required in a number of countries?

A university will be able to play these roles in advancing the economy of the country it is located in only if it has a clear perception of the part it is to play in helping to solve the socio-economic and political problems faced by that nation. It will base this perception on data and directives from governmental sources (national economic plan, manpower forecasts, ministry of education data). These forecasts may postulate the creation of considerable cadres of engineers to strengthen the infrastructure of the national economy (roads, sea and airports, power and water installations, drainage and sanitation works, housing), to exploit natural resources, or to create manufacturing industries, both for the home market and for export. The university's administration and faculty will also independently study and analyze the needs and trends of the national economy through the intellectual resources and scientific methods at their disposal. They will then conclude and decide as to which departments and laboratories should be developed. Student intake requirements for buildings, staff, and equipment will be determined accordingly.

However, a serious obstacle may arise in implementing even the best designed national and institutional plans—the lack of adequately prepared and properly motivated candidates for engineering study. In many countries, both developed and developing, engineering is not a favorite subject for young university entrants for a variety of reasons: lack of satisfactory mathematics and physics preparation; difficulty of the course of study itself; and even, as we are now witnessing in the United States, a flight from the gruesome implications of such ultimate engineering developments as nuclear weapons and ballistic missiles. In certain developing countries, potential students also are lured away by the greater social prestige and financial rewards of other professions such as law and medicine.

Education authorities and universities therefore will have to undertake a tremendous task of scholastically preparing, guiding, and informing to get an adequate number of properly motivated and instructed candidates into academic engineering schools.

I should like to postpone to the end of this paper discussing the adequate number and optimum size of a country's engineering population. Rather, before proceeding any further, I should like to clarify the term "university." As used in this discussion, it encompasses not only the classical, multidiscipline university but all institutions of higher learning; in particular, the specific phenomenon called "Institute of Technology," "Technische Hochschule," "Politechnico" and what is called in France "Grande Ecole." I even submit that for many emerging countries, it may be advantageous to set up, alongside general traditional universities, this type of academic institution whose primary task it is to create the high-level manpower and the knowledge necessary for industrialization. The heads of these institutions will not be impeded by the competing and often conflicting requirements of other departments which, in the traditional university, are sometimes considered to be of equal or even greater importance than engineering. Moreover, they will also enjoy direct access to government and other sources for their budget.

What then are the specific tasks of universities in developing countries if they are to contribute their share to the industrialization of their economies?

1. *They must provide high-level training for young men and women in those branches of engineering that offer the best prospects for the growth of local industries.* I do not believe that developing countries are the suitable environment for general programs of engineering studies. This has been introduced in several countries with a long engineering and industrial tradition where specialized knowledge and experience can be acquired in an apprentice engineering stage, after the studies have been completed. We must remember that if one wishes to avoid an excessive influx of foreign experts and all the difficulties it carries in its wake in emerging national economies, preparation of adequate high-level manpower should precede the setting up of industries.

I therefore advocate that engineering education be conducted in the accepted departmental patterns—civil, mechanical, electrical—but adjusted to the specific needs of the various countries and in accord with the most recent technological developments. We should not expect that industries in such countries will develop along the same lines as older economies, which started with rather primitive technologies and equipment and only gradually adopted more sophisticated design and production methods.

On the contrary, their chance to be competitive rests on immediately embarking on the application of the most recent technology and in thus getting a head-start over old, established, more conservative enterprises. Only on this condition will they obtain the investment capital required. A country with promising mineral resources therefore should not restrict itself to training mining engineers; its universities should also contain a modern department of extractive metallurgy and ore beneficiation. Their graduates, together with those of the chemistry and chemical engineering departments, will be able to set up and operate plants to manufacture products which will bring a much higher price than do the raw minerals. Universities in countries with a good agricultural potential will establish, besides schools of agriculture, departments of agricultural engineering with divisions of soil and water conservation, farm mechanization, and farmstead planning. They will thus help to transform traditional farming into a modern industry, the products of which will become exportable, thanks to a modern food industry headed by graduates of departments of food technology. In countries having but few natural resources, the difficult but possible task of the universities will be to train the sopisticated manpower needed for science-based industries. Here, the faculty will have the additional challenge of providing the ideas for the products turned out by these industries.

2. This last example shows that *even young academic institutions should not wait too long to establish graduate schools.* Three reasons can be given. Modern industry needs engineers trained beyond the B.S. level, universities need junior teaching and research staff who can be attracted only by graduate study and, finally, their highly qualified senior staff can be held only with the inducement of working with graduate students and research assistants.

3. This point leads to the third task imposed on a university in a developing country—to *serve as a center of both basic and applied research.* In developed countries, research is conducted in a variety of organizations: universities, industry-owned laboratories, industrial research associations, government institutions, and private research establishments. In a young economy, all this does not exist and university research laboratories have to fulfill all the tasks which, at a later stage, would be desirable and profitable to transfer to the other organizations named above. Moreover, university-related laboratories will have to routine-test local products, whereas faculty on a part-time basis consult with industry. In short, a strong and variegated institute of technology or school of engineering will reduce the need for very specific subject to be taught abroad and also will minimize the need for foreign consultants and advisors who are always handicapped by not knowing local conditions.

4. There is another point that has often been discussed in connection with the industrialization of developing countries—*whether to create facilities to train skilled workers, technicians, and practical engineers, in that order, before setting up university-level institutions.* I would decry this seemingly logical approach as being typically neocolonialist or, to say the least, short sighted. The experience of many countries has shown that, by following this precept, fatal delays were created in industrial development, thus keeping the developing countries dependent on foreign engineering knowledge. Even the lower-level technical training itself was not successful as there were no proper incentives and not enough qualified local instructor-engineers. On the other hand, where universities offered engineering training at an early stage of a country's industrial development, as for instance, in my own, there was a two-fold result. First, the young engineers felt like true pioneers and were ready to undertake all the tasks required in the new industries they built up, beginning with planning and designing, shop management, and training the worker at the machine tool, using what they had learned in workshop practice at the university. Second, university engineering departments created the proper atmosphere, the professional personnel, and the standards for setting up vocational high schools and technical institutes and lent social standing to the entire new sector of industrial occupations.

5. Universities everywhere, even more so in developing countries, play a vital role in the ever-growing field of graduate education and extension training. This concept of the university as a center of life-long learning is a gift to the world of the American national genius. It has its source in the Morrill Act of 1862 and in the Land-Grant College which changed the image of the university from an ivory tower and place to educate the social elite. Utilizing the resources and the organization of a great university to spread technical knowledge, skills, procedures, and methods among the industrial population, in keeping with the various levels of its preparation, is a university function that, in its impact on the economy of the country, may not be less important than the more strictly academic forms of university education. New technologies thus will be imparted quickly to practicing engineers and technicians; latest findings of academic research in production engineering and industrial management will benefit the operation of industrial enterprises.

And finally, a few remarks on the quantitative aspect of the student population in those branches of higher learning—the basic sciences, engineering, economics, and industrial management—which have a direct bearing on the task of preparing the high-level manpower required for a country's industrialization.

I would say that, in principle, there should be no distinction between the optimum parameters applied to developing and to fully developed countries, because high-level manpower must be conceived not as the result of development but as the condition necessary for it. What for many generations has been clear to every understanding parent—that he must invest in the education of his children to ensure their economic and general well being and future—has become, in the past twenty years, one of the fundamental principles for the economic advancement of the underdeveloped countries. Indeed, one of the milestones in this new doctrine, the "Report of the Commission on Post-School Certificate and Higher Education in Nigeria" (1960), under the chairmanship of Sir Eric Ashby, was entitled, "Investment in Education."

To create guidelines, it should not be difficult to determine figures of student enrollment in relevant university departments in the industrialized world and of the capital and current expenditure required for them, per capita of the general population. These figures should then be incorporated into the economic plans and budgets of developing countries. The only impediment to implementing this strategy of human capital development will not be the availability of the capital required—it is worthwhile to borrow it—but, as mentioned earlier, the availability of qualified and properly motivated students and teachers. The primary task of national and friendly foreign governments as well as that of international organizations therefore will be rapidly to strengthen secondary education and to train potential university staff, wherever they can, both at their own universities and abroad.

THE ROLE OF NATIONAL UNIVERSITIES, GOVERNMENTAL AND PRIVATE

Commentary by William D. Van Vorst

NATIONAL UNIVERSITIES, either governmental or private, simply mean universities in the developing nations, including "regional" universities, colleges, schools, institutes, and the like. The term "national universities," then, refers to higher education in general.

Particularly worthy of scrutiny is "engineering technology." Although the term is really quite well chosen, it is a phrase that could be used so as to take on many meanings. There is a saying that science teaches us to know, and art to do, and that the more perfect sciences lead to the creation, or development, of corresponding useful arts—astronomy the science, navigation the art, for example. The practical art which utilizes scientific knowledge may be defined as technology, and conventionally "technology" implies a strong industrial association. Indeed, the most concise dictionary definition available for technology is "industrial science." Adding the concept of "engineering" incorporates certain functions of design, planning, and decision-making elements of management. Engineering *method*ology must be recognized as an explicit component of engineering *tech*nology."

Clark Kerr (1963) in his commentary on *The Uses of the University* begins with a quotation from Alfred North Whitehead:

In the conditions of modern life, the rule is absolute: the race that does not value trained intelligence is doomed. Not all your heroism, not all your social charm, not all your wit, not all your victories on land or sea can move back the finger of fate. Today we maintain ourselves. Tomorrow science will have moved forward yet one more step; and there will be no appeal from the judgment which will be pronounced on the uneducated.

This, written in 1916, seems remarkably prophetic. I particularly call attention to the relationship, albeit inferential, between "trained intelligence" and education. The question is often raised whether we are, in fact, "training" or "educating" people in our institutions of higher learning, particularly in the "professional schools." I recognize most emphatically that there is a difference between the two, but I suggest that material entirely appropriate for "educational pursuits" in one time period becomes more appropriate to "training programs" in another. What is training and what is education depends very much on the over-all environment, I submit, rather than on absolutes. Therefore, there is no unique, specific role for higher education in developing countries. Rather, the role of higher education must be devised indigenously with respect to the environment of the times and, insofar as possible, the defined goals of the future.

With regard to engineering technology and industrialization, a pragmatic approach and an almost intimate relation with industry seems indicated. This is a very challenging role, incidentally, for though "practical" work must be emphasized in the curricula, it certainly must be based on sound knowledge of fundamentals. "Research" will be more in the nature of development or even trouble shooting for industry. Objective decision making on such problems as resource allocation or plant location, for example, might well be a service rendered the government and/or industry.

REPORT OF WORKSHOP 15

George E. Klinzing, Rapporteur

FIVE RECOMMENDATIONS were specified by Workshop 15:

1. *The efficient application of engineering technology in industrialization programs of the developing countries depends on the integral prepartion of engineers.* Engineers must have a profound knowledge of the national reality and the national plan of development. They must be balanced between managerial positions and technical works. The number of engineering schools and their graduates must meet the needs of engineering projects and management positions. Engineers should have a knowledge of the labor relations of their country, and thus the university should provide such courses in their curriculum. After leaving the university, continued education programs should be provided.

2. *The university needs to prepare engineers and scientists cooperatively with the private and public sector.* In this preparation, training in the humanities and social sciences is imperative; this training must be integrated with the engineering subjects. One possibility would be to use an all-encompassing design project, including sociological and cultural effects of such an engineering design. Group dynamics and team teaching should be employed in engineering teaching.

3. *The universities need to prepare their own researchers who are oriented to the national reality.* In research and the training of engineers, international organizations must manage programs through the universities and in close cooperation with the government. Centers of service to industry and government and for consulting should be established within the university. In this manner, projects could be directed through the center to professors with expertise in specific fields. The center also should stimulate professors to suggest projects beneficial to industry and government; foreign advisors could function most favorably in these centers.

4. *Above all, with the initiation of research programs in the universities, the primary function of the university—teaching—must not be forgotten.*

5. Care must be taken in choosing experts for programs of assistance to the developing countries. Programs should be directed from university to university, thus guaranteeing the quality of the expert. National counterparts must also be selected carefully. Matching plans and projects properly between national counterparts and the visiting expert is necessary for the optimum transfer of technology. The counterparts should work with the advisors on a full-time basis. Thus, the funding organizations must provide means to finance this full-time program.

Consensus was reached that the university is the single most vital instrument in the development of a country and also that each country is at a different point in the over-all development picture, and its needs must be planned accordingly.

19

AN INTERDISCIPLINARY TEAM APPROACH FROM THE NONENGINEERING POINT OF VIEW

Principal Paper—Melvin Kranzberg
Commentary—Kan Chen
Commentary—Jiri Nehnevajsa
Report of Workshop 16—Marlin H. Mickle, Rapporteur

Development clearly is a problem requiring inputs from many fields of specialization. This chapter concerns itself with the nonengineering view of interdisciplinary activities in development.

The Editors

AN INTERDISCIPLINARY TEAM APPROACH FROM THE NONENGINEERING POINT OF VIEW

Principal Paper by Melvin Kranzberg

HERODOTUS often is called the "father of history" and probably rightly so, for his *History of the Persian Wars* represents the first narrative account of a chronological sequence of events. Yet, historians ever since have taken as their motto a dictum which antedates the work of Herodotus—"Nothing new under the sun," from the *Book of Ecclesiastes*. Some have followed this dictum so earnestly that their histories explain the past as a series of repetitions, almost cyclical in structure. Historical investigation becomes a search for antecedent parallels, origins, and predecendents.

Some historians of science find 19th century atomic theory a repetition of the atomist views of Leucippus and Democritus of 2000 years earlier. Historians of technology compare the modern impact of the digital computer with the changes wrought by Watt's steam engine or Ford's assembly line. Religious historians find antecedents of today's religious crisis in the Protestant Reformation of the 16th century; social historians see many similarities between the moral crisis in American society and the situation in the post-Antonine Roman Empire. And, during the past few months, the diplomatic historians have busied themselves with comparing the Russian invasion of Czechoslovakia in the summer of 1968 with the Nazi rape of that hapless country some thirty years ago. Political commentary upon the 1968 presidential campaign is filled with references to George Wallace's campaign as a recrudescence of the "know-nothing" movement a century ago.

The search for origins and historical parallels is, of course, valid. It yields perspective on contemporary problems and thereby enlightens us. It helps to prevent precipitous action by building a more thoughtful basis for our attitudes and deeds.

As a historian holding paid-up cards in several professional organizations, I am, of course, obliged to remain in good standing. I have to point out that many problems involved in the application of technology to developing countries are by no means new. There are parallels in past history, and we can trace the origin and evolution of the problems as presented today. In essence, our contemporary problem is but a new version of the transfer of technology or the diffusion of techniques—problems apparently as old as mankind. These date from the time the first ancestor of *homo sapiens* was bludgeoned with a rock held by his unfriendly neighbor and resolved to imitate the technique and sock it to his neighbor in the same fashion.

Very early in history, however, we discover that imitative technology is neither nearly so simple nor spontaneous as it might seem. An example is offered by the case of the wheel, one of the seminal inventions of mankind. We know that, by 3000 B.C., wheeled carts were already in use in Mesopotamia and

Syria. The proximity of Syria to Egypt strongly suggests that the Egyptians must certainly have known about the wheel. Yet, despite its obvious advantages of transport, the Egyptians did not begin to use the wheel until about 1650 B.C.—and then only after they had been invaded by peoples from lands where wheeled carts were in common use. The reasons for this ancient "technology gap" are difficult for the modern mind to fathom.

An archaeological theory that Egypt already had an effective and sufficient water transport system in the Nile River and its system of canals seems to founder on the inevitable problems of land-to-water and water-to-land transport. The wheel certainly had obvious advantages and was simple to copy. Why was it not—and much earlier than 1650 B.C.?

The cultural anthropologists conclude that the structure of Egyptian society, already highly stratified by 3000 B.C., was so rigid that it successfully resisted all innovations, even those as advantageous as the wheel. Whatever the reason, here is an early example of resistance to technology transfer. For more than twelve centuries, the Egyptians knew about but never used wheels, although they needed them.

Most of history, however, weighs in favor of a simple diffusion of technology. The transfer of techniques and innovations usually occurred through movements of technical people themselves. Through antiquity and the Middle Ages, we find examples of various technologies diffusing with craftsmen who moved from one place to another—usually individually. Then the religous strife of the 16th century caused whole communities to move. Thus, the French Huguenots took their technical skills in glassware and textiles to England, Germany, and the Netherlands because of religious persecution (Scoville, 1961).

With the rise of mercantilist ideas in the 17th century, governments made concerted efforts to induce technicians to leave their homelands and establish manufacturing industries in more congenial areas. Thus Colbert, Louis XIV's finance minister, made strenuous efforts to attract foreign craftsmen to France (Cole, 1939). Other European states took their cue from France. When Philip V became King of Spain in 1700, "he resolutely sent his deputies abroad to recruit craftsmen with skills that were lacking at home." (LaForce, 1964.) Peter the Great of Russia not only tried to seduce foreigners into setting up manufacturing establishments in Russia, but traveled abroad himself to learn, firsthand, the technical achievements of western Europe. And he saw to it that other Russian engineers and craftsmen went abroad to acquire the information in detail (Danilevskii, 1966).

Although mercantilism fostered the transfer of technology by seeking technical people to expand manufacturing to sell goods for precious bullion, applied defensively, the same doctrine worked against technology transfer by these early examples of the "brain drain." Governments, loath to see the skills and techniques leave their countries, attempted to bar migrations of skilled workmen and of the machines, tools, and processes they used. To block the emigration of

340

her textile artisans, France placed special guards along the Spanish frontiers. England similarly watched her ports and ordered her consulates in Portugal and elsewhere to turn back Irish and English workmen who attempted to reach Spain (La Force, 1964).

Notice how simple and naive this concept of technology transfer seems today. There was little talk of resource factors, capital needs, socio-cultural barriers, absorptive capacity, and other parameters that complicate our contemporary discussions of applying engineering technology to underdeveloped countries. The early modern notion was that technology could easily be transferred from developed to underdeveloped areas through the transit of the technologists themselves. And the notion was precisely right for the times.

In the craft and pre-industrial technologies which then governed productive capacity, the essential element was indeed the workman himself and his "knowhow" laboriously acquired through years of apprenticeship and practice. The migration of the workman himself was sufficient to ensure diffusion. The American colonies through the first half of the 18th century enjoyed an easy and successful transit of technology from Britain. The craft level of British technology made it transferable without complicated machinery or large capital investments; the need for a simple craft technology in a virgin land was great; and the American colonists, having the same background as the British, were receptive (Kranzberg, 1968).

Sometimes, however, socio-cultural factors discouraged acceptance of technology even in pre-industrial societies. LaForce (1964) tells us how the opposition of the guilds, the traditional working patterns of the Spanish artisans, and the prejudices against outsiders, especially Protestants, interfered with efforts to raise the productivity level in the textile industry despite governmental efforts. In the end, the indiscriminate efforts of the Spanish kings to force certain advanced technologies on their peoples did not take hold. Similarly, over the long run, Peter the Great's efforts were scarcely successful in developing Russian technological capacity. It was already being realized that the transit of technology was no simple matter of transporting men and tools. Yet, it was to take almost 200 years before this simple fact was borne home.

Laissez-faire doctrines and industrialism at once complicated and confused problems of technology transfer from the middle of the 18th century. That mythical rational being, "the economic man," chose his activities, according to the *laissez-faire* doctrine, on the basis of a clear view of his economic selfinterest. It seemed obvious to the classic economists that "economic man" would inevitably adopt the most advanced technology. The only barriers were the artificial curbs on trade and the migration of technicians and machines. Adam Smith had pointed out that "the Chinese would naturally learn the art of using and constructing themselves all the different machines made use of in other countries" if only their mandarin rulers would free the country from foreign trade restrictions (Smith, 1937).

The classical economist saw no problem in applying technology to underdeveloped countries arising from the nature of the technology itself or the nature of the receiving countries. It was simply a matter of doing away with barriers unnatural and artificial to the diffusion of the technology.

The Industrial Revolution, which dramatically revealed the power of machines to increase productive capacity, also tended to cloak problems of technology transfer. Because industrialization seemed only to substitute machine for human labor, technological development was equated with the transfer of machines. This was a logical extension of the earlier notion that technology transfer simply involved the transit of the worker to the underdeveloped area. *Ergo,* applying engineering technology to the industrialization of developing countries was a simple matter of capital equipment export with, in some cases, a few engineers or technical personnel to show the natives how to work the machinery. Yet, even this simplistic notion of technology transfer enlarged the dimensions of the problem. The questions of what machinery to export and who and how to pay for it, raised purely economic aspects of the problem.

The study of exportable industrial development unfortunately became monopolized by the economists; it has largely remained so. The focus was on investment in the underdeveloped areas and, to a lesser extent, on the entrepreneurs and bankers required by new capital investment. On questions of the industrialization of developing countries, the dismal science had dismal results. The economists were working in too narrow a context for, by concentrating on the investment parameter to the exclusion of the other elements in the problem, they tended to oversimplify it. The economists themselves were the first to recognize this as they sharpened their analysis, acquired more quantitative data, and employed better analytic techniques. Their interest widened to take into account available local resources, manpower factors, societal structural changes, and ultimately all the complex variables involved and analyzable as factor proportions (Strassmann, 1968).

Despite the broadening inquiry into developmental matters,

various theoretical and operational aspects of the transfer of technology have been a relatively unstressed subject in economic literature. . . . Economists, . . . with some notable exceptions, have been content to deal with technology as if it had somehow arrived as a datum for incorporation via market adjustments in general equilibrium theory or a single "residual factor"—a shift in the production function. (Spencer and Woroniak, 1967.)

Increasingly aware that relatively large infusions of foreign aid monies did not necessarily bring about industrial development, developmental economists now broadened their analyses to include the environment for investment (Weiner, 1966).

Confrontation with reality also was forcing the technological people actually engaged in the transfer of technology to broaden their views. Events had belied the optimistic hopes held forth by the "bold new program" of technical assistance, embodied in Point Four of President Truman's Inaugural Address, 1949

342

(Alpert, 1963). The transfer of technical expertise in the mid-20th century proved far more difficult than did the simple migration of workmen in the pre-industrial phases of economic development two centuries earlier. Since the problem is really the transfer of knowledge, this widened the range of problems of applying engineering technology to industrialization far beyond all points reached by the economists.

Problems of exporting industrialization cannot be left either to technologists or to economists. These are socio-cultural problems that involve virtually all departments of human knowledge and activity. Many anthropologists and sociologists and a few economists had been saying this for a long time (Mead, 1955; Pepelasis *et al.*, 1958; Hirschman, 1959; Gruber, 1961; Hoselitz, 1960). They recognized that modernizing the underdeveloped regions of the globe through industrialization was "one of the great revolutionary transformations of mankind." (Black, 1966.) Applications of modern industrial techniques in developing societies require a whole range of changes in education, religion, values, the family, government, local community organization, social stratification, the communication system, science and technology, demographic factors, formal and informal social organization (Baranson, 1967).

Transfer of technology is neither simply technical nor economic but rather is a complex and pervasive process of the dynamic transformation of the entire society, with universal impact on human affairs (Black, 1966). To this, developing peoples are quite likely to reply, "Never mind your ideas. Just let us have your hardware." The truth seems to be, however, that they need the ideas too.

Recognizing that the problem of applying engineering technology in developing countries had broader parameters and more variables than had previously been considered did not result in the solutions. Instead, it complicated them with entirely new sets of problems.

Societies differ in their absorptive capacity. Cultural factors limit—or better, complicate—the application of industrial technology to underdeveloped areas. Workers are sometimes so culturally conditioned that they cannot easily make the change from peasant to factory life. Managerial and proprietary groups are often too rigid in thought and organization to introduce innovations and to provide adequate incentives for the workers. Their traditionalism may indeed be the greater problem (Strassmann, 1968; Chaplin, 1967; Granick, 1967).

A whole series of societal changes is at once a requisite for, and an accompaniment of, industrialization. A partial list is urbanization, extension of literacy, equalization of opportunity, a change in relationships between men and women, growth in the communication network, and health improvement. The process calls for social mobilization and transformation on a large scale.

All this brings us not a single step toward solutions. We have merely widened the arena, outlined a strategy, and chosen the battlegrounds already soaked with blood from anthropological and sociological controversies. One controversy is institutional versus individual change, the socio-cultural equivalent of the "chicken-or-the-egg" problem. Some scholars suggest that attitudes and values must first be modernized (McClelland, 1961). Others claim that behavioral changes through institutional adjustment can bring about the essential changes (Hirschman, 1965). Most economists are in the latter camp, urging industrialization through, not a frontal attack upon values, but a revision of institutions and structures to shift the incentive system of the backward nation and hence its values.

Psychologists stress individual before institutional changes. Cyril Black (1966), borrowing Frank Lloyd Wright's architectural dictum that "form follows function," says:

Suffice it to say that the strong bias toward the view that modernization will dissolve tradition, based on the theoretical assumption that form follows function, an essentially Westernizing view in this context, held by most sociologists and economists and by many political scientists, has not been supported by the empirical research done so far. Anthropologists and historians are by training and experience more impressed by the staying power of tradition, and political scientists are divided on this issue depending on their education and the direction of their research. It is their view that form follows function only in the limited sense of adaptation to changing function.

The issue also generates subproblems. Although political revolutionary groups always advocate the complete destruction of the old order to establish the new, does this doctrine apply to revolutionary industrialization? Can the new be introduced without destroying the old? Is it not possible to maintain some traditional values and thereby prevent complete dislocation of a society? In the American society, the rhetoric of a small-town, rural America still prevails in political discourse in high quarters, despite the reality of an urbanized, industrialized nation. Inconsistencies concerned with tradition and innovation have existed in American life for more than a century. Practically speaking, we, who have always had it both ways, look odd in insisting that old ways must disappear upon industrialization. The United States, leader in the world's jet age, still has a lot of "horse-and-buggy" people.

In this connection, it is interesting to note that there are scholars who believe industrialization can proceed even within traditional societies.[1] Even more interesting are the studies of economists who have concentrated on the technological aspect of modernization and call for the adaptation of technology itself to the needs of the developing countries.

Jack Baranson (1967) has pointed out that

a basic problem of transmittal involves choosing or adapting technologies that will enable recipient societies to utilize more effectively existing resources at emerging stages of development. Adapting technologies to social capabilities and economic conditions can ease the burden of restructuring societies to fit modern techniques and should lessen considerably the human and economic costs.

Baranson uses the telling term, "technological elasticity of a society," to describe variations in the nature and pace of the technological adjustments which different societies can and will make to foster industrialization. A corollary is that even the simple imitation of a more highly developed technology when applied to an underdeveloped area requires innovation within the new context (Spencer and Woroniak, 1967).

There is yet another facet to the problem. Must primitive communities pass through sequential steps of industrialization, repeating the pattern of our Western industrial history? Or is it possible for them to go directly from dugout canoes to jet planes without passing through, say, the railroad- and canal-building eras? (Stover, 1963; Heilbronner, 1967.) Present answers to both questions suggest the primitive state of our learning. However, there may be certain preconditions for industrialization. W. W. Rostow (1960) has set down, for example, explicit "preconditions for take-off," but Alexander Gerschenkorn (1962) has argued that not every case of industrial development has had all the preconditions postulated by Rostow.

The many dimensions of the nonengineering aspects of industrialization of developing countries suggest to pessimists that analytical solutions do not exist and that muddling through to possible solutions is enough to meet the demands of good will and rising expectations even though we do not accomplish a great deal. Certainly, much of the world's business carried on by Americans meets this soft-headed standard. If there are interdisciplinary approaches to solutions, we must face preliminary problems and disagreements about even how to state the problem. The engineers naturally see industrialization in developing countries as a matter of production efficiency; the economists, as income growth, individual and national; the social anthropologists as cultural differentiation and conflict; the sociologists, as problems of social change; and the political scientists, as power relationships, administration, nationalism, and international politics. Only we historians seem to take over-all points of view—and we are far from being in agreement.

Everyone keeps enlarging the boundaries of the problem, then investigating small segments of it. A century ago, no one recognized that there existed a problem of technology transfer; however, there were simplistic solutions. Now we discover endless problems but no solutions. We face an "information overload;" more and more data are coming into the system without any organizing principles or evaluative criteria. We have no models—theoretical, structural, or operational. Yet the real world admits of no delay. The population explosion continues. Although the nutritionists preserve us from panic by claiming that prophecies of doom are mistaken, they point out that, if existing technology were properly deployed, there would be no problem of mass nutrition or even serious malnutrition. That, of course, begs the question. The population explosion puts pressure, not on those who invent new technology, but rather on those who attempt to transfer and apply existing technologies in underdeveloped areas.

Similarly, there are mounting political pressures. The "revolution of rising expectations" has not assisted much in the application of technologies in underdeveloped areas, but expectations are still rising. The political rulers of the underdeveloped countries face hard political and economic decisions on national goals and the mobilization and allocation of resources. And they cannot wait for the scholars.

Still, several factors point encouragingly toward at least a limited degree of optimism. There is the recognition that the application of engineering technology to the industrialization of developing countries involves more than simply engineering or economic problems. A vast amount of empirical data exists, and the variety of conceptualizations suggests that the equipment, knowledge, skills, and techniques of the transfer effort must be adapted to local technical, cultural, political, and economic conditions. We have powerful techniques such as operations research and systems analysis which may enable us to deal meaningfully with situations that contain interdependent variables in dynamic and accelerating situations. This offers an orderly and rational approach, taking into account all dynamic factors. Instead of piecemeal attention, we can view the problem as a whole, identify the subsystems, simulate them, combine them, and ascertain lines of solutions at some level of optimization.

Because the systems approach takes into account major variables, it requires the cooperation and coordination of many different disciplines to identify and characterize those which are quantifiable and useful. Since "universal doctors" disappeared with St. Thomas Aquinas and Herbert Spencer, the knowledge and training required means interdisciplinary teams of specialists from many fields—economists, sociologists, anthropologists, historians, psychologists, and experts in the methods of operation research and systems analysis.

Specialist status is not enough. The interdisciplinary approach works only for men who are aware of the socio-cultural implications of technological change and development. Engineers, well trained in engineering itself but ignorant of the social and economic implications of their work, will not do. Nor will economists who accept technology as "given;" nor sociologists, anthropologists, historians, psychologists, and humanists who ignore the technological parameter in human affairs. We cannot afford such half-formed "authorities" on our interdisciplinary teams. All must have a basic understanding of the interrelationships between technology and society and more than a passing acquaintance with the country or the society of concern. This means careful study of the economy, geography, and other factors involving technological applications; specific inquiries into sociological and cultural anthropological structures to modify the technology under consideration and make it adaptable without too severe a wrench in local customs. It also requires a solid study of the local technology, political and social structure, as well as the local needs and wants as the determinants of the feasible extent of industrialization. On these last points, historians of technology might be able to make significant contributions, particularly in underdeveloped areas that lack the traditions of Western civilization. Emphasis would be on the contributions that the underdeveloped society itself might make to the technological transfer process. It could usefully bar some forms of industrialization but encourage others. There is more than one way to industrialize and, I suspect, every situation's unique characteristics are as important as those it has in common with others.

There is nothing new in holding that engineers should have some knowledge of the socio-cultural implications of their work. On the other hand, the assertion that social scientists and the other members of an interdisciplinary team should have some knowledge of how technology impinges upon and affects their own special fields is, if not new, surely refreshing and repeatable. For the sociologists, this means understanding the relationships between technology and social change. For political scientists, it means understanding how technology affects the instruments and institutions of political control; for the anthropologists, how technological changes have transformed value systems and traditional institutions; for historians, how technological developments have affected the course of history in all its ramifications; for psychologists, distinguishing the psychological factors implicit in the discipline of the factory and assembly line from the attitudes in a primitive farming community. The technological parameter must be introduced into all the specialized social science disciplines as a matter of serious study.

Indeed, it is now no secret that I think we might do away with the barriers between disciplines; they seem to me meaningless, even crippling, in coming to grips with the problems that confront man and society today. Our educational institutions might do well to reorganize themselves for problem solving rather than into traditional disciplines. Instead of having departments in sociology, economics, and anthropology, why not have departments in developing areas and urban systems? When these problems are solved, we can reorganize for new ones. This kind of approach already characterizes some of our advanced engineering schools, where old departments of chemical, civil, mechanical, and electrical engineering, derived from 19th century engineering practice, have been abandoned in favor of design, systems, materials, information, and energy.

Are we not faced with similar and equally challenging problems in the interdisciplinary aspects of applying engineering technology to the industrialization of developing countries? Perhaps our students would give up riot and rebellion if universities showed themselves more attuned to problems relevant to our society. The students, at any rate, are saying so. I can think of no better place to begin than with a problem having the ramifications and future implications of the transfer of technology to underdeveloped countries.

NOTES

1. Milton Singer, in Chapter 4 of Weiner (1966) points out that Hinduism, which Max Weber had claimed to be an impediment to modernization in India, has not, in practice, proved to be such a barrier.

AN INTERDISCIPLINARY TEAM APPROACH FROM THE NONENGINEERING POINT OF VIEW

Commentary by Kan Chen

I SHOULD LIKE to offer five points in my discussion of Professor Kranzberg's paper. The first has to do with the changing nature of change. The next three are related to the systems analysis mentioned in Professor Kranzberg's paper as a framework for interdisciplinary team approach—how systems analysis has been applied in the past, how it can be applied at present, and what needs to be done to apply it broadly in the future. The last point I shall make is on the organization of interdisciplinary teams.

THE CHANGING NATURE OF CHANGE

I agree with Professor Kranzberg that technological and social change is the most salient phenomenon in the history of mankind. However, to a technologist like myself, the nature of change itself seems to be changing, as reflected in two characteristics. First, the accelerating pace of change, caused by the rapid development of technology and the much closer interaction of a smaller world, implies significantly that prior experience seems to have become less relevant for problem solving. To put it in a more provocative way, we may be less able to learn from history. Second, as a result of technological advancement, the choices in problem solving have become much richer and more complex. Certain solutions are practical only if substantial resources are utilized. The implication is that, if a mistake were made, it could be extremely expensive. The necessity of making complex choices justifies more careful analysis by an interdisciplinary team approach.

THE USE OF SYSTEMS ANALYSIS TO FACILITATE THE INTERDISCIPLINARY APPROACH

Now I should like to move to the next point—the use of systems analysis to facilitate the interdisciplinary approach. I used to use the term "multidisciplinary" interchangeably with the term "interdisciplinary" until one of my colleagues pointed out to me the very fundamental difference between the two. The multidisciplinary approach is used when a team of experts in various disciplines offer a variety of opinions on a subject and the team leader writes a committee report that incorporates these viewpoints and tries to elicit a consensus, more or less, on political grounds. The interdisciplinary approach implies intensive interaction among the team members and expects a single, and it is to be hoped, synergistic solution superior to any solution based on a single discipline. Experience indicates that the truly interdisciplinary approach can be applied when the experts in various disciplines are focused on a single project or, better yet, on a single decision. Under these circumstances, systems analysis becomes decision analysis, which provides a language for communication between decision-makers and the interdisciplinary team members. To illustrate how such an approach has helped to integrate the inputs of engineers, financial experts, economists, and decision makers, I shall cite an example based on a project recently completed for the Mexican Power Commission.

The decision to be analyzed was whether Mexico should, in the foreseeable future, build her first nuclear power plant. Nuclear power has not generally been considered economically favorable for developing countries. However, the competitive strength of nuclear power has advanced beyond original expectations. The capital cost has come down rapidly with new reactor technology, and the increasing number of countries with capability to enrich, fabricate, and process nuclear fuel removes some of the concerns about overdependence on limited sources of fuel supply. In Mexico, the size of the interconnected power systems is growing rapidly and will be boosted substantially if and when the frequency unification plan goes through. The consideration of installing large base-load plants generally makes the nuclear alternative attractive. On the other hand, Mexico has substantial hydropower resources. Compared with the equally economic nuclear alternative, hydro plants would have external benefits of contributing to local employment, public works, and conservation of foreign exchange. The policy question related to Mexico's first nuclear plant is therefore a question that must be solved from many considerations and in the environment of an ill-defined value system.

Figure 1 shows the result of applying systems analysis to this decision problem. Only the highlights of the model will be indicated. The inputs from the left include financial, energy, technology, and market—the forecasts and data supplied by financial experts, engineers, and economists. The policy decisions from the bottom include when and where to build the first nuclear plant, whether Mexico should get involved in fuel processing and fabrication, and the investment, operating, and pricing policies of the Power Commission. The outputs, interestingly, include not only the economic criteria summarized in the profit model, but also taxes, employment, impacts of electrification, and public works, items that do not affect the Power Commission directly, but may be significant from the standpoint of social welfare in Mexico. By putting a "price tag" on these external, and sometimes nonmaterialistic, welfare functions, the decision is analytic on a rational and explicit basis, using the inputs from an interdisciplinary team.

Figure 2 shows a systematic and orderly procedure for integrating the interdisciplinary team approach to stimulate private enterprise, either foreign or indigenous, in a developing country. It is intended to provide a framework for integrating legal, political, and business considerations. The decision to be analyzed here is the incentive system necessary to induce private investment.

The comprehensive model describes the key issues in a development process and will be discussed in detail later. For the time being, suffice it to say that a development strategy or policy has been obtained through analysis based on the comprehensive model. The next step, then, is to define the roles of the various parties, which may include the national and foreign governments, as well as

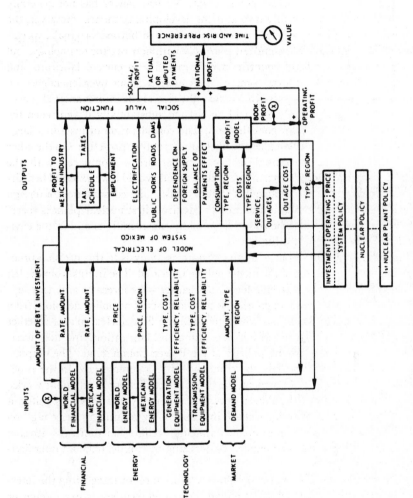

FIG. 1.—Decision Analysis model of Comision Federal de Electricidad (Mexico).

350

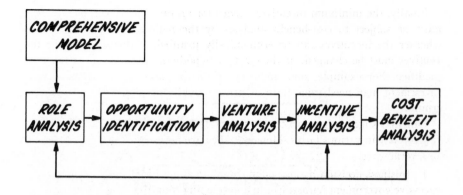

FIG. 2.—Systems approach to stimulation of private enterprise.

indigenous and foreign firms. For example, the role of the national government in industrialization may be restricted to providing infrastructure such as transportation, power, education, and health services. In the case of regional cooperation, the role of analysis may include a careful review of the comparative advantages of several nations and the types of industries to be emphasized in each nation will be specified.

After the role of private enterprise has been clarified, specific opportunities will be identified. This step may be initiated by the government or consultants, but it is best if private entrepreneurs are involved. The next step is venture analysis from the entrepreneurs' point of view. Here their primary considerations are expected profit and risk of the proposed venture or investment opportunity. Such factors as market size, labor cost, and tax holiday will affect the expected profit. Factors such as political instability, market uncertainty, and expropriation will affect risk. The investor with capital will compare the venture with other competing opportunities in terms of profit and risk. If the result of venture analysis is negative, ie profit too low and risk too high, the next step is to do incentive analysis to determine the minimum incentives necessary to induce a favorable decision by the investor. Very often, the current incentive system may have a wrong emphasis. For example, if risk is the more important negative factor affecting investment, governmental guarantee would be much more effective than tax exemption in inducing investment.

An important point should be made here—the risk in venture analysis is the felt risk, ie risk as felt by the investor. Sometimes the risk felt by foreign investors is so high that in certain developing countries they do not even bother to look carefully into the opportunities. Although this may be right in some cases, too often the felt risk so far exceeds what may be the true situation that excellent opportunities that would mutually benefit the foreign investor and the developing country are ignored. Such an information or credibility gap can be closed only by vigorous promotional programs launched by the government.

Finally, the minimum incentives needed for an investor's favorable decision must be subject to cost-benefit analysis by the national government to see whether the incentives can be economically justified; if they cannot, the incentives must be changed, or the original hypothesis of roles may have to be modified. For example, some industry originally planned for strictly private investment may need some form of private/public partnership to get off the ground.

One may suggest that, to a certain extent, the various steps in Fig. 2 are being taken today in various forms. However, they are not being taken appropriately in several ways.

1. Business decision makers often complain about insufficient incentives and excessive government harassment in a developing country without being specific as to how much more incentives and what reasonable reform of government procedures would make them decide favorably on investment.

2. National governments proclaim legal restrictions or incentives often without intimate knowledge of the major concerns of the private investors.

3. The lack of communication and, understandably, the lack of openness between government and investors make it difficult to obtain reliable (and honest) data to do the proposed systems analysis.

Realizing the importance of honest data and the need for going around the loop in Fig. 2 speedily several times to obtain effective results, I would suggest consideration of a disinterested third party—perhaps a systems consultant—to act as a broker between the government and the potential investors.

Now, let me comment on the comprehensive model based on the systems analyst's point of view. As indicated earlier, the comprehensive model is supposed to capture the key issues in a development process so that the model can be used to test various policies and development strategies. For this purpose, the model should contain at least the key elements shown in Fig. 3. To my knowledge, this kind of model is still in the early developmental stage and it may be a long time before it can become operational or useful in real policy decision-making. At the top of the figure is a set of social goals and, depending on the policy decisions, the model can be used to predict, with some measure of uncertainty, the response of the society and the implications in terms of social value at the bottom of the figure.

Most of the modeling that has been developed, even to a high degree of sophistication and quantification, is on physical aspects and the economic system. For example, to a high degree of detail, transportation systems can be modeled and simulated on computers. The costs of various transportation systems and their impact on regional economy can be obtained from the model. However, such models, though complicated, do not include enough for development policy decisions. As Professor Kranzberg points out in his paper, one wonders about the basic assumptions behind the purely economic model. When a demand arises, will there automatically be a supply to satisfy the demand?

352

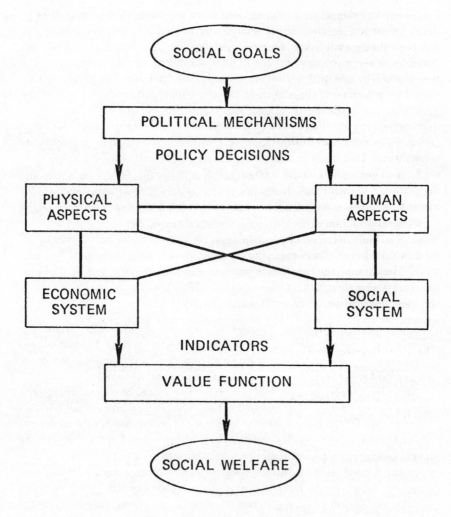

FIG. 3.—Comprehensive model.

Will everyone in the society behave like "the economic man," who will always optimize his own material benefits? With development, the coefficients in the input-output table will change. But how fast and how much will they change? To attempt to answer such questions, one must look at the development process in the broader context, including the human aspects and the social system.

Psychologist McClelland suggests a strong correlation between personality traits and development. Sociologist Hagen believes that development begins with the man. Many theories have been proposed to describe and explain development processes (some have been referred to in Professor Kranzberg's paper) but, to my knowledge, the literature concerning the human and social factors in development is suggestive rather than definitive. Very little causal connection has been firmly established. Currently, efforts are being made to identify the variables at the interfaces between the various blocks in Fig. 3. Relationships between blocks are ill defined, even though they have been suggested, as has been done a number of times at this Conference. A review of the literature suggests that the modeling of human aspects and the social system is mostly qualitative.

Superimposed on top of the four middle blocks in Fig. 3 are the political mechanisms. This block is supposed to describe who sets the social goals, how conflicts in goals are resolved, who participates in policy decisions, and how the decisions are implemented. It is quite possible that the policy decisions implemented are inconsistent with the avowed social goals.

Below are the indicators that are supposed to show the state of the society. Most of us know what economic indicators are (GNP, per capita income, capital flow). However, alone, these indicators do not tell us the quality of life in a society, how happy the people are, nor how alienated they are from each other. On the opening day of this Conference, Dr. Bronk warned us not to overlook the questions of goals. Is materialistic prosperity the real goal? We want development to what? for what? We must hope the current active work on social indicators will help us to remember these questions and articulate our answers. The value function is supposed to combine the measurements of economic and social indicators to a single-valued social welfare so that any two distinct sets of policies can be compared with each other. The road toward a useful comprehensive model is long. Obviously by purpose is presenting Fig. 3 is not to show how to do it but to suggest that it is a meaningful research subject.

THE ORGANIZATION OF INTERDISCIPLINARY TEAMS

Finally, I should like to touch briefly on the point of organizing interdisciplinary teams. First, an ideal member of the team should not only be an expert in a relevant discipline but also humble and open-minded. Humility is necessary to elicit genuine cooperation and interaction with other team members and, perhaps even more important, with the client and the beneficiaries. Open-mindedness should include one's willingness to sometimes forget his own discipline and approach the problem in an entirely free and unencapsulated manner.

Second, it would help the development of interdisciplinary team approach if our institutions, particularly the universities, would be willing to recognize the need for relevant education as well as the interdisciplinary approach as a new challenge in the modern world. To meet the challenge, our institutions should be willing to re-examine their roles, reorganize themselves, and revamp their reward system that guides, with an invisible hand, the direction of the best brains in our society.

354

Last, I should like to suggest that an interdisciplinary team should strike a balance between detachment and involvement—detached so that they maintain enough objectivity and perspective to the development problem, and involved so that they will be sensitive to the genuine needs of the people in the developing countries and the feasibility of political implementation.

AN INTERDISCIPLINARY TEAM APPROACH FROM THE NONENGINEERING VIEWPOINT

Commentary by Jiri Nehnevajsa

IT HAS BECOME obvious that all problems of socio-economic development have, as their integral components, other than purely technological dimensions. The acceptance of such a premise is by now so widespread that it calls for no further explanations. It follows, of course, that problems which transcend, in their origin, formulation, and consequence, the boundaries of any single codified body of knowledge, cannot be tackled as effectively within the confines of any single discipline as they can, at least potentially, by the concerted effort of specialists whose knowledge and experience provide for complementarity as well as integration of their respective more fractionated expertise.

Thus our main concern is not to determine whether or not interdisciplinary teams in development activities are desirable. We largely agree that interdisciplinary approaches are necessary as part of the vast armamentarium of human and physical resources to stimulate, guide, and reinforce the revolutionary process of induced change. We agree, despite some sense of frustration resulting from our recognition of the serious problems which beset the functioning of any interdisciplinary group.

We are brought together, in part, by a sense of malaise that things on the development fronts of the world have possibly not been going as well as we would like them to, or as they might. We know that there is need for improvement.

However, we are here also with a feeling of accomplishment—modest though it may seem. The life of the aggregate of men on this planet, on balance, is probably better today than it was yesterday, and it is quite a bit better than it was a decade ago. Indeed, aeons of improvement have actually passed in the course of the past quarter of a century. And this in spite of the serious setbacks in which man's inhumanity to man leaves deep and lasting scars on the paths to a truly civilized existence.

We must have teams whenever a task is too large to be handled by an individual. We must have interdisciplinary teams whenever the characteristics of the effort tax the knowhow of professionals from various fields of endeavor. What kinds of teams? What are some of the implications? These remarks are addressed to such problems.

To begin, let us discard the notion that the world is very usefully sliced up into such things as "engineering" and "nonengineering" developmental points of view or, for that matter, that it should be considered from the vantage point of "sociology" or "anthropology" or "political science." Indeed, such points of view may, and do, exist but their appropriateness as "distinct" and "separate" approaches must be open to the most serious question. Simply stated, problems of development, either *in toto* or in terms of each distinct project, are not isomorphic to the structure of contemporary scholarly disciplines. This implies the need for a careful rethinking of our very educational traditions and may well lead to the discarding of conventional thinking in terms of the usual scholarly disciplines.

At least in those aspects of each scientific and scholarly activity which is to be applied to solving actual problems of men, the problem-oriented organization of our pedagogical enterprise appears much more promising than our present prevailing educational formats.

Indeed, this leads to a kind of systems, rather than disciplinary, point of view. In no way is this an argument for doing away with scientific and technical specialization; rather, the issue is one of recasting scientific and technical specialties so that they reflect the actual properties of problems, current and, above all, anticipated.

Undoubtedly engineers need to acquire more than fleeting knowledge of the relevant elements of other disciplines, particularly the social sciences. In turn, social scientists need to acquire actual knowledge of the relevant elements of engineering and the physical sciences. This is more than learning just enough words, to "speak the other fellow's language," although the capacity to communicate with specialists outside of one's own area of expertise is certainly a minimum prerequisite. It is, in fact, surprising how little of this capacity is learned during the many years which our young people spend in schools.

One point should be clarified immediately: an idea of this type may not be readily reconcilable with a situation in which we seek to graduate as many people as possible and, in particular, as quickly as possible. At the very time we are witnessing a veritable knowledge explosion with its many accelerating dynamics, we are also making efforts to shorten the time needed to acquire some significant segments of this knowledge. This in and of itself is paradoxical.

Furthermore, we do not advocate the substitution of some engineering or physics specialization for economists in place of what economists are expected to learn. Nor is it an issue of revamping engineering curricula to include some sort of a course in sociology. Let us be explicit about the intention. We must begin to consider lengthening, perhaps even significantly, the usual university curriculum—and certainly at least at the level of graduate study or its equivalent. Above all, however, we must think through establishing programs and curricula of flexible duration to reflect a realistic time span for learning what must be learned instead of fixed-time or fixed-credit endeavors basically identical for all students, regardless of their specialties and regardless of what they plan to do with their careers. It is certainly somewhat amusing that, in the waning years of the 1960s, we still find quite frequently an attitude which presupposes that all segments of knowledge can be packaged into three-credit or n-credit bits and passed on in time segments such as trimesters, semesters, quarters, and academic years, regardless of who is doing the learning or the teaching and what it is that is being taught and learned.

The intention of these remarks is *precisely* to argue that a kind of revolutionary rethinking of our educational systems is almost prerequisite to doing a better job of development in all its aspects, domestic and international.

The next major point is that we recognize the need for teams and for some interdisciplinary blending of knowhow. By and large, however, development teams get put together via individual assignments. Not infrequently, they are established as potential teams only on location. This may well be both costly and ineffective. Might we not consider, at least with respect to the vast undertaking of development, to begin to educate development teams as teams? Might we not profit by assigning development teams as teams to their particular— and successive—missions?

Changes in our educational institutions must be viewed as longer-range prospects and none can be adopted too lightly and without the most careful scrutiny. As a shorter-range fix, however, could we not gain a great deal by setting up, educating, and deploying development teams as teams?

Whatever the characteristics of development teams, we should stay away from including people as team members so that they can "represent" some particular discipline or so that a particular discipline simply is "represented." This means that sociologists may not be needed on all development teams; political scientists may not be required on some; and anthropologists may not be called for on still others. The organization of development teams should thus reflect a realistic assessment of the relative importance of various factors which impinge on the success or failure of a program.

Once we raise the question as to the kinds of skills and knowledge needed, and who has those skills and knowledge, we are a long way from strict and largely unproductive disciplinary thinking and even from mechanical "inter"- disciplinary conceptualization.

But this also means that development teams will turn out to be not infrequently international in composition and this, too,.is as it "should" be, assuming again that what "should" be is not merely normatively determined but rather a consequence of the analysis of the specific nature of the development task. Similarly, development teams might well include, as actual participants rather than as resource persons or informants, potential beneficiaries or clients of specific projects. Development teams, more often than not, need to operate not only "for" some groups but also "with" them.

Clearly, sharing concrete developmental experience among teams and over a period of time may contribute to the over-all effectiveness of each activity by providing the kind of feedback which facilitates learning. It needs to be stressed, however, that information on less than successful, or even failing, projects and efforts is generally more important than information about successes. Unfortunately, we can expect that such information will be least systematically available and that it will remain too largely anecdotal to be of real value, if for no other reason than because project failure may get interpreted as team or personal failure. Errors from which others could learn most are, sadly enough, also most threatening to the individuals concerned. We need to think through some feedback system which handles failures and difficulties so as to depersonalize them.

An information system, sorely needed, which can provide a common pool of practical knowledge and mechanisms for its dissemination, also requires some standardization of data-acquisition procedures. We need standardized and structured instruments to monitor each project. Each program from concept through implementation, as well as the instruments, must also be interscientific in character.

The final point has to do with the obvious, but genuinely neglected, role of development teams and of each member of each team in the political process of the community in which they function. We must fully realize that development activities intervene quite directly in the political institutions of a society and that no amount of discussion about the desirability of nonintervention can do away with the fact that even complete political aloofness of development teams from the internal affairs of a society amounts to a form of intervention, perhaps more forceful and profound than deliberate attempts at impacting the political climate as well. Thus considerable thought is needed on the realistic role of development teams as diplomats and politicians, starting from the premise that their political impact, in some sense, cannot be avoided and thus might as well be made more consciously and with more insight into the relevant aspects of the political process of the developing society.

This raises many sensitive policy questions which cannot be avoided if we are serious about doing the best possible development job. We should cease pretending to ourselves that development activities do not include such things as influencing and convincing others, propagating an idea, advocating a concept, changing power relations, enhancing the prestige of some, and possibly deflating the prestige of others. We must stop pretending that the development process does not include such things as struggle against incompetence, corruption, disinterest, and that, not infrequently, the technical difficulties of development programs dwindle into relative insignificance when compared with the puzzles that are men as men and as political creatures.

Obviously, none of the points which have been mentioned here can be viewed as final or definitive. Rather, they are brief reflections on a problem common to all of us. To even think through the implications of such thoughts, we need truly interdisciplinary cooperation.

REPORT OF WORKSHOP 16

Marlin H. Mickle, Rapporteur

THE WORKSHOP'S first order of business was to discard the idea that there are such notions as "engineering" and "nonengineering" points of view about development. Development problems are not isomorphic to the structure of contemporary scholary disciplines.

One obvious conclusion at this point in the Conference is about the need for a more humanistic education for engineers as well as an engineering and scientific awareness for persons in the social sciences, and political science. The need is for more than a ritualistic course or courses included in any existing curriculum.

Interdisciplinary work appears to exist in one form or another in education at both the undergraduate and graduate level but, to be effective, such work must go deeper into the areas of research. Problem definition at a research level is an absolute necessity to make possible a realistic approach to such education in these areas at an undergraduate level. Discussion of problems and/or assumed solutions in a classroom without concrete examples is merely paying lip service to real and existing problems.

Any attempt at interdisciplinary courses within a single existing department will not satisfy the needs without a *true* interdisciplinary involvement of those preparing and/or teaching such courses.

In effect, the over-all problem in development must be approached from a team point of view. The natural consequence is not a team whose mission is to solve all problems of development but rather a team for each type of problem. Inherently implied is a hierarchy of problem definition. Not only must we identify parameters of systems under study, but current disciplines inherent in the various problems as well.

In any complete analysis of existing situations, it is as important to study successes as well as failures. Project failure can frequently be identified as team failure and not faulty problem analysis. In spite of illustrated failures, life is better in 1968 than it was in 1967.

Development has frequently been approached, and success measured, by economic factors. Two faults are inherent in this approach. The entrepreneur measures his successes in terms of economic pluses to be weighed against his own economic input which is considered as a minus. Obviously successes must be measured by other than economic factors; however, a subtle point in this analysis is that, with other than direct economic indicators, the entrepreneur can balance humanistic pluses which may be returned in exchange for development aid. Therefore, it is necessary to investigate what the underdeveloped countries may return in exchange for aid received.

It is necessary to take a systems approach in order to avoid single ventures which are completed, evaluated, and ignored. The changing nature of change itself makes it diffiuclt to categorize any individual effort. There is a distinction between a "multi"-disciplinary and an "inter"-disciplinary action. The approach which must be taken is an interdisciplinary one to account for the many interacting factors involved.

It has been pointed out, however, that the state of the art of present systems science is not the final answer to the problem. We must frankly emphasize that human considerations must be taken into account. We need to recognize that the intervention in lives and governments which inevitably occurs when aid is given is not necessarily bad or undesirable.

The final point in this analysis is that we are searching for, not a man exposed to many disciplines, but rather a Renaissance Man.

Mr. Kranzberg stated, that, at the opening of the Conference, the primary emphasis was on what we do to target countries and that, at the closing of the Conference the emphasis shifted to what we must do to ourselves. We have come to a point of selfintrospection, of questioning our whole perspective.

REFERENCES CITED

Alpert, Paul. *Economic Development: Objectives and Methods.* Glencoe, Ill., 1963.

Baranson, Jack. *Technology for Underdeveloped Areas: An Annotated Bibliography,* Oxford 1967.

Black, C. E. *The Dynamics of Modernization.* New York, 1966.

Chaplin, David. *The Peruvian Industrial Labor Force.* Princeton University Press, 1967.

Cole, Charles W. *Colbert and a Century of French Mercantilism.* 2 Vols. New York, 1939.

Danilevskii, V. V. *Nartov and His Theatrum Machinarum,* A. S. Britkin, ed. Jerusalem, 1966.

Gerschenkorn, Alexander. *Economic Backwardness in Historical Prespective.* Cambridge, 1962.

Granick, David. *Soviet Metal-Fabricating and Economic Development: Practice Versus Policy.* Madison, Wisconsin, 1967.

Gruber, Ruth, ed. *Science and the New Nations.* New York, 1961.

Heilbroner, Robert L., "Do machines make history?" *Technology and culture,* Vol. 8, No. 3 (July, 1967).

Hirschman, Albert, "Obstacles to development: A classification and a quasi-vanishing act," *Economic Development and Cultural Change,* Vol. 13., No. 4 (July, 1965).

Hirschman, Albert, *The Strategy of Economic Development.* New Haven, 1959.

Hoselitz, Bert F. *Sociological Aspects of Economic Growth.* Glencoe, Ill., 1960.

Kranzberg, Melvin, "The transfer of technology to Colonial America," *Preceedings of the XIIth International Congress in the History of Science,* Paris, 1968.

Kranzberg, Melvin and Carroll W. Pursell, Jr., eds. *Technology in Western Civilization.* Oxford, 1967.

LaForce, J. Clayburn, "Technological diffusion in the 18th century: The Spanish textile industry," *Technology and Culture,* Vol. 3 (Summer, 1964).

McClelland, David C. *The Achieving Society.* Princeton, 1961.

Mead, Margaret. *Cultural Patterns and Technical Change.* New York, 1955.

Pepelasis, Adamantios, et al. *Economic Development.* New York, 1958.

Rostow, Walt W. *The Stages of Economic Growth.* Cambridge, 1960.

Scoville, Warren C., "Minority migrations and the diffusion of technology," *Journal of Economic History,* Vol. 21, No. 3 (Fall, 1961).

Smith, Adam. *The Wealth of Nations.* Modern Library Edition, 1937.

Spencer, Daniel L. and Alexander Woroniak, eds. *The Transfer of Technology to Developing Countries.* New York, 1967.

Stover, Carl S. *The Technological Order.* Detroit, 1963.

Strassmann, W. Paul. *Technological Change and Economic Development.* Ithaca: Cornell University Press, 1968.

Weiner, Myron, ed. *Modernization: The Dynamics of Growth.* New York, 1966.

20

AN INTERDISCIPLINARY TEAM APPROACH FROM THE ENGINEERING POINT OF VIEW

Principal Paper—Maurice L. Albertson
Commentary—Victor B. Sullam
Commentary—Lawrence Bass
Report of Workshop 17—G. Fauconneau, Rapporteur

Interdisciplinary teams have been a standard engineering device for many years. This chapter analyzes the function of such groups in development from the engineering point of view.

The Editors

AN INTERDISCIPLINARY TEAM APPROACH FROM THE ENGINEERING VIEWPOINT

Principal Paper by Maurice L. Albertson

ENGINEERS, in general, have had very little training and experience in a truly interdisciplinary approach to problems. In certain cases, this approach may involve such additional disciplines as biology, economics or law, and, frequently, teams of engineers from different branches. Seldom is the engineer involved in a truly interdisciplinary team approach which would include, all at one time, a considerable number of such disciplines as sociology, political science, economics, biology, law, agriculture, business management, mathematics, physics, chemistry, education, and engineering.

Although the need for the interdisciplinary approach has always existed, it has never been as apparent as it is today:

1. Developments of almost any kind take place today with much greater speed than they have in the past: therefore, we have not the time to use the pseudo-experimental approach which permits us to make even slight errors in an initial solution to a problem and then, later, over a longer period of time, make the adjustments necessary to perfect the solution. Today, the other disciplines must be involved from the outset so that the solution will be as free from error as possible and will reduce or eliminate the later adjustments necessary to perfect the solution.

2. Today, many of our activities which previously were almost entirely domestic involve international components with different cultural, sociological, economic, political, educational, and other backgrounds with which we are relatively unfamiliar. Consequently, it is necessary to involve specialists in other disciplines in the planning and development of a solution. When we have not done this, we frequently have serious difficulty in accomplishing our objective most efficiently and effectively.

In an effort to gain a better understanding of the factors involved and of how they are inter-related, consideration is first given to the development process itself, then to the importance of human resources and the different disciplines, and finally to the team approach.

THE DEVELOPMENT PROCESS

As we have learned more and more about the development process, we have reached the conclusion that development is the result of interaction among several different components and resources such as:

1. Manpower (human) resources
2. Natural resources
3. Institutional resources
4. Works, facilities, and equipment
5. Energy

363

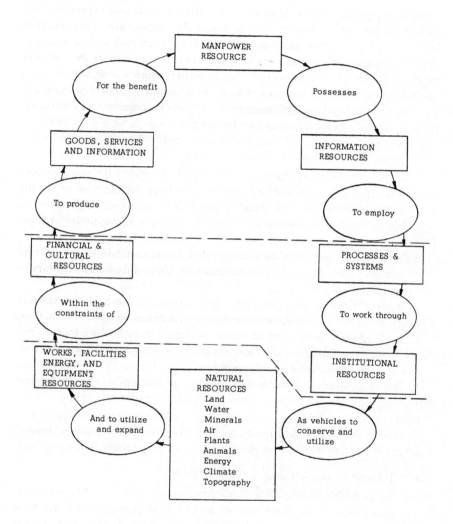

FIG. 1.—The development wheel, illustrating the development process.

6. Information
7. Financial resources
8. Cultural resources
9. Processes and systems

For development to occur most efficiently and effectively, it is necessary that these components be combined and utilized in a certain manner. The necessary inter-relationship is illustrated by the development wheel in Fig. 1. This wheel shows the sequential nature of the development process as well as the interdependence of the various resources utilized in development together with the actions which must be taken for development to occur. The resources are enclosed in boxes and the actions in ovals. The development wheel also shows that, in a sense, the development process is a chain composed of links so that if any link is weak or missing, development is inhibited or stopped completely.

From the wheel concept, it is also evident that, basically, man is the critical and central resource who provides the initial motivation and energy to start and keep the development wheel rolling. Without man to perform this function, all development stops. Specifically, the development process is dependent upon:

1. Man's knowledge and understanding of the information resources available to him.

2. Man's motivation and ability to utilize the information.

3. The existence of institutions which man can use as vehicles through which he can function; without institutions man can act only as an individual.

4. Various natural resources—with land, water, and air as a minimum —which man can utilize and modify to produce goods and services.

5. Various man-made resources such as works, facilities, equipment, and energy which man utilizes as he produces goods, services, and information and as he builds or fabricates additional resources.

6. The constraints of financial and cultural resources which can either stimulate or inhibit development through the production of goods, services, and information.

7. Goods, services, and information, in turn, then being used by man for consumption or for further development.

IMPORTANCE OF HUMAN RESOURCES

From the foregoing, it is evident that manpower resources are of paramount importance in the development process. In fact, man is so central to development that, without him, development does not take place.

The manpower resource is composed of both quality and quantity. The importance of this distinction is evident from a consideration of the Marshall Plan and the subsequent Point 4 Program conducted abroad by the United States. Through the Marshall Plan immediately following World War II, a supply of money and materials made it possible to rebuild Europe very rapidly. On the basis of this success, it was believed that money and materials would be all that was needed to build the less-developed countries (LDCs) in the world. Much to our dismay, we found that, regardless of the amount of money, materials, and equipment poured into the LDCs, progress toward development was almost imperceptible. This is still true today.

In this example, it is important to note that the necessary quantity of manpower for development, however, was strikingly different. The manpower of Europe was already trained to set the development wheel in motion and to keep it moving. Many of the processes and systems had been used before. Much of the institutional structure existed or had existed previously—even though it may have been destroyed or dormant—and could be quickly rebuilt. Natural resources were known even though they might be limited in extent or variety. With this background, it was possible quickly to rebuild the institutional resources and the works, facilities, and equipment to again produce goods, services, and information—the criteria for development.

In the LDCs, on the other hand, the required manpower resources with the necessary training, experience, skills, and knowledge did not exist in sufficient number and the necessary institutional structure did not exist at all, even to set the development wheel in motion—much less to keep it in motion.

Unfortunately, leaders of development programs in the past have not realized the importance of the institutional resource and the quality of the manpower resource as a prerequisite for development in the LDCs. Consequently, inadequate emphasis has been placed on building these resources in preparation for development.

IMPORTANCE OF DIFFERENT DISCIPLINES

The foregoing analysis shows that many disciplines of knowledge and training are of paramount importance if the development wheel is to begin turning and to keep turning. The following is a list of roles which can and must be played in order for development to occur.

1. Educational institutions must be involved in training manpower resources.

2. Personnel in the various social sciences must be involved in analyzing and developing the social systems enclosed in the broken-line area of Fig. 1. This includes first analyzing the systems as they are presently organized as well as designing modifications or entirely new systems.

3. The engineer must be involved in the planning, design, and construction of works, facilities, and equipment; but he must operate within the constraints of limited funds, cultural resources, and institutional resources.

4. Agriculturalists must be involved in the production of plants and animals for food and fiber and they too must operate within the constraints of limited funds, cultural resources, and institutional resources.

5. Management specialists, economists, natural resources specialists, homemaking specialists, industry specialists, finance specialists, and business special-

ists must all be involved to enable a complete study, analysis, plan, and design to be prepared within the various constraints imposed.

The foregoing professional skills are needed in a coordinated fashion to accomplish development on a most efficient and effective basis—especially in the complex systems with which we are involved today. The input of each is needed first in the clear definition of objectives and then in the preparation and execution of a plan to attain these objectives.

THE INTERDISCIPLINARY TEAM APPROACH
Commentary by Victor B. Sullam

TODAY EVERYBODY pays at least lip service to the idea of an interdisciplinary approach. Politicians have their philosophers or poets in residence, nutritional surveys include sociologists, and no transport survey team would be complete without agronomists, industrial specialists, and tourist advisors. Recently a team that studied the reorganization of a large corporation in the Carribbean included agronomists, engineers, economists, sociologists, anthropologists, educators, and management specialists. In the Italian South, anthropological and social studies of the available manpower have accompanied the design of industrial plants and the establishment of vocational training programs. This approach produced some interesting reports but had no apparent impact either on the success of the plants or on the productivity of labor.

Doubtless we have all learned in recent years the advantages of using the tools of various disciplines to solve old and new problems. Feasibility studies, transport surveys, land reform programs, and industrialization plans are but a few examples of tasks in which the interdisciplinary task is generally accepted, at least in principle.

Only too often, however, the end product is anything but interdisciplinary; rather it is essentially a series or sequence of unrelated and, above all, unintegrated reports prepared by specialists and, perhaps, edited by the team leader. The contributions of each group of specialists are accepted and utilized without discussion or evaluation. Seldom, if ever, does one reap the benefits of a true interplay of thoughts of persons of different backgrounds, training, and approaches. Yet these are the real benefits of the interdisciplinary approach.

In other words, what we get today may be compared to the *Civil Affairs Handbooks* of World War II, which covered in separate volumes, all possible aspects of a country or area, from agriculture to transport, from the structure of the churches to the penal code; they were imposing in size and scope but did not yield a true picture of the subject. Another illustration may be an agricultural survey filled with data on climate, soils, and land tenure, but without any indication of the productive potential. Works of this kind may be multidisciplinary but are certainly not interdisciplinary.

To arrive at a true interdisciplinary team approach, I believe we must be aware of certain pitfalls and develop special techniques of communication and cooperation.

Let me address myself first to the question of pitfalls. The engineer is indeed experienced in the interdisciplinary approach in that he utilizes many disciplines and relies on many specialists, such as soil scientists, geologists, and meteorologists, for certain inputs. In the field of economic development, however, the engineer encounters a different breed of technician, the agricultural specialist. Most of the projections—in terms of infrastructure, transport and storage—needed by the engineer are based upon forecasts of the impact of agricultural investment and innovation. These forecasts are supplied by technicians who must also be ardent advocates of the projects they propose. They must, in fact, be endowed with that peculiar missionary zeal needed to introduce innovations in a highly traditional society. The agricultural specialists usually find a highly sympathetic and uncritical audience among the specialists of other disciplines; the backwardness of native farming and the benefits of modern agriculture are only too obvious, and an increase in agricultural productivity appears to be the key to economic development. Moreover, most laymen are unwilling to make even a small effort to understand the nature of agricultural innovations, whether they be the introduction of new crops or the shift from dry farming to irrigation. Thus, we find that too many projects are based on oversanguine projections of agricultural production; in many cases production facilities, such as irrigation projects, remain idle or innovations fail to find widespread acceptance. These pitfalls of agricultural investment stem in part from technical errors (to a much greater extent than we are willing to admit) and in part from a failure to appreciate the interplay of cultural, social, and economic factors that work against agricultural change. The impact of these factors should, in theory, be forecast by the behavioral scientists. Yet, in practice, it is difficult to utilize their knowledge in true interdisciplinary fashion. First of all, some of this knowledge does not seem to apply to actual conditions, eg the "cattle complex" in East Africa. Second, some findings of behavioral scientists appear to be misleading or altogether wrong, eg the cultural obstacles to the diffusion of hybrid corn. Finally, in many cases even an intimate knowledge of a given society does not seem to yield any information of real significance to the engineer and the economic planner. Few social groups, I believe, have been studied as exhaustively by sociologists and anthropologists as the cane cutters of the Caribbean. Yet the results of these studies do not explain the shortages of native cane cutters in the poverty-stricken Dominican Republic, nor do they suggest ways and means to enhance the productivity of imported labor. Thus, one can understand why engineers who are accustomed to accurate quantitative answers of obvious significance may be somewhat baffled by the pronouncements of behavioral scientists.

One last pitfall may be mentioned; at first blush, the economist may appear to the engineer to be a trustworthy member of the sliderule brotherhood. Formulas, derivatives, charts—these hallmarks of accuracy and reliability are, of course, very misleading when used by the economist, but most engineers learn to distrust economists only from bitter experience.

Some of the pitfalls I have mentioned might be avoided by special training—by teaching social sciences to engineers and agricultural specialists. However, this approach may be too costly and time-consuming. A better solution may be to reevaluate our past experience in the field of economic development in interdisciplinary terms. Developmental activities may be grouped under relatively few headings, such as irrigation, land reclamation, land settlement, improvement of major crops (wheat, corn, rice, sorghum), road construction and maintenance, and cottage industries. For any given subject, it should be possible to assemble data on the actual experience of different countries and regions. Thus, we could compare what happened in advanced and in less-developed countries. This examination should be carried out by an interdisciplinary team after the members have been made fully aware of the nature of the innovation and of its known social and economic implications. Obviously, from this type of comparative study one would gain exceedingly useful information regarding the rate of diffusion of the innovation. Spurious cases and absurd claims would stand out and be easily identified as such. Some of the problems encountered could be illustrated by the experience of our own country or of countries similar to ours in terms of culture, ease of communication, and reliability of data.

The first yield of this approach would be a series of "coefficients of acceptance" to be applied to the projections of the technicians. Coefficients of this kind are used in irrigation projects to compare the "acreage irrigable" to the much smaller "acreage actually irrigated." In many parts of the world the latter is less than one-third of the former. How would we feel about a factory that operates at one-third capacity?

The availability of these coefficients, based on actual experience, would strengthen the position of the layman *vis-à-vis* the technician. The latter would maintain his role of advocate but would also have to show why the coefficients cannot be applied to his particular project. Past experience suggests that technicians, when confronted with this type of information, are quite willing to adopt a more conservative approach. The sectoral analysis I suggest also would yield a series of "do's" and "dont's," to be kept in mind in the design and implementation of specific projects, for example the problem of maintenance of ditches, weirs, canals, machinery, and equipment. The availability of this information in the literature would depersonalize any conflict between the technician and the lay members of the team. An engineer, for instance, cannot be charged with being "against agriculture" if his objections are based on generally accepted information.

Nor should the elaboration of past experience be confined to agricultural projects. The developing world is clamoring for industrialization, and the experience gained in the depressed areas of the West and of Japan may become exceedingly useful in that connection. We know, for instance, of the recurring shortages of certain types of skilled workers, such as welders and carpenters. We also know that illiteracy or lack of skill does not rule out the utilization of farm laborers in the assembly lines of many factories, because neither literacy nor skill is needed to perform the repetitive motions of an assembly line. The difficulties encountered in industrialization stem from concepts of "time," "work," and "leisure" prevalent in rural societies, concepts quite different from those of the industrialized world.

The assembling and elaboration of experience gained elsewhere and the well-integrated effort of social and political scientists and technicians also may help us to cope with some of the thorniest issues of development planning, such as the disposal of a bankrupt railroad that is a source of patronage and employment or the handling of the uneconomic power station or mine that has become a national symbol.

Two difficult problems deserve special attention. First is the identification of alternative lines of development that provide for lower capital/output ratio and greater employment. This vitally important approach is often suggested by economists and political analysts, but I have yet to see an interdisciplinary team working on alternative technologies for the relatively few productive activities that are feasible for developing countries. The few suggestions that appear in textbooks on economic development are monumental absurdities from the engineering standpoint. The second problem concerns another "fact of life" of the developing world, public enterprises engaged in industrial and agricultural production as well as in the operation of transport and other public services. The essential need for an interdisciplinary team approach in dealing with public enterprise is only too obvious. Engineers and other technicians, by themselves, are virtually useless because, by instinct, they tend to criticize the philosophy rather than the structure and performance of the public enterprise. Economists, too, may tend to overplay the profit factor, which need not be the *raison d'être* of the public corporation. Political scientists are thus needed to temper and mold the opinions of the technicians and the economists.

Once again, the interdisciplinary team approach presupposes a great deal of information on comparable ventures. The mixed economies of the West offer innumerable examples of public enterprises engaged in an extraordinary variety of activities, from steel to automobile production, from mining to food distribution. The end products of these enterprises are often well known to, and admired by, the technicians. Reports on these enterprises and on their counterparts in Southern Europe, Asia, and Latin America could be extremely useful to interdisciplinary teams.

In short, the interdisciplinary team approach is, in my opinion, essential to the efficient design and implementation of development projects. This approach, however, presupposes effective communication and cooperation among members of the team. In turn, these conditions can be achieved by exposing all members of the team to a re-elaboration and synthesis of past experience in similar undertakings.

MANAGEMENT OF INTERDISCIPLINARY TEAMS FROM THE ENGINEERING POINT OF VIEW

Commentary by Lawrence Bass

TASK FORCES or interdisciplinary teams are being more widely used to coordinate the inputs of a mixture of professional skills to attack complex problems. When used with up-to-date managerial techniques, they lead to sounder and faster solutions. They speed up analysis, conclusions, and recommendations and, further, they bring about implementation of projects with greater certainty that the major factors have been given suitable weighting.

The multipdisciplinary approach stresses concurrent feed-in of facts and opinions, in contrast to the less direct paths of feedback cycles among different groups or cells of specialists. It encourages the interplay of varied skills with appropriate intensity and timing. It helps the transfer of knowledge and expertise from step to step. It leads to better use of trained manpower, promotes professional development, and stimulates *esprit de corps*. Developing countries can make improved use of limited resources of specialized personnel and ensure that feasibility studies are on a broader base, reducing the risks of new undertakings. When mixed teams of foreign and local professionals are involved, which is recommended practice, the close relationships between the two bring about more effective transfer of expertise to the latter.

EVOLUTION OF INTERDISCIPLINARY MANAGEMENT

In up-to-date practice, multidisciplinary teams, sometimes called task forces, have the following managerial pattern:

1. Designation of a team leader with responsibility and authority for assembling and coordinating a group of specialists with a suitable array of skills to carry out the assignment; the membership usually crosses the formal lines of organizational structure and the team operates as a unit with only general supervision.

2. Definition by the leader of the proposed program, the nature and extent of participation by each member (often on a flexible part-time basis), the communication procedures within the team, and the setting up of budgetary control of the expense generated by individual participants.

3. Indoctrination of the team members by the leader and coordination of their activities until the project has been completed.

4. Submission of a final report including findings, conclusions, and recommendations.

Engineers began to use these principles many decades ago for large projects and have now perfected managerial techniques. In earlier days the teams were recruited by the principal engineer among individual practitioners; this still happens in many cases. The rise of large engineering organizations with a spectrum of skills, sometimes reinforced by outside specialists, has encouraged the trend toward an interdisciplinary approach.

Thus far, these techniques have been used in a systematic way in only a few other professional activities. Although company managers sometimes organize a task force to meet an emergency, they revert to formal communication channels when the crisis has passed. Several decades ago an occasional research and development organization consisting chiefly of consultants, began to adopt these concepts, which are also quite widely used by consulting management engineers and some other professionals in group practice. More recently, the handling of large and complex projects has resulted in the rise of systems engineering and such managerial procedures as "critical path methods" (CPM) and "program evaluation and review techniques" (PERT).

Multidisciplinary teams, in the systematic sense in which they are here discussed, are used infrequently by industrial firms in the United States, and still less in other countries. Engineering departments in these companies, however, are likely to be employing similar principles in estimating and controlling project costs.

There are four main reasons that engineers pioneered the development of this valuable managerial technique. First, the complex nature of large projects required a massive approach, including a variety of expertise. Second, the development of engineering specialties and the professional attitude of engineers encouraged the recognition of the importance of proficiency in individual skills. Third, the nature of engineering tenders required the preparation of cost estimates, both aggregate and subdivided, of different professional inputs. Finally, underlying all these points, are the systematic processes of the engineering mind.

Interdisciplinary teams, then, are so commonly used for engineering problems that it seems warranted to limit this discussion to general principles and advantages. In this connection, engineers have long employed well-established techniques for administering their activities. Today there is relatively little literature or discussion on how to manage an engineering department, except for such innovations as systems procedures, whereas the subject of organizing and directing research and development has brought forth a flood of conferences and publications.

When engineers are engaged jointly with representatives of other disciplines, however, the latter often have not been exposed to task force operations. Two types of projects of this kind which have great impact on the progress of industrial development and public works in developing countries are discussed later: (a) complex feasibility studies involving, and perhaps directed by, nonengineering personnel; and (b) research and development projects of which only segments are primarily of an engineering nature.

ADVANTAGES OF INTERDISCIPLINARY PROGRAMS

The scope, flexibility, and dynamics of multidisciplinary teams carry important benefits for the projects undertaken, for the individual professionals, and for the organizations as a whole. These advantages exist even when the administrative procedures are not so rigorous as optimum performance requires. The arguments for adoption of the techniques are so strong that the only obstacle appears to be reluctance to depart from ingrained practices.

Some types of work, such as basic research or short-term applied assignments, however, are usually left as the responsibility of individuals, although most other activities may be carried out by interdisciplinary groups.

Project Improvement of Activities. Task forces by their very nature produce a continual refinement of objectives because the broader analysis from different points of view sharpens the criteria for examining progress and for programing future work. Major obstacles to success come to light at earlier stages. Better information is available for adjusting the amount of effort upward or downward in the various disciplines or even for postponing or stopping work.

The course of development toward practical application is speeded up by the continual refinement of objectives. Implementation of results is more rapid because of the earlier participation of representatives of operating departments. Knowledge and expertise are transferred from step to step by proper make-up of the team as the project advances.

Professional Development of Individuals. Most professional workers flourish under this system. The nature and value of their contributions to projects are recognized by their peers from other disciplines. This recognition stimulates morale and develops initiative. Contacts with a broad range of specialists widens their horizons; they become organization-minded rather than narrowly selfcentered and develop managerial capabilities, especially with respect to scheduling their own work. The degree of success of their interaction with co-workers on common problems stimulates a better comprehension of their professional flexibility and personal traits.

Advantages to the Organization. Introduction of interdisciplinary principles improves the effectiveness of an organization by reducing the number of administrative layers or echelons. This leads to pruning of decision trees; less work has to be re-done due to omitted factors which should have been considered earlier.

Task forces make for better deployment of all the available specialized skills. They reduce the empire-building tendencies of individual groups by providing a mechanism for obtaining expertise from elsewhere in the organization. Larger firms which have established "corporate development" or "corporate planning" departments responsible to top management find this a particularly important benefit; instead of requiring a large and costly staff of specialists for these functions, multidisciplinary teams can be recruited from individuals within the company.

Finally, this technique raises morale and initiative, improves communications, and promotes better interpersonal relations in the organization as a whole.

MANAGEMENT OF MULTIDISCIPLINARY TEAMS

A project team system represents a fundamental departure from the conventional, hierarchical mode of management. Instead of having all authority flow through formal channels of the organization, a dual parallel system is required: (1) the usual managerial control, as embodied in an organization chart, for administrative matters (employment conditions, indoctrination and guidance, and general overseeing of activities); and (2) professional responsibility to the various team leaders under whom the individual carries out project activities.

Prerequisites for Successful Team Operation. The team concept calls for changed attitudes and behaviors at all levels of the organization. Unless these changes are adopted wholeheartedly, the system becomes merely another mechanism for laying out work assignments, but even this may have real value as an aid to better programing.

Delegation of responsibility and authority to team leaders for carrying out project activities must be recognized and accepted by top management and the departments concerned. The existence of separate channels for administrative control and coordination of professional activities must be made clear to all members of the organization involved in task force operations.

A project system is needed to define goals, programs, schedules, and budgets. There should be a procedure for recording expenditure of technical man-hours to control the deployment of personnel on different activities.

An atmosphere must be created in which each member of a team becomes personally dedicated to using his talents constructively for group success on the project. The head of a task force is purposely called a "leader"—not a "director" or "manager"— to emphasize the fact that he should adopt a style of operations which brings forth the initiative and creativity of his colleagues. The levels of supervisors above the team leader and individual members must avoid actions which undermine the responsibility and authority of the leader.

Procedure for Setting up Project Teams. Preliminary analysis of the proposed idea should be made by the appropriate manager or committee to determine its justification and scope and to select a team leader. The leader should take part in the further discussion of the project to define the goal, outline a program, select a team, and propose a budget and schedule; he may need to do exploratory work before the final request is submitted for authorization at the proper level.

After the project plan has been approved, the team leader secures agreement of his members to serve, obtaining concurrence from their supervisors as necessary. He indoctrinates them regarding the goal and program and informs them of the expected nature, extent, and timing of their participation. He coordinates all activities, communications, conferences, and interim reporting. When the program has been completed, he is responsible for the final report and for follow-up with management as to disposition of the results.

An important benefit of a project team system is the need to estimate the total cost of each program, providing the basis for cost-benefit comparison between the expense of doing the work and its probable value. Research men usually resist this procedure on the plea that one can never foretell how long it will take to complete an assignment. After a trial period, however, most of them find they can make better estimates than they thought possible. Engineers in particular are much more accustomed to this type of scheduling.

Budgetary control is established by tabulating the number of man-hours proposed for each team member and converting these into monetary units which should include a pro-rata proportion of the overheads of the organization. The man-hour is the most common basis for accounting, but one successful system has used quarter-hour intervals for many years. Even if the unit is as large as a half or full day, systematic planning of the use of technical manpower is encouraged.

Successive Teams on Multistage Projects. Many programs need to be broken down into major stages which require different arrays of skills. For examples, the development of an innovative new product from original concept to commercial introduction will fall into several phases, some of which may in part be carred on concurrently:

1. Product definition
2. Product development
3. Process development
4. Internal evaluation
5. Field evaluation
6. Process confirmation
7. Market confirmation
8. Comprehensive review of all commercial and technical aspects
9. Management decision regarding implementation

In a large company the skills required to carry out such a comprehensive program would be distributed among a number of different organizational units, for example: applied research, product development, process and engineering development, market research, marketing, corporate central engineering, purchasing, manufacturing, finance and accounting, patents and legal, and of course, top management. The dominant skill or discipline would change at the various stages, and it might be advisable, therefore, to use a different "subteam leader" where such changes occur. Further, the make-up of each "subteam" will vary but, to ensure continuity in the transfer of expertise and to secure the advice of those who will be responsible for later phases, representatives should be included in each new subteam of the preceding and succeeding subteams. To make sure of a smooth succession of subteams, coordination may be effected by a senior executive.

Steps for the Introduction of a Project Team System. Because interdisciplinary operations of this type represent such a radical change from the usual administrative patterns, great care should be taken in the manner in which they are introduced. The author has had much experience with a number of American companies which have adopted these techniques for research and development projects and is therefore familiar with the problems encountered. Multidisciplinary teams are also being tried out in development projects, at the author's suggestion, in two countries in the Far East, one in the Middle East, and at least one country in Latin America.

If task forces are started precipitately for the bulk of the program, administrative chaos is likely to result. It takes time and experience for supervisors and members of their sections to understand and accept the changed relationships. Instead, one or two carefully selected projects should be undertaken on a trial basis with careful explanation of the solutions to problems which arise. Only then should the techniques gradually be extended to other studies.

ILLUSTRATION OF A COMPLEX FEASIBILITY STUDY

Entrepreneur ABC, a successful industrialist in a developing country, advocated the establishment of a fixed nitrogen plant for fertilizers. His idea was enthusiastically endorsed by the government, and he was assured of a six-year loan of federal funds under favorable terms to provide a large part of the financing for investment and initial working capital. To satisfy the government and some private investors, ABC needed a well-documented feasibility study or prospectus. He made an agreement with a foreign consulting firm to carry out this assignment.

General Background. Consumption of nitrogenous fertilizers is increasing throughout the world. In this particular country government data on imports indicated local needs of 20 000 tons/year of ammonia equivalent, with a current annual growth rate of nearly 15 per cent per year. In addition, it was believed that about 3000 tons/year could be exported to neighboring countries as ammonium sulfate.

The technology and engineering for synthetic ammonia operations are well established. A number of foreign engineering contractors are prepared to furnish complete designs and install turn-key plants.

Scope of the Study. Because the technology was readily available, the market outlook was of prime importance. Minimum economic size of synthetic ammonia plants is now at least 100 tons/day in areas of restricted competition for this basic commodity. This represents 35 000 tons/year for such a plant operating 350 days during an annual period. In highly competitive situations, it should be noted, minimum economic plant capacity is about 600 tons/day.

The marketing study required the confirmation of estimated present consumption and the outlining of a sales program. The data on volume could be checked by analysis of government import data and discussions with local importers and foreign exporters to the country. Marketing aspects involved a survey and critique of the existing distribution system, including pricing policies and trade channels, practices, mechanisms, formulations, and packaging, together with such additional factors as technical service and promotional efforts.

To examine the potential for growth, the views of agricultural economists, agronomists, and soil specialists would be needed. Subjects to be investigated would include review of government programs to train agricultural extension workers, conduct soil analyses, and educate farmers on the advantages of more modern farm practices, including the use of fertilizers. Other pertinent topics would be export trends for farm products and the prospects for better correlation for specific crops between soil analyses and growth response to fertilizer application.

From the production point of view, the following subjects would need to be evaluated: optimum plant location, selection of process and equipment to suit local conditions, site preparation factors, availability and cost of raw materials and supplies, availability and expense of labor for construction and operation, transportation costs, import duties on equipment and materials to be purchased abroad, and level of inventory of replacement parts.

Conduct of the Study. The consulting firm used a field team of three specialists, headed by a fertilizer marketing expert who had originally been trained as a chemical engineer. The other members were a process engineer and an agricultural development engineer. These three individuals were senior men with broad international experience in evaluating fertilizer projects; otherwise it would have been advisable to use a larger team. They received back-up assistance on some aspects from specialists in their home office. In addition, ABC assigned an engineer and a marketing man from his own staff to work with them as needed to assist with local contacts and information and acquire some experience in methodology.

The conclusions of the consultants were that the undertaking had a sound basis with a profit margin that would provide for pay-out of the investment within a satisfactory period. The data for current demand were found to be factual and the growth outlook indicated that the design capacity of 35 000 tons/year would be in balance with sales within two years after production started. The plant and operating cost estimates included a liberal contingency for escalation to take care of the inflationary trend between the date of estimation and completion; even in highly developed countries failure to provide for inflation between preparation of estimates and delayed implementation of projects is likely to be the cause of criticism of an engineering department.

In this particular case, the cost of producing ammonium derivatives would not be competitive in some areas. Lower distribution costs, however, because of location close to the market, provided economic justification for ABC's project. The national benefits were the conservation of foreign exchange and the creation of employment, although the latter effect would be more apparent chiefly in satellite operations, because a synthetic ammonia plant is capital-intensive and operates with a small staff.

REPORT OF WORKSHOP 17

G. Fauconneau, Rapporteur

THE DISCUSSION revolved around the following three basic points:

1. Need for an interdisciplinary team approach
2. Problems encountered in the past in the use of such teams
3. Management of interdisciplinary project teams

The discussants recognized the essential necessity of an interdisciplinary approach to development. The need is made urgent by the speed at which development occurs in the developed countries and should occur in the less-developed countries. As a result, opportunities to improve solutions as they evolve are diminished, requiring from the outset the participation of sociologists, political scientists, social anthropologists, economists, and historians, along with engineers. The contributions from nonengineering fields are particularly needed in many present-day activities that involve international components with which the engineer is relatively unfamiliar.

In recent years the advantages of using the tools of various disciplines in the solution of problems have received recognition. The end products, however, have often failed to be truly interdisciplinary. These failures are the result of certain pitfalls which must be recognized. Often, the members of an interdisciplinary team act as special advocates of some approach or theory, and thereby reducing the crossfertilization needed for a truly integrated solution. Often, too, specialists' suggestions have no bearing on the problem at hand. The problem is compounded by the difficulty encountered in interpreting suggestions cast in language unintelligible to the engineer. The solution offered by the workshop was to create a body of past experience in the field of economic development, re-evaluated in truly interdisciplinary terms. In this fashion, existing pitfalls could be avoided, a series of "do's" and "dont's" could be established, and the difficult problem of the prestige items (eg nuclear power plant, dam, railroad) in developing countries could be handled in a more rational fashion. Only if all members of the team are exposed to a re-evaluation and synthesis of past experience in similar undertakings can they effectively communicate and cooperate.

Paramount among the factors essential to the success of an interdisciplinary team are its proper management and basic principles of its operation:

1. A team leader must be designated; it is his responsibility to assemble a group of specialists with the needed skills. The specialists must not only be competent in their own fields, but also be sensitive to the content of the other specialists' fields.

2. The team leader must define the proposed program, the nature of each member's participation, and the reporting procedures. The definition of the task must not only be clear, but also broad enough to avoid undue constraints in shaping the solution.

3. The members must be indoctrinated and their activities coordinated.

4. The final report of findings, conclusions, and recommendations must be submitted.

Through these steps, the effectiveness of multidisciplinary teams in accelerating the sequence of stages in development can be noteworthy.

REFERENCES CITED

Bass, L. W. *The Management of Technical Programs.* New York: Praeger, 1965.

Bass, L. W. and F. N. Woodward, "The management of multidiscipline project teams," *Chemistry and Industry,* London, November 11, 1967.

"Product and process development," *Handbook of Business Administration,* New York: McGraw-Hill, 1967.

United Nations Industrial Development Organization (UNIDO). *Manual on the Management of Industrial Research Institutes in Developing Countries.* New York, 1968.

UNIDO. *Manual on the Management of Industrial Research Institutes in Developing Countries.* New York, 1966.

SUMMARY OF THE CONFERENCE PROCEEDINGS
Carl Beck

THE CONFERENCE participants were distressed by the increasing gap that exists between the rich and the poor nations. All saw industrialization as a means of bridging that gap. All saw a direct relationship between technology and industrialization by means of which technology could serve as an instrument of economic development. Countries cannot industrialize without the application of modern engineering technology, yet less-than-modernized countries find it difficult, if not impossible, to incorporate modern engineering technology into their industrial and agricultural activities.

A recurrent question in these proceedings was, "what are the factors which accelerate or impede the application of modern technology?" Among factors cited were the physical and educational, as well as those related to social and political structure, social, and political behavior. The participants recognized that they were discussing a complex of interrelationships and called for increased and continuous inventories of natural resources, of investments in education, and of research and development; for more sensitivity to social and cultural conditions; for better planning; and, in general, for greater activity by both public and private agencies, domestic and international, in the application of modern technology.

We have concluded the proceedings with a better understanding of the difficulties involved in applying modern technology, better understanding of the reasons for frustration, frustration which will increase because most of the projections for the immediate future seem dour.

Something obviously is inadequate about the mechanisms we have been utilizing to analyze the problem structure and to develop solutions. On one level we lack well-ordered hypotheses which integrate the varied interrelationships associated with the application of technology. On another level we lack strategies for creating a proper setting for technology. For example, it has been impossible for many Asian nations to achieve the relatively low-level goal of investing 1 per cent of their Gross National Product in research and development. Too many problems intervene that must be confronted; too many immediate demands deluge the government.

Implicit in a number of the Conference papers and explicit in quite a few is the thought that the basic problem is not so much closing the technological gap through specific projects as it is developing a milieu in which technological innovation becomes selfgenerating.

The creation of a milieu for technological innovation has not been a deliberate aspect of the planning process on either the domestic or the international scene. We have realized here that each country has thought of its problems in an essentially autarkic manner. Existing models of development are not international; indeed, the "model" that seems most accepted is that based essentially upon the experiences of Western Europe and the United States. This particular "model" unfolded in an era in which the structure of society, politics, economic assumptions, and perceptions of the ability to manipulate the external world were quite different from what they are today. Then, social norms were patterned and, perhaps more important, the decision-makers were less accessible to social and political pressures.

The autarkic model of development was costly enough in human and economic terms as it was evolved. In an era of mass communications, an era in which political and economic leaders of all countries are immediately accessible to a myriad of immediate pressures, the instability of the crisis of political participation and the instability of dramatically changing relationships within and between social aggregates suggest that the autarkic model of development will not be very successful. Even progressive autarky under optimum conditions may well contribute to a widening of the technological gap. The goals and strategies implicit in an autarkic model are goals and strategies of the past.

In his luncheon address (Chap. 1), A. J. Aizenstat stated:

The vigorous leaps made by the highly industrialized countries who are now in the midst of what has already been called the Second Industrial Revolution seem to have lifted the issues of industrialization out of their traditional context and planted them in a new and as yet uncharted territory.

Without oversimplifying the case, we can characterize the traditional context as domestic, the uncharted as international.

As we analyzed development, we came away impressed with the staying power of tradition. It is not just the tradition of less-than-modernized societies but also the tradition of our modes of analysis and modes of action that must impress us. We need to find ways to view the problem as a whole, to identify the subsystems that are operating, and to isolate critical predictors. As academics we need to create research and teaching mechanisms to do these things.

We are faced with two major problems. The first is that of developing a set of lenses that will assist us to see more clearly the variables that impact the development of technological innovation as a selfgenerating system, as well as the interaction of these variables. This calls for new research ventures and, I would argue, a new form of research milieu.

The second problem is one of creating new forms of instruction. The topic of technology and society is by its very nature interdisciplinary. The systematic pursuit of the interrelationships discussed above demands the perspectives of a number of experts in continuous discourse with others. Concerted research in this area is going to require not only the development of research teams but also the cooperation of a number of research institutions reaching across universities, public and private enterprises, and national boundaries. In the past the transfer of technology has often been related to a specific project in a developing country. Although the particular edifice may stand once the project is completed, such a research and project strategy has two major weaknesses: the research or project is not related to a global strategy for technological innovation, and the institutions involved are usually placed in a dependency relationship rather than in a parity relationship. For research as well as projects we must push aside our isomorphic and parochial concerns and create an international network of accrued research from which program manipulation and experimentation can evolve. The development of an international interdisciplinary milieu will contribute not only to the specific problem but to the professional development of the individuals involved. It is in such a context that effective research hypotheses can be developed and explored and learning take place.

The problem of creating new forms of instruction is also related to our isomorphic and parochial modes of behavior. Jack Baranson writes:

Engineers are typically called upon to design plants and equipment under existing supply and demand conditions. A much more challenging role for engineers would be to design industrial systems which economize on scarce or underpriced factors, such as foreign exchange and managerial skills, and make more use of relatively abundant factors, such as low-level skills and raw materials.

This suggests a new role for the engineer. He must become, as we all must become, more cognizant of the factors that impinge upon his ability to perform his tasks successfully and be aware of alternative ways to define his task. We cannot lay out now the exact skills that are going to be required in the future. However, the Conference proceedings suggest that the engineer must become a participant in an educational milieu which aims at systematically confronting the interplay of environmental factors—domestic and international—assumptions which underly *ad hoc* policy decisions and suggest alternative lines of procedure. How many university settings have an opportunity for our students, researchers, and faculty to share their concerns and, through sharing, come to grips with impediments and accelerators of technological innovation? How often do we bring the skills of analysis, the corpus of experience, the variety of perspectives in a continuing teaching and research milieu?

The Conference has presented us with a number of challenges: challenges to the way in which we have conceptualized the problem area, challenges to the implicit models for development which we have adopted, challenges to the way in which we defined our academic roles, challenges to how we relate to other institutions, challenges to our mode of educating. If we can build upon these challenges we shall continue to advance both our knowledge and our effectiveness.

APPENDIX 1
Biographical Data of Participants

The following are photographs and brief biographical sketches of those who participated in the Conference program. As might be suspected, it has not been easy to condense the relevant background experiences of these participants. To do so, we have had to omit references to many honors, awards, publications, and other achievements by those who accepted key roles in the Conference. The Conference Planning Committee believes that the participants are among the most qualified people in the world to address themselves to the multidisciplinary topics under consideration. These scientists, engineers, economists, lawyers, physicians and scholars are dedicated men whose education and vast experiences form a sound basis and frame of reference for their participation in this effort.

The University of Pittsburgh and the Conference Planning Committee wish to express their gratitude to each of the following participants who came together from Africa, Asia, Europe, South America, the Middle East and from many parts of North America to consider the unique and diverse problems relating to the industrial development of the emerging countries of our world.

Aron Jose Aizenstat, an Argentine economist, is director of the United Nations Industrial Development Organization (UNIDO) Office in New York. Mr. Aizenstat has served in the United Nations Secretariat for the last 15 years in various senior positions. He was closely connected with United Nations work in the fiscal and financial fields, having contributed to many publications on the subject. As head of the Technical Assistance Office for Latin America he was instrumental in developing United Nations advisory services in economic programming, including the provision of assistance to Latin American governments in establishing programming cadres and in formulating overall development plans. The latter eventually became the keystone for assistance to countries under the Alliance for Progress.

For the last six years Mr. Aizenstat was fully devoted to the creation of a United Nations machinery to promote the industrialization of the developing countries. As special assistant to the United Nations Commissioner for Industrial Development, he steered the organization, first, of the United Nations Center for Industrial Development and more recently of the United Nations Industrial Development Organization (UNIDO) which currently has its Headquarters in Vienna. Mr. Aizenstat represents UNIDO in New York at many official meetings and professional gatherings in and outside the United Nations Headquarters.

Previous to United Nations service, Mr. Aizenstat was connected with private industry in Buenos Aires. He also served as Argentine representative on United Nations programs and for a brief period as consultant of the International Program on Taxation of Harvard University Law School.

He has traveled extensively in the developing countries and represented the United Nations in negotiations with governments on major economic development projects.

387

Maurice L. Albertson is professor of civil engineering at Colorado State University. He is principal investigator for a national study of the Research Needs and Requirements in Civil Engineering cosponsored by the National Science Foundation and the American Society of Civil Engineers. Mr. Albertson is the United States Coordinator for the SEATO Graduate School of Engineering in Bangkok in Thailand and was director of the Congressional Study in 1960–61 of the advisability and practicability of a Peace Corps.

He has had 25 years' experience in fluid mechanics, hydraulic engineering, water resources research, and international development engineering. He has been concerned

primarily with problems of design and development of hydraulic structures, energy dissipation, alluvial hydraulics, boundary layer studies, and diffusion. He pioneered in the development of the use of a wind tunnel to study meteorological and climatological phenomena. In 1958 he established the Office of the Colorado State University Research Foundation and was its Director until 1963. In that year he established the Office of International Programs at the Colorado State University.

Professor Albertson holds the M.S. and Ph.D. degrees in hydraulic engineering from the State University of Iowa and the degree of Doctor of Physical Sciences from the Université de Grenoble in France.

P. C. Asiodu is permanent secretary, Federal Ministry of Industries in Nigeria, serving also as government director of boards of several jointly owned (Nigerian/Foreign) enterprises

388

such as the Nigerian Industrial Development Bank, the Nigerian Cement Company, the Nigerian Sugar Company, and the Nigerian Paper Mill. He has been a member of Nigerian delegations to several international economic conferences.

Mr. Asiodu has served in the Federal Ministry of Health, the Ministry of Lagos Affairs, and the Ministry of External Affairs, Lagos. In 1960–62 he was the first secretary in the Permanent Mission of Nigeria to the United Nations and was a member of the Nigerian delegations to the 15th, 16th, and 17th U.N. General Assemblies.

In 1958 Mr. Asiodu served in Nigeria House in London. He has been attached to British High Commissions in Australia and New Zealand.

He received his education at King's College in Lagos and at Queen's College, Oxford.

Jack Baranson has been an economist with the World Bank since 1966 and has been an economic consultant to the bank since 1965. Previously, he was a research associate at the Brookings Institution, as staff associate of the Committee for Economic Development, and a research associate of the International Development Research Center at Indiana University.

Mr. Baranson has written two books on trade and industrialization policies toward developing economies, particularly as they relate to technological transfer and the role of technology in development. He is now completing a study on Automotive Industries in Developing Economies.

Mr. Baranson received his Ph.D. in Economics from Indiana University and also attended the Johns Hopkins School of Advanced International Studies and the University of Wisconsin.

Curtis H. Barker is university relations officer for the Agency for International Development. In his position, he is concerned with AID-university polices, academic resources relevant to foreign aid, and institutional arrangements for making these resources available to the Agency. He joined AID in 1964 and has worked with programming, administering, and evaluating contract research on the social science aspects of international development.

Earlier in his career, he conducted small-group research at the Institute for Social Research in Ann Arbor; education and training research at the Air University in Alabama; research on Chinese "thought reform," urbanization, and the Science-Politics Relationship at the Center for International Studies, MIT; and research on arms control, East-West communication patterns, and socio-political barriers to development in Iran, at the Institute for Defense Analyses in Washington.

He received a Master's degree in social psychology from the University of Michigan and has completed his coursework for the Ph.D. in political science at MIT.

Leland Barrows is director of the Economic and Social Development Program in the University of Pittsburgh's Graduate School of Public and International Affairs.

He has had broad experience in many levels of government, serving most recently as United States Ambassador in Cameroun in West Africa from 1961 to 1966. His career in government service began in 1934 with the U.S. Department of Agriculture; then followed successively with posts in the War Relocation Authority, Office of Price Administration, and the Federal Public Housing Authority. In between he served as a second lieutenant with the U.S. Coast Guard Reserve in World War II.

Moving into the international field, he was named deputy director in the Office of Information and Educational Exchange, Department of State, in 1947, and a year later served with the Economic Cooperation Administration in Europe. Under the Marshall Plan, he was appointed director of U.S. operations in Greece in 1952, and in 1954 was named director of U.S. economic and technical assistance in Vietnam. From 1958 to 1960 he was regional director of Near East and South Asia Operations, ICA.

His affiliations include Phi Beta Kappa, American Foreign Service Association, and the Council on Foreign Relations of New York. He received his A.B. and M.A. degrees in political science from the University of Kansas.

Merton R. Barry is director, Engineering Foreign Programs at the University of Wisconsin, which has programs currently under way in India, Mexico, and Singapore.

He has been with the university on and off since 1943, starting as a teaching assistant in engineering graphics. He also has been an assistant professor at Central Washington State College. For six years, until 1966, he was Wisconsin Campus Coordinator, AID contract-engineering education, India.

He has conducted a number of studies on engineering education and belongs to the AAUP, ASEE (currently, he is chairman, International Engineering Education Committee), and the American Craftsmens Council. He is a practicing artist and craftsman, has exhibited frequently, and is represented by a Seattle gallery.

In 1949 Mr. Barry was a Fulbright Fellow at the Rijksuniversiteit Utrecht, Netherlands. He received his M.S. from the University of Wisconsin and attended the University of Zurich and the Kunstgewerbeschule in Zurich.

Lawrence W. Bass is consultant (formerly vice president), Arthur D. Little, Inc., and has been an executive of Mellon Institute, New England Industrial Research Foundation, and Arthur D. Little, Inc., for nearly 25 years. Earlier, he was a technical director in industry for 15 years and was engaged in basic reseach in the U.S. and abroad for another 7 years.

In 1964 he retired as vice president of Arthur D. Little but continued as a consultant and took on a number of professional assignments for the United Nations Industrial Development Organization. His major interests are management of research and development, corporate organization and planning, and the economics of developing countries.

Mr. Bass has headed economic development projects in Egypt and Iraq; he has planned and participated in R & D conferences in Italy and the United Kingdom; he planned, organized, and headed a team which presented a three-week training course on R & D management in Cairo under Ford Foundation auspices for 38 Egyptian technical executives—believed to be the first course of the kind ever given in a developing country; he wrote the basic manuscripts and was a member of the International Committees which prepared UNIDO manuals on the Administration of Industrial Research Institutes (1966) and the Use of Consultants in Developing Countries (1968); he has surveyed programs for development in Japan, the Philippines, Singapore, and Thailand; and has participated in conferences and symposia in Austria, Columbia, England, Italy, Peru, the Philippines, Scotland, Sweden, and the United States.

Mr. Bass received his Ph.D. from Yale and has held official positions in a number of national organizations.

392

Carl Beck is professor of political science and director of the Center of International Studies at the University of Pittsburgh. His teaching and research interests are in comparative communist political systems, bureaucratic theory, elite theory, and information systems. Under a grant from the Carnegie Corporation he established a Comparative Communism program of teaching and research at Pitt.

He is chairman of the Information Science Committee of the American Political Science Association and was, in 1967, codirector of the

Consortium Research Conference on Political Elites. He is chairman of Computer Center Inter-Action Committee of the Social Sciences and chairman, Information Retrieval Sub-Committee, Council of Social Science Data Archives. Mr. Beck is a member of the executive board, Inter-University Consortium for Political Research.

He received his Ph.D. at Duke University and studied at Wesleyan, the University of Munich, and Pitt.

Nicky Beredjick is Senior Industrial Development Officer for UNIDO. He has been responsible for evaluating feasibility reports on the establishment of new chemical industries in Latin America, Africa, Asia, and the Far East; for industrial and marketing surveys in Algeria; and for pre-investment studies in Pakistan. In connection with his surveys in Algeria, Mr. Beredjick prepared the guidelines and an outline for a worldwide survey for the demand and supply of petrochemical products including marketing projections for the next 20 years.

Dr. Beredjick previously held various senior technical management positions with Union Carbide Corporation in Chicago, Standard Oil Company in Indiana, and the Ford Motor Company in Detroit. He has published widely in the fields of chemicals as well as contributing extensively to various United Nations publications.

Dr. Beredjick obtained his Ph.D. in chemistry from Syracuse University and has done other graduate work at the University of Chicago and McGill University in Montreal.

Warren J. Bilkey is in the Departments of Marketing and International Business in the School of Business at the University of Wisconsin. He has been teaching Behavioral Methods in Marketing, Marketing Research, Advertising, National Economic Development of Central America, International Marketing, and Industrial Development. His research has been conducted in El Salvador, Costa Rica, Peru, the Dominican Republic, and, of course, the United States. He has written extensively on industrial development, consumer behavior, and marketing. He is currently conducting industrial research on El Salvador.

His past experience includes being an economist with the Central Bank of the Dominican Republic and as an economic advisor to President Juan Bosch and his Minister of Industry and Commerce; serving on the economics faculty of the Universities of Notre Dame and Connecticut; and serving as an economist with the U.S. Office of Price Administration.

Mr. Bilkey received his Ph.D. in economics from Harvard and also studied social psychology and business administration there.

394

William Bollay is visiting professor in aeronautics and astronautics at Stanford University. He has worked extensively in teaching and research and development in astronautics, missiles, rockets and jet propulsion, guidances systems, and VTOL aircraft. He is a director of the American Institute of Astronautics and Aeronautics and a director of the Science and Engineering Council of Santa Barbara, Inc.

Among the institutions with which Mr. Bollay has been associated are MIT, UCLA, Harvard, and the California Institute of Technology (where he instituted the first Caltech program in rocket research). He was the founder and president of Aerophysics Development Corporation and founder and technical director of the Aerophysics Laboratory, North American Aviation, Inc. He has been a consultant to U.S. Government agencies and industries. He is a member of the U.S. Department of Commerce (National Inventors Council), NASA (Meteorology Sub-committee, Space Science and Applications Steering Committee), and the National Academy of Sciences Subcommittee on Industrial Research.

Mr. Bollay received his Ph.D. in Aeronautics from the California Institute of Technology. He also studied at Northwestern University and received an honorary degree from that institution in 1959.

Detlev W. Bronk is past president of The Rockefeller University in New York City, and serves on the board of trustees of Bucknell University, the Johns Hopkins University,

395

Rockefeller Brothers Fund, the Rockefeller University, Rensselaer Polytechnic Institute (where he is Chairman of the Board), the University of Pennsylvania, and many others. He has received 52 honorary degrees from institutions in this country and abroad and 14 awards including the most recent, the Benjamin Franklin Medal of the Royal Society of Arts in 1967.

Mr. Bronk was president of the Johns Hopkins University from 1949 to 1953 and was director of the Johnson Research Foundation for Medical Physics at the University of Pennsylvania for twenty years.

From 1957 to 1963, Mr. Bronk was a member of the President's Science Advisory Committee. He is a member of the Board of Directors of the New York State Science and

Technology Foundation and is a foreign member of the Royal Society of London, the French Academy of Sciences, the Royal Danish Society of Sciences and Letters, the Swedish Royal Academy of Sciences, the USSR Academy of Sciences, the Brazilian Academy of Sciences, and the Swiss Academy of Sciences. He is an honorary fellow of University College, London, and an honorary member of the eight national and international associations and societies.

He also has been associated with Swarthmore College and the Air Surgeon's Office and is a former chairman of the National Research Council, former president of the National Academy of Sciences-National Research Council, and former president of the American Association for the Advancement of Science.

George Bugliarello is professor of biotechnology and civil engineering and chairman of the Biotechnology Program at Carnegie-Mellon University. He was previously a research associate in the Hydrodynamics Laboratory at MIT and assistant to the chair of special hydraulic projects, University of Padua.

Besides lecturing at numerous U.S. institutions, Dr. Bugliarello has been invited to participate in seminars at the Technische Hochschule (Karlsruhe); the IAHR Conferences in Yugoslavia, London, and Leningrad; the Israel Institute of Technology; the First International Conference on Hemorheology, Iceland; the U.S. Delegation of Joint U.S.-Japan Symposium on Instrumentation for Hydraulic

Research, Tokyo; the NATO Advanced Study Institute on Surface Hydrodynamics, Italy; and he served as Chairman of the Engineering Session, Education and World Affairs Regional Conference at the University of Pittsburgh in 1967.

Professor Bugliarello was a Fulbright Scholar, has received the 1967 Research Prize from the Society of Civil Engineers, and in 1968 was awarded a NATO Senior Post Doctoral Fellowship to the Technical University of Berlin.

After completing undergraduate studies at the University of Padua, Mr. Bugliarello earned an M.S. at the University of Minnesota and his Sc.D. at MIT.

Robert A. Charpie has been president of Bell & Howell since March of this year. Formerly he was with Union Carbide Corporation, first as a physicist at Oak Ridge National Laboratory, then as assistant director of ORNL, and in 1958 as director of the Reactor Division. In 1961 he moved to Union Carbide's New York offices as manager of advanced developments. In quick succession he became general manager of the Development Department, director of technology, and finally president of the Electronics Division.

Dr. Charpie served as deputy United States delegate to the United Nations Advisory Committee on Atomic Energy in 1954–55, and in 1955 was Scientific Secretary for the First International Conference on the Peaceful Uses of Atomic Energy in Geneva in Switzerland. Also in 1955 he was named one of America's Ten Outstanding Young Men by the United States Junior Chamber of Commerce.

He is a member of a number of national and international organizations including the President's Science Advisory Committee—Panel on Oceanography. He also serves on the Visiting Committee for the Department of Nuclear Engineering at MIT.

He received his D.Sc. in theoretical physics from Carnegie Institute of Technology.

Francis S. Cheever is Dean of the School of Medicine and Vice Chancellor, School of the Health Professions at the University of Pittsburgh. Before coming to Pittsburgh, Dr.

Cheever taught for many years at the Harvard Medical School. He has written numerous articles and is a member of several learned and technical societies.

Dr. Cheever received his undergraduate and M.D. degrees from Harvard University. He also holds an honorary D.Sc. degree.

Kan Chen is assistant director of Stanford Research Institute, a position in which he is responsible for assisting the Systems Sciences Area management in launching new programs and in assuming project leadership for many activities in which Stanford University interacts with other academic institutes.

Before his present position, he developed, with Standard University, a program designed to provide a combination of consulting, training, and research functions in engineering-economic systems

Mr. Chen previously was manager of Systems Technology Research and Development at Westinghouse Electric Corporation in Pittsburgh. He was with Westinghouse for more than ten years and was responsibile for a number of programs aimed at creating new systems opportunities for the company.

Mr. Chen received his B.E.E. from Cornell University and his M.S. and Sc.D. from MIT. He is a senior member of IEEE and is active in the Group for systems science and cybernetics. He also is a lecturer in the Engineering-Economic Systems Department of Stanford University.

398

W. L. Chilton is an international economist with the Ford Motor Company in Dearborn, Michigan. He has worked in international business with Joel Dean Associates; Hastings-on-Hudson, New York Management Consultants; and Columbia University's Graduate School of Business. Earlier, Dr. Chilton was an export traffic manager with International Freight Forwarders.

Mr. Chilton received his Master's degree in economics from New York University and his Ph.D. from Columbia University's Graduate School of Business. He is a member of Beta Gamma Sigma and held a Doctoral Dissertation Fellowship of the Ford Foundation under its program of Economic Development and Administration.

Walter A. Chudson is professor of international business in the Graduate School of Business at Columbia University. Previously he was the assistant director of the United Nations Industrial Development Organization. He has served in the United Nations Secretariat since 1946, formerly attached to the U.N. Department of Economic and Social Affairs as staff

economist concerned mainly with problems of international trade and finance.

Professor Chudson has been with the Secretariat since 1946 and also has held positions with the U. S. Board of Economic Warfare, the Department of State, and the United Nations Relief and Rehabilitation Administration.

In education, Dr. Chudson has been asso-

399

ciated with Columbia University, the University of Oregon, the College of the City of New York, the Yale University Law School, and the Economic Development Institute of the International Bank.

Mr. Chudson attended Oxford University as a Rhodes Scholar and received his Ph.D. in economics from Columbia University.

Elbert T. Culver is manager of project sales for Koppers Company, Inc. (International Operations) and vice president of Koppers (Far East), Inc. He graduated from the Newark College of Engineering in 1949 with a bachelor's degree in chemical engineering, and has done graduate work at the University of Pittsburgh.

Mr. Culver has been with the Koppers Company for 19 years and has served in the fields of chemical plant design and sales, in the research and development program on iron ore reduction, and for the past 6 years in international sales of iron and steel plants. In this latter capacity he has traveled extensively and had the opportunity to participate in industrial plant study programs in developing countries in Asia, Africa, South America, and the Near East.

John C. Cutler is director, Population Division, and professor of international health in the Graduate School of Public Health at the University of Pittsburgh.

Formerly, Dr. Cutler was assistant then deputy director of the Pan American Sanitary

Bureau, Regional Office of the World Health Organization. His experience includes service as health officer for the Central District, Allegheny County (Pennsylvania) Health Department when the district was being developed as a training and research area for public health practice in cooperation with the Graduate School at Pitt.

Dr. Cutler was assistant director of the National Institute of Allergy and Infectious Diseases, National Institutes of Health in 1958 and served for 1-1/2 years as Assistant Surgeon General of the U.S. Public Health Service.

Dr. Cutler received his M.D. at Western Reserve University and his Master of Public Health at the Johns Hopkins University School of Hygiene and Public Health. He is a Diplomate of the American Board of Preventive Medicine and Public Health.

Paul Henri David is Inspector, General Inspection of Construction, with the Ministère de l'Equipement et du Logement in Paris. He studies housing markets, plant locations, and regional development in France, the United Kingdom, and the United States.

Mr. David is a member of the American Industrial Development Council and the Association Française de Science Economique Régionale.

He received the diploma of the Industrial Development Institute from Oklahoma University; the diplome d'Etudes Supérieures de Droit Public, Université de Lyon; and the Diplome d'Etudes Supérieures d'Economie Politique, Université de Lyon. He also attended the Ecole Nationale d'Administration and the Ecole Pratique de Hautes Etudes, Section Economique in Paris.

Julien Engel is professional associate in the Office of the Foreign Secretary, National Academy of Sciences, and head of Middle East-South Asian Affairs. In the current academic year, he also has been staff officer for the U.S.-Brazil Joint Study Groups on industrial research and norms, measurements and testing; and staff officer, U.S.-China Workshop in the application of science and technology to the industrial development of Taiwan in Taipei.

He is a member of task forces under bilateral cooperation programs between the academy and counterpart institutions in a number of developing countries on the application of science and technology to economic development.

Formerly, he was senior officer in charge of French-speaking Africa and director of the African Training Program for the African-American Institute in New York. He has served as an editorial associate for the Foreign Policy Association-World Affairs Center and was a Time-Life correspondent at Oxford in 1955–56.

He holds his M.A. from Oxford University (Worcester College) and attended Princeton University's Woodrow Wilson School of Public and International Affairs.

Tom J. Farer is assistant professor of law at Columbia Law School. Previously, he was with the firm of Davis, Polk, Wardwell, Sunderland & Kiendl, a research associate at MIT in the Sloan School, a legal advisor to the Government of Somali Republic, a special assistant to the General Counsel of the Department of Defense, and International Relations Officer for AID.

402

He is the editor of *African Economic Development* and is the author of several papers on national and international legal problems.

Mr. Farer is a graduate of Princeton University and the Harvard Law School and was a Fulbright Scholar in the United Kingdom.

Herbert I. Goodman was elected Far East coordinator for the Gulf Oil Corporation early in 1967 and is responsible for negotiations and policy matters concerning Gulf's interests in that area of the world. He is headquartered in Pittsburgh, where he joined Gulf in 1957. In 1958, he was transferred to London as coordinator, crude oil sales for Gulf Eastern Company, a wholly owned subsidiary.

In 1960, Mr. Goodman moved to Tokyo as assistant manager of the Crude Oil Department—Far East. Later that year he became manager—Crude Oil, Far East, and manager of Pacific Gulf Oil Limited, another subsidiary. He was elected executive vice president and general manager of that subsidiary in 1961 and, until 1963, also served as Gulf's area representative to Japan, Formosa, and the free countries along the mainland from Korea to Burma. In 1964 he returned to Pittsburgh.

Before he joined Gulf, Mr. Goodman was a foreign service officer stationed in U.S. embassies in Copenhagen, Saigon, and Phnom Penh (Cambodia); and in Washington, D.C.

Mr. Goodman is a graduate of the University of Pittsburgh and has received an M.B.A. from Harvard Business School and an M.A. from Harvard Graduate School of Arts and Sciences.

Maximo Halty-Carrere is chief of the Technological Development Unit, Department of Scientific Affairs, Pan American Union in Washington, D.C. The general objective of the unit is to promote the technological development of the Latin American countries. Until 1964 he was a researcher in the Institut d'Etude du Développement Economique et Social at the University of Paris, where he was in charge of the research group of educational and human resources planning in Latin America.

Born in Montevideo in Uruguay, he has held positions with FUNSA, the largest enterprise in that country; the University of California; and the University of Uruguay. He has organized or participated in some 50 meetings and conferences concerned with engineering training, economic and social development, industrialization, and productivity mainly as they concerned Latin American countries.

He attended IEDES, Université de Paris, the University of Uruguay, the University of California, the American University, and the Lycée Français in Montevideo.

Howard B. Hamilton is professor and chairman of the Electrical Engineering Department at the University of Pittsburgh. Before assuming his present post, he was adjunct professor and chief of party for Pitt's program at the Universidad Tecnica Federica Santa Maria in Valparaiso in Chile. Before that, he was a professor of electrical engineering at the University of Wichita.

Professor Hamilton is a consultant to the Ford Foundation, Recommendation and Evaluation Team for the University of Santa

Maria, and to the Knowledge Availability Systems Center at the University of Pittsburgh. He has been a consultant for such companies as Boeing and K. M. Hale Company, and he has served as an expert witness and investigator in numerous litigations involving accidental deaths.

Recently, Dr. Hamilton was awarded a National Science Foundation grant for develop-

ment of an undergraduate course in "power processing." His main interests are electric machinery, direct energy conversion processes, electric power systems, and control systems.

Professor Hamilton received his Ph.D. at Oklahoma State University and has studied at the University of Minnesota and the University of Oklahoma. He initiated the electrical engineering program at the University of Wichita.

Minor Clyde Hawk is the director of the Office of International Programs, director of the Office of Continuing Education Studies, and lecturer in the department of Civil Engineering at the University of Pittsburgh's School of Engineering. During the past two years he has also served as the University's campus coordinator for the AID-sponsored program at the Universidad Tecnica Federica Santa Maria in Valparaiso in Chile.

Immediately prior to his present position Mr. Hawk served as engineering coordinator and then assistant director of the NASA-sponsored program of space and technology transfer in the Knowledge Availability Systems Center.

Mr. Hawk has taught in several other institutions of higher learning including Washing-

ton and Jefferson College and the Carnegie Institute of Technology where he served as chairman of the Engineering Graphics Division of the Mechanical Engineering Department.

Professor Hawk has served as a consultant to several industries and is the author of an engineering textbook which has been published in several languages with worldwide distribution. He has also written many articles and has presented professional papers dealing with technology transfer.

Mr. Hawk has been an active member of several professional organizations and has been cited in Who's Who in Engineering.

Mr. Hawk received his graduate degree from the University of Pittsburgh.

Harold E. Hoelscher is dean of the School of Engineering at the University of Pittsburgh, director of the Space Research Coordination Center at Pitt, and professor of chemical engineering.

He came to Pitt from The Johns Hopkins University where he was chairman and professor of the Department of Chemical Engineering. He was with Johns Hopkins from 1952 until 1965. Previously he was on the faculties of the University of Cincinnati and of Washington University.

Dean Hoelscher has written and published extensively in the field of chemical engineering, chemical engineering education, engineering education, and university development. His chemical engineering publications generally are in the field of chemical reaction engineering and kinetics.

His consulting activities have taken him to India as a UNESCO expert, and he has served as senior Fulbright lecturer at Alagappa Chettiar College, University of Madras, India.

Mr. Hoelscher received his Ph.D. in chemical engineering from Washington University and attended Princeton University.

Bert F. Hoselitz is professor of social science; director, Research Center in Economic Development and Cultural Change; and chairman, Committee on the Divisional Master's Program at the University of Chicago.

He was formerly director of studies, Committee on International Relations at the University of Chicago and was an expert in industrial economy with the United Nations Technical Assistance Mission to El Salvador.

406

He has taught at the University of Chicago, Carnegie Institute of Technology, and Manchester College in Indiana. He also was a research assistant in Economics and International Relations at the Institute of International Studies at Yale University. Mr. Hoselitz was visiting professor of economics at the University of Frankfurt in Germany and a fellow, Center for Advanced Study in the Behavioral Sciences, Stanford University.

From 1953 to 1961, Professor Hoselitz was editor of *Economic Development and Cultural Change*. He was an editor of the Encyclopedia of the Social Sciences, a Guggenheim Fellow, and a Visiting Professor of Economics at Santa Cruz University. Mr. Hoselitz was organizer, in 1960, of the North American Conference on the Social Implications of Technological Change sponsored by UNESCO and before that, worked on metropolitan planning under a Ford Foundation project with the Ministry of Health and Local Government in New Delhi.

He received the Doctor of Law degree at Vienna and the Master of Arts in Economics from Chicago.

Warren Seabury Hunsberger is professor of economics at the American University in Washington, D.C., a consultant to the United States Department of State, and a lecturer on Asian economic problems at the Foreign Service Institute.

He has been a professor of economic programming at the Johns Hopkins University, Institute for International Development, School of Advanced International Studies; adjunct professor of economics at the American University; a research fellow for the Council on Foreign Relations; and has lecturered at the Salzburg Seminar in American Studies. He also has been associated with the University of New Hampshire and Princeton University.

Dr. Hunsberger has held U.S. Government positions as a Far East regional economist, as a program officer in Brazil, and as an economist on the President's Materials Policy Commission. Dr. Hunsberger also served for over 3 years as Ford Foundation economist in an Economic Planning Unit in Malaysia.

His publications have concentrated on Japan's trade, international trade policy, and development.

Dr. Hunsberger received his Ph.D. in economics from Yale.

407

John M. Ide is director of the Division of Engineering of the National Science Foundation, a post he has held since June, 1964. Previously, he served for three years as director, SACLANT Antisubmarine Warfare Research Center at La Spezia, Italy, a NATO Center for research in oceanography and underwater acoustics and for scientific studies of military operations.

Earlier, he was in the Pentagon, where for a year he was head of the Ballistic Missile Defense Program, and before that was technical director of the Underwater Sound Laboratory, a U.S. Navy laboratory located in New London, Conn., and devoted to research and devel-

opment of electronics equipment for submarines and other problems of undersea warfare.

His career includes experience in university teaching, in industrial research, and in research and development for governmental agencies. He has published on electronics, geophysics, and acoustics. In 1958, he received a career service award from the National Civil Service League, which cited him for "outstanding achievements in research, development and organization." Mr. Ide received his doctor's degree from Harvard University and studied at Pomona College in southern California, where he was awarded an honorary Doctor of Science degree in 1965.

Robert William Iversen is professor of social science at Syracuse University. He has been on the faculties of Pennsylvania State University, Columbia University, Drake University, and the State University of Iowa.

Mr. Iversen's government service includes a two-year period as deputy director of training for the U.S. Peace Corps and consultant service for the Office of Personnel, Agency for International Development and Bureau of Executive

408

Manpower, U.S. Civil Service Commission. Mr. Iversen is a graduate of the University of Minnesota and received his Ph.D. in American history from the State University of Iowa.

Govind Pandurang Kane is officer on special duty with the Ministry of Industry in New Delhi, India. He has been deputy director general and senior industrial advisor to the Development Wing in the Ministry of Commerce and Industry, and earlier in his career he was professor and reader in chemical engineering in the Department of Chemical Technology, University of Bombay.

Dr. Kane was responsible for the planning and development of chemical and allied industries in India from 1955 to 1965. He was the leader of the Indian delegation for pharmaceuticals, drugs, and dyestuffs to the USSR, East Germany, West Germany, Italy, and Switzerland in the 1950s. He was a United Nations consultant at a conference on petrochemicals held at Teheran in 1964 and was vice chairman and chairman of two ECAFE seminars. He also has been chairman of technical committees of Government for development of industries. At present he is promoting a public sector paper corporation for the production of pulp, paper, and newsprint.

Mr. Kane received his Ph.D. and D.I.C. in Technical Chemistry from the Imperial College in London. He also studied at the Indian Institute of Science, Bangalore.

Augustus Braun Kinzel is past president and chief executive officer of the Salk Institute for Biological Studies, a position he held from 1965 to 1967; before that was with the Union Carbide Corporation for 39 years in a variety of positions including chief metallurgist, vice president and president of Union Carbide and Carbon Research Laboratories, and director of research for the entire Union Carbide Corporation. Later he served as vice president for research.

Dr. Kinzel is the founding president of the National Academy of Engineering and a member of the National Academy of Science and the American Philosophical Society. He holds honorary Doctor of Engineering degrees from New York University, Rensselaer Polytechnic Institute, Worcester Polytechnic Institute, and the University of Michigan. In 1960 he received the James Douglas Gold Medal Award from the American Institute of Metallurgical Engineering and in 1966 was given the Washington Award from the Western Society of Engineers.

Dr. Kinzel has held a number of U.S. Government advisory posts including membership in the Manhattan District Committee for World Control of Atomic Energy. He is a Trustee of the California Institute of Technology and was the first Gwilym Price lecturer at the University of Pittsburgh.

He was educated at Columbia University and MIT and holds advanced degrees from the University of Nancy in France.

Hibberd V. B. Kline jr. is professor and chairman of the Department of Geography at the University of Pittsburgh. He has been acting dean of the Division of the Social Sciences at the University of Pittsburgh and was associate professor at Syracuse University.

Dr. Kline has been visiting professor at Columbia University, the University of Sierra Leone, and the University of Ghana. In his past positions, he has been a research analyst for the Library of Congress, chief of the Cartography Division, Office of Strategic Services and Department of State. He has served as a consultant and member of mission, U.S. Foreign Aid Programs to Africa. He is founding member of the African Studies Association; was a coordinator of Peace Corps training for Liberia. He is a director of the United Nations Association of Pittsburgh and president of the Pitt Resources Development Institute.

Professor Kline is an author, consultant, and lecturer on tropical Africa, social science education, and applied geography. A Commander in the U.S. Naval Reserves, he is cited in *Who's Who* and *American Men of Science*.

Mr. Kline received his Ph.D. from the University of Wisconsin.

Melvin Kranzberg is head of the Graduate Program in History of Science and Technology at Case Institute of Technology. At Case, Mr. Kranzberg also holds the position of professor of history. He has been on the faculties of Amherst College, Stevens Institute of Technology and Harvard University and has held visiting professorships at Springfield College, Washington

University, and the University of Colorado. In addition, he has served as a consultant to the Operations Research Office of the Johns Hopkins University.

Earlier in his career he was administrative assistant to the chief of the Service Trades Branch, Retail Trade and Services Division, Office of Price Administration, Washington, D.C.

Mr. Kranzberg this year was cochairman of an International Symposium on the Industrialization of the Underdeveloped Lands as an Historical Process, held in Paris. He has written on engineering education, history of science and technology, French history, and general European history. He has been a consultant to two encyclopedias and editor of several technical publications.

Mr. Kranzberg received his M.A. and Ph.D. from Harvard University and has two honorary degrees.

Matthew J. Kust is in the international legal practice in Washington, D.C. He is a member of the New York, District of Columbia, and the United States Supreme Court bars. Before 1951 he was in law practice in New York City, associated with the firm of Sullivan and Cromwell.

From 1951 to 1954, he was a Department of State Legal Advisor at New Delhi, India, for the economic and technical assistance programs in South and Southeast Asia.

He is the author of *Foreign Enterprise in India, Laws and Policies,* which has been called a "pioneering study of the laws governing foreign enterprise in India."

412

Mordechai Lador is with the Israeli Ministry of Foreign Affairs, Division for International Cooperation, in charge of all technical assistance activities in Asia, the Middle East, and Latin America. In 1966 he was a member of the Israeli delegation to the United Nations General Assembly and from 1964 to 1967 was counselor to the Israel Embassy in Washington.

His earlier positions include Chargé d'Affaires, Kathmandu, Nepal; and handling contacts of the Political Department, Histadrut, with African and Asian labor movements. For two years he was on mission for the Jewish Agency to the Scandinavian countries and for seven years was secretary of the Productivity Department of the General Federation of Labour, Israel.

Mr. Lador received his education in Hamburg.

John D. Lauer is clinical professor of occupational medicine in New York University's postgraduate medicine program and medical director of International Telephone and Telegraph Corporation.

Dr. Lauer began his career in general practice and surgery at St. Paul, Minnesota, in 1938, later becoming a fellow in industrial medicine at the University of Pittsburgh, assistant professor of occupational medicine at Kettering Lab, University of Cincinnati; medical director of Jones & Laughlin Steel Corp., and clinical associate professor of occupational medicine at Pitt.

He is a Diplomate in public health and occupational medicine of the American Board of

413

Preventive Medicine and belongs to a number of national and international associations.

Dr. Lauer received his M.D. from the University of Minnesota and his doctorate in Industrial Medicine from the University of Pittsburgh.

Lawrence D. Lee is an associate professor of law at the University of Pittsburgh. He teaches such subjects as Land-Use Planning, Problems of Doing Business Abroad, and Uniform Commercial Code.

Previously, he was visiting associate professor of law at SMU School of Law and before that, a teaching fellow at Harvard Law School and research assistant for the School's International Legal Studies. As a researcher, he conducted field studies of urban affairs and problems of financing urban development in Uruguay and Mexico.

His varied career includes a period when he was director of Public Relations for the Costa Rican Revolutionary Army. He also has operated businesses engaged in import-export.

He received the LL.M. from Harvard, the J.D. from the University of Southern California.

Alberto Leon is dean and professor, Engineering Division, Universidad del Valle, Cali, Colombia. He is also professor, Graduate Program, Social Sciences-School of Economics at the university.

Previously, Dean Leon was an associate in

414

research at the Sloan School of Management at MIT and an assistant in research at the Mental Health Research Institute at the University of Michigan, and taught at the University of California at Berkeley. He is particularly interested in computers and learning processes, data storage, and retrieval systems. He was consultant on computers and the nervous systems (mathematical learning models) for the Mental Health Research Institute at Michigan and is now consulting for the Information Sciences Center at Bogota in Colombia.

Mr. Leon graduated as a civil engineer from the Universidad Nacional de Colombia, Facultad de Mathematicas e Ingenieria. After graduation he worked for the same general engineering firm, Sideico Limitada, Bogota, in different technical and administrative positions. Professor Leon received his Ph.D. in Operations Research and Systems Engineering from the University of Michigan.

Kenneth S. Levick is associate assistant administrator for technical assistance in the Office of Program and Policy Coordination, Agency for International Development in Washington, D.C.

He has been with AID since 1950 and has been chief, Institutional Development Division, Bureau of Near East and South Asia; industry and loan officer, AID Mission for the UAR; assistant director for Program, AID Mission to India; and deputy industry officer, AID Mission to India. He held previous assignments in Paris, Oslo, and Washington.

Mr. Levick received his Master's degree in Economics from Columbia University.

415

Mordechai M. Levy is with the Technion-Israel Institute of Technology in Haifa. He has held a variety of positions there, including lecturer in sociology, academic secretary, and assistant to the president. He arranged academic and practical training programs abroad for Technion staff and graduates and represented the institution on national and international bodies. Since 1944 he has been acting chairman, Board of Directors, World University Service in Israel; advisor to Israel Government on evaluation of foreign academic degrees; and a member of the Executive Board, Israel National Commission for UNESCO. He has been in charge of liaison with Israel Government departments, foreign governments, and United Nations representatives in Israel, and he has been in charge of Technion's programs to assist developing countries.

Mr. Levy has been a consultant to the United Nations Economic Commission for Africa, Addis Ababa, Ethiopia, and a UNESCO advisor on national and international training. For one year he was cultural attaché in the Israel Embassy in Washington, D.C.

He received his Ph.D. in sociology and history from the University of Cologne.

K. T. Li is minister of economic affairs in the Republic of China and serves concurrently as vice chairman of the Council for International Economic Cooperation and Development. He is a member of the National Security Council and was vice chairman of the National Reconstruction Planning Committee.

As early as 1953, Minister Li began working

416

toward the economic development and industrialization of the Republic of China. He was a member of the Industrial Development Commission of the Economic Stabilization Board; secretary general of the Council for United States Aid; chairman of the Industrial Development and Investment Center; and convener of the Industrial Planning and Coordination Group of the Ministry of Economic Affairs.

He helped formulate the successive four-year economic development plans, making effective use of United States aid in Taiwan. He and his colleagues have been largely responsible for the improvement of investment climate in general and the establishment of industrial districts and export processing zones in Taiwan in particular since 1960. Mr. Li has represented China at many international meetings and promoted the setting of binational economic cooperation conferences with Vietnam since 1960, with Korea since 1966, and with Thailand in 1968.

He has led a number of economic goodwill missions and has pushed a technical cooperation program with some 26 countries in the free world.

Mr. Li has received a number of honors including the Order of Brilliant Star (Republic of China) and decorations from the Korean, Spanish, Vietnamese, Thai, and Malagasy governments. Just a few months ago, he received the Magasysay Award for Government Service for his vigorous, rational guidance of the Republic of China's economy, generating one of the world's most rapid rates of industrial growth.

Carl R. Lovitt is vice president and manager of foreign operations for Sverdrup and Parcel, Engineers-Architects. He has had more than 35 years of professional engineering experience including more than 20 years directly related to foreign operations in Northwest Canada, Alaska, Western Europe, Southeast Asia, Japan, and Okinawa.

As general manager for the firm's operations in Thailand and Southeast Asia, he was responsible for the $100 million Yanhee Hydroelectric Complex and numerous highway, airfield, and industrial projects. With the U.S. Corps of Engineers, he was identified with all engineering activities of the Northwest Division and Northwest Service Command in Northwest Canada and Alaska as well as the design and construction of the military establishment on Okinawa and U.S. and NATO installations in Western Europe.

He received his degree in civil engineering from the Los Angeles College of Engineering and took advanced studies at Carnegie Institute of Technology and the University of New Mexico.

George McRobie is chief executive of the Intermediate Technology Development Group and last year was part of a British government socio-economic survey team to the Gilbert and Ellice Islands. For three years he was with the Ford Foundation in Hyderabad in India as a program specialist attached to the Small Industries Extension Training Institute.

Earlier he had been Assistant to the Economic Adviser to the National Coal Board and a research assistant in political and economic planning. Until 1950, Mr. McRobie first worked as a coalminer and a journalist. He is the author of numerous papers and articles on public corporations, industrial organization, and development economics, and is now working on a book on district development in India.

He is an economics graduate of the London School of Economics and attended Fordyce Academy in Scotland.

Ralph L. Miller is staff geologist, Director's Office, U.S. Geological Survey and is the Director's representative on the International Activities Committee of the Geological Survey.

Dr. Miller served as a staff advisor in Mexico and Central America, as a technical advisor under the auspices of AID for geologic programs in Costa Rica, Nicaragua, and Salvador, and for a new Minerals Exploration Program for Colombia, and as a technical assistant under the auspices of International Cooperation Administration to Afghanistan, Guatemala, and Mexico.

Mr. Miller earned a Ph.D. in geology from Columbia University.

418

Ward Morehouse is director of the Center for International Programs and Services, State Education Department, University of the State of New York. In his past positions he was resident director, Educational Resources Center, New Delhi, India; educational director, Asia Society, New York; executive secretary, Conference on Asian Affairs, Inc., New York; instructor, Department of Government, New York University; and executive secretary, International Conference on Asian Problems, New York.

The center he currently directs is developing programs to strengthen Asian, African, Latin American, and other non-European fields of study in schools, colleges, and universities throughout the state of New York, as well as organizing and encouraging educational exchange activities and overseas service projects. He has written extensively on science and public policy.

Mr. Morehouse is a graduate of Yale University and has done graduate work in Middle Eastern studies and political science at the Asia Institute in New York City and at New York University, where he has taught.

Jiri Nehnevajsa is professor of sociology at the University of Pittsburgh and, as joint appointee, professor of economic and social development in the Graduate School of Public and International Affairs. As principal scientist and head of the program in social planning, he is affiliated also with the System Development Corporation, Santa Monica, California. Previously, Dr. Nehnevajsa was on the faculties of Columbia University and the University of

Colorado.

Professor Nehnevajsa has been visiting professor at the University of Heidelberg and the University of Mannheim. He served as member of the Executive Board of the Inter-University Program in Institution Building, and as research director of this program. Dr. Nehnevajsa has conducted numerous studies of political and social development in a number of countries, and has served as consultant to various research organizations.

Professor Nehnevajsa was educated at Masaryk University in Czechoslovakia, the University of Lausanne, and University of Zurich, from which he received his Ph.D. degree in sociology.

Alfred Kurt Neumann is at present chief of the Division of International Health at UCLA. Previously he was a lecturer in the Department of International Health at Johns Hopkins University School of Hygiene and Public Health and for two years was visiting assistant professor at the Christian Medical College in Punjab in India.

Dr. Neumann has also taught at the Massachusetts General Hospital School of Nursing, the Tufts University School of Medicine, the Harvard School of Public Health, and the Boston College School of Nursing. He has received grants to study tropical public health and medicine in West Africa, intermediary metabolism, public health, and heart perfusion. He has been a public health physician for the Massachusetts Department of Public Health and assistant medical director for the department's Division of Adult Health.

He received his M.D. at New York University's Bellevue Medical Center School of Medicine and his M.P.H. at the Harvard School of Public Health. He has a Master's degree in economics from the University of Wisconsin.

Bax Nomvete is director, Industry Division, United Nations Economic Commission for Africa. Previously, he was faculty fellow at the Center for International Affairs at Harvard and at one time was on the faculty of the Department of Economics at the University of Hull in England. He has been a senior scientific officer, Department of Scientific and Industrial Research, United Kingdom; and research officer, Department of Economics at the University of Natal in South Africa.

He holds graduate degrees from Cape Town University in South Africa and the University of Manchester in England.

Robert B. O'Connor is vice president, health services, United States Steel Corporation at Pittsburgh. Previously, he was the medical director at U. S. Steel. Dr. O'Connor also is adjunct professor of occupational medicine at the University of Pittsburgh's Graduate School of Public Health.

For three years he was editor-in-chief of the Journal of Occupational Medicine and has taught at Harvard's School of Public Health. He formerly was Medical Director, Loss Prevention Department, Liberty Mutual Insurance Companies; before that he was on the attending staff in surgery and orthopedics at St. Joseph's Hospital in Paterson, N.J. He also was medical director, Wright Aeronautical Corporation, Paterson, N.J.

He is a member of a number of public health and industrial health associations and is on the President's Committee on Employment of Handicapped. He did his undergraduate work at Boston College, received his M.D. from Harvard Medical School, and is certified by the Specialty Board in Occupational Medicine.

C. H. G. Oldham is a senior research fellow in the Science Policy Research Unit at the University of Sussex. He is responsible for the program of research related to science policies in developing countries. He also has been serving as a consultant on science and development problems for OCED in Turkey and Portugal and for UNESCO in Brazil and Cuba.

Previously he was a fellow with the Institute of Current World Affairs studying the Chinese language, and problems of utilization of science and technology in eight Asian countries.

He also has been with Standard Oil Company in the exploration research laboratories and in the foreign exploration subsidiary as a senior geophysicist. For three years he was concerned with oil exploration in Latin America.

Mr. Oldham is a graduate of the University of Reading in England and received his Ph.D. in physics, specializing in geophysics, at the University of Toronto.

Wesley Leland Orr is professor of engineering at the University of California at Los Angeles. He spent seven years with the U.S. Department of Agriculture in dam design and construction, irrigation works, water supply, flood control, soil conservation, regional planning, and dust bowl control. For one year he was with the U.S. Engineers Office in the design of military installations.

Mr. Orr has been with the University of California for 26 years as assistant dean; vice chairman of academic activities; vice chairman of the faculty of engineering; head, Division of Design, Management and Planning; and

422

campus coordinator and chief of party of the UCLA Indonesian Project. He was formerly a member of the Planning Commission of the City of Santa Monica.

His overseas experience was gained in Pakistan, Indonesia, Thailand, and Vietnam. He has been a consultant to SEATO and AID, a member of the Board of Directors of International Student Center, and a member of the Board of Advisers of the SEATO Graduate School of Engineering in Bangkok.

Robert L. Oshins is director of the Industrial Services and Institutions Division, United Nations Industrial Development Organization (UNIDO). Mr. Oshins spent the last 26 years with the various United States government agencies responsible for overseas economic aid. He was attached to the Mission for Economic Affairs in London and then was assigned to SHAFE as a U.S. Naval Officer in the Civil Affairs Division.

Mr. Oshins was appointed to the White House Staff under President Truman as Secretary of the Cabinet Food Committee and was one of the first staff members of the Marshall Plan organization. He served in Paris and Athens with the Plan, then returned to Washington to serve with the successor to the Marshall Plan, the Mutual Security Agency, and established the Private Enterprise Program.

During the 1960 presidential campaign he was director of research of the Democratic National Committee. Before joining UNIDO he was with the Department of Commerce as Director of the Office of International Investment. Mr. Oshins is a founder of the Society for International Development and is a member of its board. He initiated the program to encourage business executives to participate in developing countries known as the International Executive Service Corps.

He is a graduate of the University of Chicago and did graduate work in public administration at the Maxwell School, Syracuse University.

423

Logan C. Osterndorf is a UNESCO program specialist in the U.S. Office of Education. He was previously on the board of directors of the Council on International Educational Exchange and director of educational programs for the National Education Association.

He conducted a Ford Foundation faculty research seminar on international trade and development at Duke University. For six years, he was an assistant professor in political science and economics at Virginia Polytechnic Institute.

Mr. Osterndorf is an honors graduate of the School of Foreign Service of Georgetown University and earned an M.S. degree in political science from the University of Wisconsin.

Arthur Paul, the Asia Foundation's adviser on regional economic affairs now based in Hong Kong, has worked in Asia for the past nine years, including five years as an adviser to the Minister of Commerce in Afghanistan and two years in a similar capacity in Ceylon. He has had a distinguished career in business and government.

He served as a member of the U.S. delegation to the International Labor Office in Geneva; as executive director of the Foreign Economic Administration in Washington, D.C.; as director of the Office of International Trade; and as assistant to the U.S. Secretary of Commerce. He has had numerous articles on international trade published in foreign trade periodicals.

A graduate of Princeton University, Mr. Paul has studied at the University of Pennsylvania, the New York University Graduate

School, and the Woodrow Wilson School of Public and International Affairs at Princeton, where he specialized in international economics.

Charles H. Peake is provost of the University of Pittsburgh and was formerly vice chancellor for the academic disciplines. Dr. Peake came to the University in 1956 as assistant chancellor for student affairs. He has served as dean of the college at Knox College and as assistant dean of the college at the University of Michigan, and has taught English both at the University of Michigan and in the Detroit public schools.

Dr. Peake has travelled widely and coordinated numerous international programs for the University of Pittsburgh. His special area of interest and competence is Asia.

Dr. Peake received his Ph.D. from the University of Michigan.

Jesse D. Perkinson jr. is director of the Department of Scientific Affairs, Pan American Union, Organization of American States; executive secretary of the Inter-American Nuclear Energy Commission; and director of OAS Regional Scientific and Technological Development Program.

Previously, he was in charge of training and education programs for the U.S. Atomic Energy Commission; was professor of biochemistry in the medical units of the University of Tennessee; and senior scientist in the Medical Division,

425

Oak Ridge Institute of Nuclear Studies, Tennessee.

He is a member of the Panel on International Transfer of Technology, Commerce

Technical Advisory Board and has been a consultant to government and education.

He received his Ph.D. in biochemistry from the University of Rochester.

Stuart S. Peters is special adviser to the president of the Canadian International Development Agency. He has been the Deputy Minister of Resources and more recently was made Director-General for planning in the Department of Community and Social Development of the government of Newfoundland and Labrador.

Dr. Peters has been a visiting lecturer at the Memorial University of Newfoundland and was chief biologist and director of Wildlife Management Programs for the government of Newfoundland and Labrador. Very early in his career, he was partner-manager of the Peters Seed Company in Kingston, Ontario.

Dr. Peters received his bachelor's, master's, and Ph.D. degrees from Cornell University.

Wesley Wentz Posvar became the 15th chancellor of the University of Pittsburgh in June, 1967. He was born in Topeka, Kansas, and when the family later moved to Cleveland he attended public schools there before his appointment to the United States Military Academy at West Point. He was graduated first in his class in 1946, and went to England as a

426

Rhodes Scholar at Oxford, where he earned the B.A. and M.A. degrees in philosophy, politics, and economics. He later earned the Master of Public Administration and the Ph.D. degrees in political science at Harvard. He holds an honorary Doctor of Laws degree from Carnegie-Mellon University.

Dr. Posvar was a Littauer Fellow in the Graduate School of Public Administration at Harvard from 1962 to 1964 and a research fellow at the MIT Center for International Studies in 1963 and 1964.

Dr. Posvar's first teaching post was as instructor at West Point from 1951 until 1954. He was appointed to the faculty of the Social Sciences Division of the Air Force Academy in 1957 and was faculty chairman of the division when he was appointed chancellor of the University of Pittsburgh. His military posts included duties in strategic planning and service in overseas theaters.

He has written and lectured on international politics, national security, decision theory, systems analysis, and arms control, and has served as advisor to government agencies on policy issues.

K. Nagaraja Rao is employed by the Ford Foundation as program officer, Science and Technology for Latin America and the Caribbean. Previously, he was with the Dunwoody Industrial Institute; the Ministry of Economic Affairs, Government of Indonesia; the Institute of Gas Technology; and the Korean Technical Institute.

He holds several awards and has written on technical education, chemical engineering, and economic development. He is a member of the board of the National Association for Foreign Student Affairs.

Mr. Rao received his Ph.D. in chemical engineering from the Illinois Institute of Technology and also attended the University of Mysore.

427

Alvin Roseman is associate dean of the Graduate School of Public and International Affairs at the University of Pittsburgh and professor of public and international affairs. Previously, he was assistant director general of the United Nations Educational, Scientific and Cultural Organization in Paris, and earlier served with the International Cooperation Administration as regional director for the Far East. He has held administrative posts in the missions to Cambodia and Greece; was with the Mutual Security Agency; was representative to UN agencies at Geneva; and was chief of International Activities for the U.S. Bureau of the Budget.

He was cited for outstanding public service in 1957 and received the Distinguished Public Service Career Award in 1959.

He received his LL.B. in public law from Western Reserve University and his M.A. in social administration from the University of Chicago.

Hassan Saab is a professor of political science at the Saint Joseph University of Beirut and at the Lebanese University of Beirut. He has been associated with the Institute of Arab Studies in Cairo and the American University of Beirut. He is co-founder of "The Christian-Muslim Dialogue" Group of Lebanon.

Mr. Saab's diplomatic experience includes serving as cultural counselor in North America in Washington, D. C. and serving as director of Political Affairs for the Ministry of Foreign Affairs in Beirut and as counselor and head of the Department of Arab Affairs. Professor Saab was earlier a vice consul in Istanbul in

428

Turkey and an attaché, Lebanese Legation in Paris. Mr. Saab is a graduate of the University of Cairo and received his Ph.D. in political science from Georgetown University.

Jorge Alberto Sabato is head of the Technology Branch at the Comision Nacional de Energia Atomica of Argentina, where he organized the Department of Metallurgy. Earlier he organized a research laboratory at Guillermo Decker Co., Argentina.

Mr. Sabato has written a number of papers in physics, the teaching of physics, process metallurgy, recrystallization of metals, basic and applied research in metallurgy, and scientific policy and economic development. He has been visiting lecturer of the National Science Foundation and in 1967 he was adviser before the OAS Multinational Program in Science and Technology.

Mr. Sabato received his degree in physics from the Instituto del Profesorado in Buenos Aires, did graduate work in metallurgy at the University of Birmingham in England, and was a research fellow at Stanford University.

Antonio Salgado is vice rector of the Universidad Central in Quito in Ecuador. Previously he was dean of the engineering faculty at the university and earlier was president of the Modulo Concrete Construction Company. In previous positions he was general director of National Public Works, proprietor of Sania Construction Company, and cost chief of

Empressa Electrica in Quito. He has been a professor of engineering at Quito since 1948.

Mr. Salgado is a former director of the Society of Engineers and Architects and is one of the founders of the College for Civil Engineers. He was a delegate from Ecuador at the 12th World Conference of Road Builders in Rome in 1964 and this year was a delegate to the Congress on Pan American Road Building in Quito.

He received his engineering degree at Central specializing in design, supervision, and construction of buildings; and in projects for providing potable water, electricity, bridges, and roads.

Edward I. Salkovitz is professor and chairman of the Department of Metallurgical and Materials Engineering at the University of Pittsburgh. He has taught at the University of Maryland and at Howard University and has conducted research for the Naval Research Laboratory, where he was head of Metals and acting associate superintendent of the Metallurgy Division.

Mr. Salkovitz has served with the Office of Naval Research and the Advanced Research Projects Agency. He is a member of the Governor's Science Advisory Council and the Solid State Science Panel for the National Academy of Science. He has 55 publications in materials, metal physics, and biomaterials, and holds two patents in magnetic materials. He has received six U.S. Civil Service Performance Awards.

Mr. Salkovitz received his D.Sc. in physics at Carnegie Institute of Technology.

430

Antonius G. O. Smit is at present serving as the first commercial secretary at the Netherlands Embassy in Washington, D. C. He has also served at the embassies in Yugoslavia, Italy, and Brazil. Prior to his foreign service, Mr.

Smit worked in the Department of Foreign Affairs at The Hague in the Netherlands.

After graduating from the Utrecht School of Law, Smit worked in the Institute of Criminology and the Amsterdamsche Bank.

W. Paul Strassmann is professor of economics at Michigan State University. He was previously an international economic analyst specializing in Central America for the Commerce Department. He has conducted research in Peru, Colombia, Venezuela, Mexico, and Puerto Rico. While a visiting staff member at the London School of Economics two years ago he studied the economic aspects of European building research.

Mr. Strassmann is on the editorial boards of *Technology and Culture* and *The Journal of Developing Areas*. He has written two books: *Risk and Technological Innovation* and *Technological Change and Economic Development*.

Mr. Strassmann is a graduate of the University of Texas; he received his M.A. from Columbia and a Ph.D. from the University of Maryland.

431

Sidney C. Sufrin is professor of economics in the Maxwell Granduate School of Citizenship and Public Affairs at Syracuse University. He has taught at Ohio State University and has been a guest lecturer at Notre Dame, American University, and the University of Georgia. He was a Brook Fellow at Queensland University in Australia.

During the early days of the Roosevelt administration, Mr. Sufrin was with NRA, NERA, and Resettlement Administration. He has been a consultant to the National Resources Board on questions of industrial growth. He has also been a consultant for government and

industry.

Mr. Sufrin served on the War Production Board. During his time in the Army he worked with economic problems in overseas areas and subsequently was appointed Chief of the ECA mission to Spain to determine the economic status of that country prior to the Military Aid Program. In the field of foreign economic development, Mr. Sufrin was the United States member of the Emergency Economic Committee for Europe.

Mr. Sufrin received his Ph.D. from the Ohio State University.

Victor B. Sullam is U.S. representative of the Italian Federation of Farmers' Cooperatives, private economic consultant, and lecturer on European affairs at the School of Advanced International Studies of the Johns Hopkins University.

Previously, he was international trade analyst, Office of Regional Affairs, FAO, Washing-

432

ton. For about six years he was senior consultant to the Continental Allied Company in Washington; and he was consultant to the ICA Institute of Development Programming at Johns Hopkins. He was a lecturer in the ICA Training Program in Washington and has lectured at Howard University, American University, and North Carolina State College.

He has been with the U.S. Embassy in Rome and with the UNRRA Mission to Italy. He was a desk officer, Greece, MSA/FAO, Washington.

Mr. Sullam received his degree in agronomy at the Royal University in Florence in Italy and received an M.S. and did postgraduate work in economics at North Carolina State College.

Charles Süsskind was born in Prague and educated there and in England. After service with the U.S. Air Forces during World War II he attended the California Institute of Technology and Yale University, where he received the doctorate in 1951. He was a research associate and lecturer at Stanford University for four years and then joined the faculty of the University of California at Berkeley, where he is now professor of engineering science. His technical specialty is bioengineering, and he is also professionally interested in the history of technology. He is currently a National Science Foundation science faculty fellow at the Graduate Institute of International Studies, University

of Geneva, engaged in the study of relationships between modern technology and society.

Professor Süsskind is the editor of *The Encyclopedia of Electronics* (Reinhold, 1962) and co-author of *Fundamentals of Microwave Electronics* (McGraw-Hill, 1964). More recently, while serving as assistant dean of the University of California's College of Engineering, he made an investigation of the careers of foreign students who had received advanced engineering degrees at Berkeley during a 12-year period; the results were published in book form by the Institute of International Education in New York as *Exporting Technical Education* (1968).

Alberto Eusebio Do Carmo Tangari is acting chief of cabinet to the Minister of Industry and Commerce in Brazil and acting secretary-general of the Industrial Development Commission. He is with the Bank of Brazil. He also is a representative of the Ministry of Industry and Commerce at the Latin American Association of Free Commerce.

Previously, he was director of the Brazilian Company of Industrial Projects, representative of the Ministry in the Executive Council of the National Superintendency for Supplies, and special consultant to the Latin American Economic Commission.

Mr. Tangari was born in Brazil and graduated from Rio de Janeiro Law School. He is a licensee in economics of the Federal Council of Professional Economists.

B. R. Teare jr. is University Professor of engineering at Carnegie-Mellon University and consultant to a number of companies and universities. He has been with Carnegie-Mellon since 1939 and had previously been with General Electric Company.

His major areas of research concern hysteresis motors, copper-covered steel conductors at high frequencies, electrical studies of living tissues, and skin effect in bimetallic conductors. He has pioneered in the development and coordination of engineering analysis courses in which the student learns to deal with professional problems. Dr. Teare has been a consultant to engineering education in Pakistan and is current chairman of the Steering Committee of the Kanpur Indo-American Program. He is on steering committees for projects at the Univers-

434

ity of Kabul, the University of the Philippines, and Mindanao State University.

Professor Teare received a B.S. and an M.S. in electrical engineering from the University of Wisconsin and earned his D.Eng. at Yale.

A. C. Van Dusen if vice chancellor for Program Development and Public Affairs at the University of Pittsburgh. Among his other responsibilities, Dr. Van Dusen is charged with developing and maintaining programs for effectively relating the University to particular international interests abroad.

Prior to his present position, Dr. Van Dusen served the University of Pittsburgh as vice chancellor for the professional schools. Before coming to Pittsburgh he was vice president of Northwestern University.

Dr. Van Dusen has served as a consultant to industry and government both here and abroad. He has also helped to establish and maintain cooperative educational programs in Africa as well as in Central and South America.

Dr. Van Dusen received his bachelor's and master's degrees from the University of Florida and his Ph.D. degree from Northwestern University. He is a member of several honorary and scientific societies and has written many professional articles.

William D. Van Vorst is professor and head of Engineering Systems Division, Department of Engineering, UCLA. He has had more than 20 years experience in professional consulting and teaching in the areas of engineering thermo-dynamics, energy conversion, chemical reactor design, engineering economics, and engineering aspects of international development. Last year he was a consultant to UNESCO on "A Science Policy for Thailand" and on recommendations for the UNESCO program in Indonesia.

Earlier in his career he was head of the Engineering International Development Laboratory at UCLA and chief of party of the UCLA Engineering-University of Gadjah Mada project in Indonesia.

Mr. Van Vorst participated in one of the earliest AID type programs, the Stanford University-University of the Philippines project, and initiated curriculum and laboratory development in chemical engineering at the University of the Philippines.

Mr. Van Vorst holds the Ph.D. degree.

Kenneth F. Vernon is director of the Agency for International Development's Office of Engineering. Previously, he was chief engineer of AID's Near East-South Asia Bureau's Engineering Division and special assistant to the chief engineer for the Bureau.

Mr. Vernon's overseas service included three years as chief of the Public Works Division of the United States Operations Mission to Pakistan and nearly five years as water resources advisor to the Iraq Development Board and Ministry of Development. In this position he served as director general of the Ministry of Development's first technical section which had charge of Iraq's nearly $500 million irrigation, flood control, and drainage program being financed from Iraq's oil revenues. Mr. Vernon was also a consultant to the Jordanian Development Board and to the FAO Mediterranean Regional Project.

The U.S. Bureau of Reclamation had Mr. Vernon's services for 20 years during which time he was also chairman of the American Section of the Joint Engineering Committee between the U.S. and Canada. He has received many honors and in 1965 was the recipient of the Distinguished Honor Award, AID's highest honor.

436

Myron Weiner is professor of political science at the Massachusetts Institute of Technology. He also is senior staff member of the MIT Center for International Studies. He has taught at Princeton and at the University of Chicago.

Mr. Weiner has written extensively on political organization and political participation, particularly in South Asia. He has done extensive field research in India, and he was in Paris and the Balkans conducting research.

Mr. Weiner is a member of the Advisory Panel of the Bureau of Near Eastern and South Asian Affairs of the State Department, a member of the board of directors of the Association for Asian Studies, and a consulting editor of the Rand-McNally series on political change.

Professor Weiner is a graduate of the City College of New York. He received his M.A. and Ph.D. from Princeton.

Bunroku Yoshino is minister extraordinary and plenipotentiary, Embassy of Japan, Washington, D.C. Previously, he was councillor, Bureau of Economic Cooperation, Foreign Ministry in Tokyo and counselor, embassy of Japan in Germany. In 1960 he was the first secretary in the Embassy in Washington.

Mr. Yoshino was born in Matsumoto, Nagano Prefecture, and entered foreign service in 1941 as an attaché in the embassy in Germany. Later he was secretary, Treaties Bureau, Foreign Ministry in Tokyo.

He graduated from the law faculty at Tokyo University.

APPENDIX 2
List of Rapporteurs and Presiders

The following men served as Rapporteurs or Presiders during the Conference. The responsibilities of the Rapporteurs included the recording of pertinent issues brought forth in the workshop or panel sessions. In many instances the Rapporteur, in concert with the Principal Participant, presented the workshop report to the General Assembly. The Presiders chaired the several plenary sessions of the Conference and were quite effective in maintaining the program schedule. Some of the Presiders also served as Conference Discussants and their photographs appear with their biographies at the beginning of this section.

438

Joel I. Abrams, Chairman
Department of Civil Engineering
School of Engineering
University of Pittsburgh

Max Bishop, Director
World Affairs Council of Pittsburgh

A.E. Axelrod, Associate Dean
School of Medicine
University of Pittsburgh

Stephen Blank, Professor
Political Science Department
College of Arts & Sciences
University of Pittsburgh

Daniel S. Cheever, Director
International Affairs Program
Graduate School of Public and
   International Affairs
University of Pittsburgh

Guy Fauconneau, Professor
Department of Mechanical Engineering
School of Engineering
University of Pittsburgh

David M. Cohen, Professor
School of Law
University of Pittsburgh

Norman K. Flint, Professor
Department of Earth & Planetary Sciences
College of Arts & Sciences
University of Pittsburgh

440

George E. Klinzing, Professor
Department of Chemical & Petroleum
  Engineering
School of Engineering
University of Pittsburgh

Robert O. Krueger, Professor
Business Administration
Graduate School of Business
University of Pittsburgh

Arnold Kroner, Professor
Department of Economics
College of Arts & Sciences
University of Pittsburgh

Carmelo Mesa-Lago, Acting Director
Center for Latin American Studies
University of Pittsburgh

Marlin H. Mickle, Professor
Department of Electrical Engineering
School of Engineering
University of Pittsburgh

Roland Robertson, Professor
Department of Sociology
College of Arts & Sciences
University of Pittsburgh

Robert T. Norman, Professor
Urban Affairs
Graduate School of Public & International
 Affairs
University of Pittsburgh

Hamlin Robinson, Professor
Social & Economic Development
Graduate School of Public & International
 Affairs
University of Pittsburgh

442

Arthur Roe, Head
Office of International Science Activities
National Science Foundation

Edward B. Stuart, Chairman
Department of Chemical & Petroleum
  Engineering
School of Engineering
University of Pittsburgh

Maurice A. Shapiro, Professor
Environmental Health
Graduate School of Public Health
University of Pittsburgh

Walter R. Turkes, Associate Dean
School of Engineering
University of Pittsburgh

James B. Way jr., Executive Assistant
Center for International Studies
University of Pittsburgh

APPENDIX 3
Alphabetical List of All Participants, Discussants, and Rapporteurs

Dr. Joël I. Abrams, Chairman
Department of Civil Engineering
University of Pittsburgh
Pittsburgh, Pennsylvania 15213

Dr. A. J. Aizenstat, Director
New York Liaison Office, UNIDO
United Nations Plaza
New York, New York

Dr. Maurice L. Albertson
Department of Civil Engineering
Colorado State University
Fort Collins, Colorado 80521

Mr. P. C. Asiodu
Permanent Secretary
Federal Ministry of Industries
Lagos, Nigeria

Dr. A. E. Axelrod, Associate Dean
School of Medicine
University of Pittsburgh
Pittsburgh, Pennsylvania 15213

Dr. Jack Baranson
International Bank of Reconstruction
  and Development
Economic Department
1818 H Street
Washington, D.C. 20433

Mr. Curtis H. Barker
University Relations Officer
Agency for International Development
New State Department Building
Washington, D.C. 20523

Professor Leland Barrows
Director, Economic and Social
  Development
Graduate School of Public and
  International Affairs
University of Pittsburgh
Pittsburgh, Pennsylvania 15213

Professor Merton R. Barry, Director
Engineering Foreign Programs
The University of Wisconsin
651 University Avenue
Madison, Wisconsin 53706

Dr. Lawrence Bass, Engineering
Consultant
Arthur D. Little, Inc.
1735 Eye Street, N. W.
Washington, D.C. 20006

Dr. Carl Beck, Director
International Studies Program
Social Science Building
University of Pittsburgh
Pittsburgh, Pennsylvania 15213

Dr. Nicky Beredjick
UNIDO Liaison Office
Room 3261
United Nations Plaza
New York, New York

Professor Warren J. Bilkey
School of Business
1155 Observatory Drive
The University of Wisconsin
Madison, Wisconsin 53706

Mr. Max Bishop, Director
World Affairs Council of Pittsburgh
Kaufmann's Tenth Floor
400 Fifth Avenue
Pittsburgh, Pennsylvania 15219

Dr. Stephen Blank
Professor of Political Science
2328 Cathedral of Learning
University of Pittsburgh
Pittsburgh, Pennsylvania 15213

Dr. William Bollay
4592 Via Vistosa
Santa Barbara, California 93105

Dr. Detlev W. Bronk
President
The Rockefeller University
New York, New York 10021

Dr. George Bugliarello
Department of Civil Engineering
Carnegie-Mellon University
Pittsburgh, Pennsylvania 15213

Dr. Robert Charpie, President
Bell and Howell Company
McCormick Road
Chicago, Illinois 60645

Dr. Daniel S. Cheever, Director
International Affairs Program
Graduate School of Public and
  International Affairs
University of Pittsburgh
Pittsburgh, Pennsylvania 15213

Dr. Francis S. Cheever
Dean, School of Medicine
and Vice Chancellor
School of the Health Professions
University of Pittsburgh
Pittsburgh, Pennsylvania 15213

Dr. Kan Chen, Assistant Director
Systems Sciences Area
Stanford Research Institute
Menlo Park, California 94025

Dr. W. L. Chilton
Economics Office
Ford Motor Company
The American Road
Dearborn, Michigan 48121

Professor Walter Chudson
Columbia University
Graduate School of Business
New York, New York 10002

Professor David M. Cohen
School of Law
University of Pittsburgh
Pittsburgh, Pennsylvania 15213

Mr. Elbert T. Culver
Manager of Project Sales for
  Koppers Company, Inc.
(International Operations)
Vice President of Koppers
  (Far East), Inc.
Grant Street
Pittsburgh, Pennsylvania 15219   ○

Dr. John C. Cutler
Director, Population Division
Professor of International Health
Graduate School of Public Health
University of Pittsburgh
Pittsburgh, Pennsylvania 15213

Mr. Paul Henri David
Inspection Générale de la Construction
Ministère de l'Equipement et du
  Logement
32, avenue du President Kennedy
Paris 16e, France

Mr. Julien Engel
National Academy of Sciences
2101 Constitution Avenue
Washington, D.C. 20418

Dr. Thomas J. Farer
250 Riverside Drive
New York, New York 10025

Dr. Guy Fauconneau
Department of Mechanical Engineering
University of Pittsburgh
Pittsburgh, Pennsylvania 15213

Dr. Norman K. Flint
Associate Professor of Geology
Earth and Planetary Sciences
University of Pittsburgh
Pittsburgh, Pennsylvania 15213

Mr. Herbert I. Goodman
Far East Coordinator
Gulf Oil Corporation
Gulf Building
Pittsburgh, Pennsylvania 15230

Mr. Maximo Halty-Carrere, Chief
Technology Development Unit
Department of Scientific Affairs
Pan American Union
Washington, D.C. 20006

Dr. Howard B. Hamilton, Chairman
Department of Electrical Engineering
University of Pittsburgh
Pittsburgh, Pennsylvania 15213

Professor Minor C. Hawk, Director
International Programs
405 Engineering Hall
University of Pittsburgh
Pittsburgh, Pennsylvania 15213

Dr. Harold E. Hoelscher, Dean
School of Engineering
University of Pittsburgh
Pittsburgh, Pennsylvania 15213

Dr. Bert F. Hoselitz
Department of Economics
The University of Chicago
Chicago, Illinois 60637

Dr. Warren S. Hunsberger, Professor
Department of Economics
The American University
Washington, D.C. 20016

Dr. John Ide, Director
Engineering Division
National Science Foundation
Washington, D.C. 20525

448

Dr. Robert Iversen
507 Scott Avenue
Syracuse, New York 13224

Dr. G. P. Kane
Officer on special duty
Development Wing (Pulp & Paper)
Ministry of Industry
Government of India
Shahajahan Road
New Delhi, India

Dr. Augustus B. Kinzel
1738 Castellana Road
La Jolla, California 92037

Dr. Hibberd V. B. Kline jr., Chairman
Department of Geography
University of Pittsburgh
Pittsburgh, Pennsylvania 15213

Dr. George E. Klinzing, Professor
Department of
  Chemical/Petroleum Engineering
University of Pittsburgh
Pittsburgh, Pennsylvania 15213

Dr. Melvin Kranzberg
Division of Special
  Interdisciplinary Studies
Case Western Reserve University
Cleveland, Ohio 44106

Professor Arnold Kroner
Department of Economics
University of Pittsburgh
Pittsburgh, Pennsylvania 15213

Dr. Robert Krueger
Professor of Business Administration
Graduate School of Business
University of Pittsburgh
Pittsburgh, Pennsylvania 15213

Mr. Matthew J. Kust
Attorney at Law
1001 Connecticut Avenue, N.W.
Washington, D.C. 20036

Mr. Mordechai Lador
Ministry for Foreign Affairs
Jerusalem, Israel

Dr. D. John Lauer, Medical Director
International Telephone &
  Telegraph Corporation
320 Park Avenue
New York, N.Y. 10022

Dr. Lawrence D. Lee
School of Law
University of Pittsburgh
Pittsburgh, Pennsylvania 15213

Professor Alberto Leon B., Dean
Division of Engineering
Universidad del Valle
Cali, Colombia

Mr. Kenneth S. Levick
Associate Assistant Administrator
  for Technical Assistance
Department of State
Agency for International Development
Washington, D.C. 20523

Dr. Mordechai M. Levy
Assistant to the President for
  Academic Liaison
Technion—Israel Institute of Technology
Haifa, Israel

Dr. Kwoh-Ting Li, Minister
Ministry of Economic Affairs
No. 3 Lane 44
Linyi Street
Taipei, Taiwan
Republic of China

Mr. Carl R. Lovitt
Sverdrup and Parcel International, Inc.
Engineers—Architects
800 N. 12th Boulevard
St. Louis, Missouri 63101

Mr. George McRobie
Intermediate Technology Development
  Group, Ltd.
9 King Street
London, W.C.2, England

Dr. Carmelo Mesa-Lago
Acting Director
Center for Latin American Studies
University of Pittsburgh
Pittsburgh, Pennsylvania 15213

Dr. Marlin H. Mickle
Department of Electrical Engineering
University of Pittsburgh
Pittsburgh, Pennsylvania 15213

Dr. Ralph Miller, Staff Geologist
U.S. Department of the Interior
Geological Survey
Washington, D.C. 20242

Dr. Ward Morehouse, Director
Center for International Programs and Services
The State Education Department
The University of the State
of New York
Albany, New York 12224

Dr. Jiri Nehnevajsa
Professor of Sociology
College of Arts and Sciences
University of Pittsburgh
Pittsburgh, Pennsylvania 15213

Dr. Alfred Neumann, Chief
Division of International Health
School of Public Health
University of California
Los Angeles, California 90024

Dr. Bax Nomvete
United Nations Economic Commission
for Africa
Industry Division
P.O. Box 3001
Addis Ababa, Ethiopia

Dr. Robert T. Norman
Assistant Professor of Urban Affairs
Program Development & Public Affairs
University of Pittsburgh
Pittsburgh, Pennsylvania 15213

Dr. Robert B. O'Connor
Vice President, Health Services
United States Steel Corporation
525 William Penn Place
Pittsburgh, Pennsylvania 15230

Dr. C. H. G. Oldham
The University of Sussex
Unit for the Study of Science Policy
Sussex, England

Dr. Wesley L. Orr
Department of Engineering
University of California
Los Angeles, California 90024

Mr. Robert L. Oshins, Director
Industrial Services and
Institutions Division
United Nations Industrial
Development Organization
Felderhaus, Rathausplatz 2
Vienna, Austria

Mr. Logan C. Osterndorf
UNESCO Program Specialist
Office of the Associate Commissioner
for International Education
Department of Health, Education
and Welfare
Office of Education
Washington, D.C. 20202

Dr. Arthur Paul
c/o William D. Ferguson
2232 Land Title Building
Philadelphia, Pennsylvania

Dr. Charles H. Peake, Provost
University of Pittsburgh
Pittsburgh, Pennsylvania 15213

Dr. Jesse D. Perkinson, Director
Department of Scientific Affairs
Organization of American States
Pan American Union
Washington, D.C. 20006

Dr. Stuart S. Peters
Special Adviser to the President
Canadian International Development
Agency
75 Albert Street
Ottawa 4, Ontario, Canada

Dr. Wesley W. Posvar, Chancellor
University of Pittsburgh
Pittsburgh, Pennsylvania 15213

Dr. K. N. Rao
Program Associate for
Latin America and Caribbean
The Ford Foundation
320 East 43rd Street
New York, New York 10017

Professor Roland Robertson
Visiting Associate Professor of Sociology
University of Pittsburgh
Pittsburgh, Pennsylvania 15213

Professor Hamlin Robinson
Economic and Social Development
Graduate School of Public and
International Affairs
University of Pittsburgh
Pittsburgh, Pennsylvania 15213

Dr. Arthur Roe, Head
Office of International Science Activities
National Science Foundation
Washington, D.C. 20550

450

Dr. Alvin J. Roseman, Associate Dean
Graduate School of Public
  and International Affairs
University of Pittsburgh
Pittsburgh, Pennsylvania 15213

Dr. Hassan Saab, President
Development Studies Association
Beirut, Lebanon

Sr. Jorge A. Sabato
Comision Nacional de Energia Atomica
Dependiente de la Presidencia de la Nacion
Avenida del Liberatador 8250
Buenos Aires, Argentina

Sr. Don Antonio Salgado
Vice Rector
The Central University
Quito, Ecuador

Dr. Edward I. Salkovitz, Chairman
Department of Metallurgical
  and Materials Engineering
University of Pittsburgh
Pittsburgh, Pennsylvania 15213

Dr. Maurice A. Shapiro
Professor of Environmental Health
227 Graduate School of Public Health
University of Pittsburgh
Pittsburgh, Pennsylvania 15213

Dr. Antonius G. O. Smit
Netherlands Embassy
Washington, D.C.

Professor W. Paul Strassmann
Department of Economics
Michigan State University
East Lansing, Michigan 48823

Dr. Edward B. Stuart, Chairman
Department of Chemical/Petroleum
  Engineering
University of Pittsburgh
Pittsburgh, Pennsylvania 15213

Dr. Sidney C. Sufrin
Department of Economics
Syracuse University
Syracuse, New York 13210

Mr. Victor B. Sullam
Room 401
711 14th Street, N.W.
Washington, D.C. 20005

Dr. Charles Süsskind
Graduate Institute of
  International Studies
132 rue de Lausanne
Geneva, Switzerland

Dr. Alberto Tangari
Rue General Glicerio 400
Apartment 201
Rio de Janeiro, Brazil

Dr. Richard Teare
Carnegie-Mellon University
Schenley Park
Pittsburgh, Pennsylvania 15213

Professor Walter R. Turkes, Associate Dean
School of Engineering
University of Pittsburgh
Pittsburgh, Pennsylvania 15213

Dr. A. C. Van Dusen, Vice Chancellor
Program Development and Public Affairs
123 Cathedral of Learning
University of Pittsburgh
Pittsburgh, Pennsylvania 15213

Dr. William D. Van Vorst, Chairman
Engineering Systems Division
University of California
Los Angeles, California 90024

Mr. Kenneth F. Vernon, Director
Office of Engineering
Department of State
Agency for International Development
Washington, D.C. 20523

Mr. James B. Way jr., Executive Assistant
Center for International Studies
University of Pittsburgh
Pittsburgh, Pennsylvania 15213

Dr. Myron Weiner
Professor of Political Science
Massachusetts Institute of Technology
Cambridge, Massachusetts 02139

Mr. Bunroku Yoshino, Minister
Embassy of Japan
2520 Massachusetts Avenue, N.W.
Washington, D.C. 20008

APPENDIX 4
Conference Committees

452

The following committees have been of invaluable assistance:

The Conference Planning Committee

Jack Baranson, International Bank for Reconstruction and Development
Carl Beck, University of Pittsburgh
Nicky Beredjick, United Nations Industrial Development Organization
Max Bishop, World Affairs Council of Pittsburgh
Howard Burnett, Koppers Company
Jerry Chang, University of Pittsburgh
Lewis Conta, National Science Foundation
Fred Draper, Agency for International Development
Roy Galloway, Union Carbide Corporation
Minor C. Hawk, University of Pittsburgh
H. E. Hoelscher, University of Pittsburgh
Burkart Holzner, University of Pittsburgh
Arthur Lindsley, Aluminum Company of American
Hamlin Robinson, University of Pittsburgh
Alvin Roseman, University of Pittsburgh
Irwin Sanders, Education and World Affairs
Saadia M. Schorr, TEMPO-General Electric Company
John Singleton, University of Pittsburgh

The University Pre- and Post-Conference Committee

Carl Beck, Director, Center for International Studies, Professor of Political Science, College of Arts
and Sciences
Jerry C. L. Chang, Professor of Civil Engineering, School of Engineering
John Cutler, Director, Population Division, Professor of International Health, Graduate School of
Public Health
Frances Drew, Professor of Preventive Medicine, School of Medicine
Norman Flint, Associate Professor of Geology, Department of Earth and Planetary Sciences, Col-
lege of Arts and Sciences
William Frederick, Professor of Business Administration, Graduate School of Business
Minor C. Hawk, Director, Office of International Programs, School of Engineering
H. E. Hoelscher, Dean, School of Engineering
Burkart Holzner, Chairman, Department of Sociology, College of Arts and Sciences
Harold Lancour, Dean, Graduate School of Library and Information Sciences
Edward Sell, Dean, School of Law
John Singleton, Associate Professor, International and Development Education, School of Educa-
tion
Alex Spoehr, Professor of Anthropology, College of Arts and Sciences
Hamlin Robinson, Associate Research Professor, Economic and Social Development, Graduate
School of Public and International Affairs
Alvin Roseman, Associate Dean, Graduate School of Public and International Affairs

We also acknowledge the chairmen of the following committees:

Faculty Host & Rapporteurs—Walter Turkes, Associate Dean of Engineering, School of Engineer-
ing
Hostesses—Betty Pavlovich, Administrative Secretary to the Dean, School of Engineering
Housing—Wesley Rohrer, Professor of Mechanical Engineering, School of Engineering
Publicity—M. Daniel Henry, Administrative Assistant to the Dean, School of Engineering
Publishing—H. E. Hoelscher, Dean, School of Engineering; M. C. Hawk, Director, Office of
International Programs
Registration—Mrs. Esther Denson, Secretary, Office of International Programs, School of Engi-
neering

453

Sessions—Merton Barry, Director, Engineering Foreign Programs, University of Wisconsin
Transportation—Charles Hwang, Professor of Mechanical Engineering, School of Engineering
Visual Aids—William Rudoy, Professor of Mechanical Engineering, School of Engineering
Women's Program—Mrs. H. E. Hoelscher

The following faculty members were kind enough to serve as hosts to our Conference participants from abroad:

Joel Abrams, Civil Engineering Department
Edward Barnes, University-Community Education Program
N. Lewis Buck, Mechanical Engineering Department
Shun-Hsin Chou, Department of Economics
Juan DiPrimio, Metallurgical and Materials Engineering Department
Guy Fauconneau, Mechanical Engineering Department
Norman Flint, Earth and Planetary Sciences Department
Howard Hamilton, Electrical Engineering Department
Albert Holzman, Industrial Engineering Department
Kaanan Kano, Electrical Engineering Department
Hibberd V. B. Kline jr., Geography Department
George Klinzing, Chemical and Petroleum Engineering Department
Robert Krueger, Graduate School of Business
Takesi Nagata, Earth and Planetary Sciences Department
Hamlin Robinson, Graduate School of Public and International Affairs
Alvin Roseman, Graduate School of Public and International Affairs
George Saliba, Mechanical Engineering Department
Maurice A. Shapiro, Graduate School of Public Health
Donald Smith, University-Community Education Program
T. W. Sze, Electrical Engineering Department
Andras Szeri, Mechanical Engineering Department

The special hostesses serving the Conference participants were selected from members of the Mortar Board, a national honorary society. The secretaries were from the School of Engineering and the chauffeurs were selected from the Student Cabinet in the School of Engineering.

INDEX

456

458

460

462